Odyle
Visited Yuki's
homestay on
1st April
2003.

Bali Moon

This book is dedicated to the island of Bali and its people. To a link that spans lifetimes, transcends reason and can never be broken. My heart sets eternal on your shores.

To those spirits of light that walked forever by my side through the dark journey of my soul.

Bali Moon

A Spiritual Odyssey

Odyle Knight

Published in Australia by
SANDSTONE PUBLISHING,
56 John Street, Leichhardt, NSW, 2040.

odyleknight@hotmail.com

Knight, Odyle.

Bali Moon : a spiritual odyssey.

ISBN 1 86505 138 1

1. Knight, Odyle - Journeys - Bali Island. 2. Spiritual biography - Indonesia - Bali Island

A823.3915.98604

All characters in this book are fictional. Any resemblance to actual persons is purely coincidental.

Printed in Australia by Griffin Press Pty Ltd, Netley, South Australia.

CONTENTS

ACKNOWLEDGMENTS

My deepest gratitude to Putu Sugiarta for his valuable contribution. He remains a constant source of inspiration and support.

For all those wonderful people who helped in the writing of this book, they will find recognition within these pages. In some small part, I hope they have shared the journey with me.

Thank you.

PROLOGUE

'Miss Knight, Miss Knight! Are you there?' The heavy thumping on the door continued but I chose to ignore it, turning up the volume on my Walkman instead. The sound of the waves soothed my frayed nerves as I shrank further under my desk, safely closeted from the outside world.

Opening the travel brochure, I stared deep into the photo, imagining myself there by the pool, sipping a cool cocktail and basking in the tropical sun. Nothing to do but breathe in and out. Paradise.

A ball banged hard against the window, jolting me back to the present. I looked out through the bars to the rain-spattered schoolyard. Children were running amok in the cold grey drizzle. A bulldozer crunched into the hardened asphalt, ripping it apart and my mind along with it.

'I'm sure she's in there,' a vaguely familiar voice cried. 'Miss Knight, can you hear us? Little Craig's having a nervous breakdown.'

'Breakdown? I know *exactly* how he feels.' I flicked over to the next page. 'Mmm, that beach looks nice. It's perfect.'

Reluctantly I got up from my hiding place and steadied myself against the wall. Having stacked my files neatly on the desk, I snapped shut my attache case and scribbled a note... 'GONE TROPPO!' Smoothing down my dress, I took a deep breath and walked outside.

'I didn't think you were here,' the secretary sputtered.

'I'm not. I'm far, far away ... in Bali.'

*

CHAPTER ONE
Kuta Nights

Kuta streets were dirty and congested, a jumble of shops and stalls spilling out onto the narrow pavements. All my wondrous visions of Bali were disintegrating as the bus inched its way through the chaos.

'Lia Knight - Sunsea Beach club,' the tour guide called, ticking me off his list before speeding onto the next hotel. After a quick welcome drink the room-boy led me to my bungalow, set amid a cluster of ripe tropical palms. Standing on the thatched balcony, immersed in the balmy sea air, my mood softened with every waft of perfumed scent from the overhanging blossoms.

'Which way to the ocean?' The young man smiled deliciously, then pointed across the lush gardens. He was barely out the door before I'd ripped off my clothes and flung on a costume. I needed to bask in the warmth of the sun and erase any trace of Sydney's winter from my mind.

The heat on the beach was intense, the blaze of the sun igniting the sand. Running across it, I escaped into the welcome shade of a solitary tree. The sea stretched out forever, an endless blue. Huge waves rolled to shore, streaked with brilliant shards of crystal light. This was the Bali of my imaginings. Mythically beautiful and full of exotic promise. Another wave crashed to shore, the sound rippling off the horizon. My dream had come true; I had created my own reality.

Lulled by the intrinsic beauty of the scene, I sat entranced, until rudely interrupted by an odd collection of feet shuffling towards me. The stampede had begun and I was the hapless victim.

'Massage?' a syrupy voice crooned. Hidden under a large straw hat and layers of tattered clothing, the old woman grinned at me like a toothless banshee. 'I give you good price, morning price.' Without warning she pummelled my body, ploughing into me with the force of a Sumo wrestler. 'Me dark, no good - you lucky, skin white. Number nine best - you tell friends. No forget.'

Meanwhile, her bony friend had me in a headlock. 'Plait your hair?' she warbled in nauseating niceness, twirling a few strands of my hair around her stringy fingers. 'Nice beads ... you got lotta hair but I do cheap for you.'

Rising up from the sand dunes, another girl plonked down beside me and grabbed hold of my foot. Painting a sample toenail bright cherry red, she held me in a vice. 'Pedicure? I do flowers ... make you very sexy.'

A barrage of heaving humanity had invaded my secluded spot. My view of the ocean was obliterated by a sea of waving hands thrusting all manner of things at me. All I wanted was a little privacy, but that was obviously the last thing I was going to get. My hopes were dashed further with the arrival of fresh troops.

'You buy silver?' A tray of metal trinkets was shoved in my face. 'Cheap silver for you, missy.' Cheap was *hardly* the word for it.

'You like woodcarving?' A squat, offensive man stood directly in my line of sun, blocking any chance of a tan. 'I got chess set. Buddha?' He gestured to the solid carved head balanced on his own.

'You want sarong?' Piles of batik were being unfurled on the sand. 'Where you stay? When you come?' the stranger gabbled, addressing me like an intimate friend. 'First time in Bali? *Suti*, remember me for later.'

'Look, I don't want anything,' I protested. 'Could you all please just leave me alone. What I really need is a rest.'

'You promise with me,' an obese woman in a worn batik sarong barked, ripping up the rest of the mob by their roots. The ground groaned as she thundered towards me. 'You promise to buy yesterday. Why you not buy? You not good person, break promise!'

'Whoa! I never *promise* to buy anything yesterday, because I only got here today. Understand? Comprende? Now go away.' They looked at me blankly, refusing to budge. 'What's more, I don't have any money because I haven't had time to change it yet.'

A look of horror swept their faces as the message registered. My foot, of no further value, was dropped onto the scorching sand, the sticky polish melting into a congealed mess. The massage lady rose muttering a string of obscenities before disappearing into the distance along with the rest of her brood. Peace, at last.

Hiding under my book, I refused to show my face again in case I was subjected to another attack. I shouldn't have worried; news of my poverty had gone public and I was avoided by all but a few stray dogs who nosed around this lifeless lump in the sand with disinterest.

Anchored to the spot until dusk, I watched an army of people amble along the beach, hoping to see or be seen. Even the famous Kuta sunset fizzled out, swallowed up by an expanse of dull cloud.

Once back in the room, I stripped off and stared in horror at my reflection in the mirror. Huge red welts were rising on my body where the fierce tropical sun had left its mark. I tried to wash them off under the trickle of tepid shower water, but they were indelible.

Taking refuge under a flowing robe, I headed for the comfort of the dining room. It was packed with nubile teens sporting bouffant perms. Milling around the buffet table, they picked at the food whilst eyeing off the dashing array of males jammed against the bar. Clad in standard stubbies and singlets stood a visual assault of the worst kind: the flower of colonial manhood.

The Sunsea club had been a last minute booking. It was high season and the hotels were packed. My travel agent had advised me with great relish that the club was strictly for eighteen to thirty-five year olds and I had just edged in with a shove. I remembered feeling particularly humble. Plucking a skewered *sate* stick off the buffet table, I bit into it, plotting how I could best exact revenge on my return.

A smorgasbord dinner was included in my voucher, so I piled as much food as I could onto my plate as a form of culinary compensation. Trailing bits of fruit salad across the floor, I found the closest seat and wedged myself into a table bursting with young Wollongong lasses in designer lycra.

The girls were engaged in heavy conversation. Blue-eyed Debbie had spent the previous night in a torrid encounter with young Shane from the adjoining bungalow. It was clear from the laughter and lewd comments coming from the bar, that Shane was corroborating Debbie's story. His mates were rapt in the telling, squeezing their beer cans and snorting at all the good bits. 'Pass her round when you've finished, Shaney boy!'

Meanwhile, back at the table, Debbie's friend, Cheryl, was beside herself with lust. 'Geez, Deb, he's sure a spunk. He can leave his runners under my bed any time! Tell us *all* and don't leave out the juicy bits.' The girls tittered, leaning inwards in readiness. Cheryl took a drag of her cigarette, refusing to exhale until she answered. It was Debbie's finest hour.

With a sly smirk, Debbie ran her hand provocatively along the stem of her glass. Dipping her finger in the stale wine, she pulled it out and sucked it slowly. Shane started howling at the bar and his mates had to forcibly restrain him from running over and mounting Debbie on the dinner table.

'Dickhead,' a skeletal brunette sneered. You could tell from her assertive nasal tone that Francine was leader of the pack. Extracting her glomesh compact from her bag, she glared into the mirror before launching into a full-scale attack. 'How many times do I have to tell you,' Fran said, smearing on her magenta lipstick, 'if you want them to respect you, you have to wait until the second night. Now for sure he'll think you're a moll. I hope you weren't so bloody pissed that you forgot to be careful,' she added, cutting through Debbie's euphoria like a blunt knife.

'Well, you know how it is,' Debbie faltered, 'I sort of forgot. Shane said it would be alright, said he'd be real quick. Come to think of it, he was so fast I'm not sure if anything *really* happened.'

'Deb, you're a dead loss,' Fran moaned, 'you could have at least borrowed one of Cheryl's pills before you went to his room.'

It was hard to resist the temptation to comment at this stage. One look at hefty Shane in his shag-pile hair and footie shorts, and I could only presume they were referring to a Valium or at the very least an aspirin. On reflection, Debbie would have needed a double dose of both to have made it through the night.

'Don't give me a hard time,' Debbie wailed, 'you're just jealous. Now can we eat, I'm *so* hungry I could swallow a horse.' The irony of her statement was lost on the girls.

As they hoed into their food platters, Fran caught the look of consternation on my face and realised for the first time that I was actually there. Her eyes glazed over as her chest began to heave.

'Who are you?' she challenged. All eyes turned. Debbie choked on her noodles, sensing the presence of an intruder in their midst. 'How did you get here,' she asked cagily, 'are you someone's mother?'

'No', I answered, horrified. 'Why, has somebody lost one?'

I slid off my chair and beat a hasty retreat to the bar. It was long since deserted, Shane and the boys having left to attack a large plate of prawns at the buffet. I was a non-drinker, but decided this would be the perfect opportunity to start. I flicked through the bar list and picked the closest drink to my state of mind. 'One Tropical Nightmare, please.'

I was handed a deadly green brew in a martini glass. Brushing aside the glacé cherries and paper umbrella, I took a sip and gagged. As I attempted to recover my composure, a shadowy figure sidled over, his dark onyx eyes bursting with lust and hidden motives.

'I'm Romeo, the Entertainment Officer. Having a good time?'

'Terribly,' I replied, refraining from elaborating on the point.

'Well, I'm here to make sure you do.' He took my hand and started nibbling on my fingers. I snatched my knuckles away before he could draw blood. 'Call on me if you need anything, *anything* at all.' Dense clouds of musky aftershave wafted through the air flooding my brain with a torrent of obscene carnal longing. I was mesmerised by his smell, pure heaven with just the slightest hint of hell. 'What about tonight? Are you taken?'

Thrusting his pelvis close to mine, Romeo leaned forward, exposing a taut brown chest studded with a cluster of dangling gold medallions. He stared hard, then flashed a knowing smile. The man had teeth to die for. The image, right down to the deep vocal monotone and intense gaze, was very slick. What glaring oversight had allowed the club to exclude Romeo from their current brochure? Resolving not to become one of the notches on his belt, I got up from my stool and removed myself from his clutches.

'Excuse me, it's been a long day. I need some sleep.'

'May I walk you to your bungalow? It's *so* dark tonight.'

'Thanks, but I'm sure I can manage.' Walking down the path, I was confronted by a maze of signposts and the distant sound of Shane and the gang in a drunken brawl. I stopped and reconsidered. There was no risk. Having been deprived of a man and the moonlight for so long, the danger lay more for him than me. 'Maybe you could show me the way.'

'Great, we can stop at the beach to admire the view.'

'Only the most direct route,' I insisted.

Romeo was on his best behaviour, restraining himself as far as the bungalow, but the scent of a bed in close proximity triggered his overactive libido and he made a last minute dive. He was an opportunist and not about to let this one go by.

He lunged, falling upon me. With the first touch of his lips, forbidden feelings began to fester. Twinges of passion surfaced as the smell of his body seared a path through a barrage of repressed emotions. The *kundalini* was rising, I thought the inner flame had snuffed it long ago.

Throwing care to the wind, I gave myself fully to the pleasure of the moment until my mind was distracted by a painful sensation. Something hard and unpleasant was being pressed against me. Having determined that it was not Romeo I turned to come face to face with a giant *Garuda* bird statue. Its massive stone beak was wedged between my vertebrae, cutting off all circulation. It was a sign. The lack of feeling jolted me to my senses.

'If you let me in,' Romeo pledged admiring his reflection in the window, 'I guarantee you the most exciting night of your life.'

Realising his pleas fell on deaf ears, he slicked back his hair, hitched up his trousers and wandered down the path in search of new quarry.

Weary beyond belief, I slipped into bed and tussled with the sheets. They scraped raw against my sunburn. Just as I was about to fall asleep, there was a light knock on the door. I stumbled over to open it, expecting to find the persistent Romeo, but was instead confronted by a seedy security guard.

Ogling me, he stammered, 'I think I love you ... can I come in?'

'You must be mad,' I yelled, slamming the door in his face. 'Go away! Everyone's insane around here!' Crawling into bed, I tossed the blanket over my head in a vain attempt to block out the events of the day. There was another knock on the door, this time more urgent. I yanked it open. It was the same man.

'What is it now,' I seethed, rapidly losing any semblance of patience. Mobilising for attack, I looked around for a weapon, but the toilet brush was the most lethal thing I could find.

'I love you more now,' he said limply. '*Now* can I come in?'

'If you don't go immediately,' I snapped, 'I'll be forced to call the security guard.' Even as I said them, I realised how ridiculous my words were. However, they did the trick. Shrugging his shoulders, he vanished into the bushes. I sighed deeply. This had been my first day in Bali. I hoped it wasn't a taste of things to come.

In a bid to recuperate, I collapsed into the solace of my bed. Swept away to a far-off place where my body could find much needed rest, I slept as I'd never slept before. The days floated by as if in a dream, with no way to gauge the passing of time. Only the muffled voices of the room-boys provided a clue. The *Do Not Disturb* sign proved an adequate deterrent and they left me in peace, allowing me the space to recuperate and heal.

In my dream state I soared far into the heavens, high amongst the clouds, until Sydney's city skyline faded far from view. All stress left behind, swallowed up by the bleak, cement horizon. Pressures shrunk into the distance with the last trace of civilisation. Up here I was invincible; nothing could touch me. Up here in the heavens I was master of my world.

Through the scattered cloud, rich bands of coastal green merged into a vast expanse of red barren earth. Tracts of lifeless, clay-baked desert, steeped in ancient memory, sprawled out for miles as the heart of my country lay bare and desolate below me.

Without clearly knowing why, I had turned my back on an ageless land and headed for a far-off place: the mystical island of Bali. It was the ultimate escape. My life was falling apart, so I had made the difficult decision to sever all connections with the past and aim towards the future. I needed to forget who I was for a while and more importantly, to learn who I could become.

Driven by an understanding that my life was charged with a mission, I let the universe guide me. In the past, my faith had served me well. Through the dreamy haze, an island glowed in the distance. Lush green and mysterious. Bali. Now at last the first clues could be revealed. Now if fate decreed, I could find my destiny.

Replenished by the vision, I awoke to a beautiful day. Flinging open the doors to my bungalow, I inhaled the fresh ocean air. My stomach rumbled so I flagged down a passing waitress. After demolishing a huge plate of banana and coconut pancakes topped with honey, I scanned my surroundings for signs of life.

Even though it was early, the grounds were a hive of activity. The gardener was noisily sweeping the grass with a clump of dry thatch, while several young girls strolled through the bushes, picking fresh blossoms to decorate the statues along the path. The garden was alive with flowers, a beautiful palette of colour.

A gracious woman dressed in a pastel sarong walked by, a tray stacked with offerings balanced firmly on her head. Burning incense drifted behind her, leaving a subtle perfume trail. Kneeling in front of the temple, she placed some baskets on the altar, delicately waving her hands in prayer.

Across the way I spied Debbie with stilettos in hand, creeping home after a heavy night out with Shane. Dishevelled beyond repair, she scuttled past her friends' hut, frantically wiping off a thick layer of sand encrusted on her body. No prizes for guessing where she'd spent the night.

'What should I do today?' I thought languidly. The beach was definitely out, my skin was already peeling. I could go for a leisurely stroll and look at the shops or perhaps explore the local sights. Unable to muster the energy to move, I spread out on the bamboo lounge and wallowed in the infinite pleasure of doing nothing.

❁

By mid-afternoon, I was ready to venture out onto the streets. Dodging an onslaught of soup-trolleys and bicycles, I plodded along the main road pitted with potholes. These were hazardous enough without the legion of pesky watch-sellers blocking the way like marauding sharks. One, snapping the lid of his case defiantly, refused to budge, so I took refuge in the nearest shop.

Once inside I was able to peruse undisturbed, the salesgirls being far too engrossed in the soapies on television. Lying on the floor, slurping their *bakso*, the local meatball soup, with an intimate circle of friends, they remained oblivious to my presence and I had to step over their inert bodies to get to the racks.

Everything was size eight or under, so I gave up and wandered down the street past a staggering array of clothing, silver and leather-ware. Exhausted, I followed the blare of music into a huge cassette shop lined with innumerable posters of Madonna in various stages of undress. Selecting some tapes, I put on the headphones expecting to be soothed by the relaxing tones of Kitaro. Instead, I was blasted with a dose of Cold Chisel. 'Excuse me,' a voice called out, jerking at the cord, 'but I think you've plugged yourself into the wrong hole.'

'Sounds like the story of my life!'

'Then you must have led an interesting one,' the tall blond laughed, holding out a perfectly manicured hand flecked with diamonds. 'I'm Kate.' Her broad smile was warm yet there was a hint of haughtiness that suggested a more intricate character. 'Sorry that didn't come out quite right.'

'Don't worry, I guarantee nothing you could do or say would phase me. I've been in Bali for over twenty-four hours and survived!'

'Don't be so sure,' she countered, flicking back a mane of tawny hair. 'I've lived here for over six months and the place still never ceases to amaze.'

'Should I start packing my bags?'

'No, there's lots of compensations.' Right on cue, the young stud opposite took off his headphones and winked. A twinkle lit up Kate's wide hazel eyes. 'If you're not busy tonight, I'll show you how it's done. Prepare yourself for lesson number one!'

The restaurant was packed and people were queuing at the bar for a table. The waiter recognised Kate and we were whisked ahead and led to an intimate booth beside a fish-pond brimming with lotus and golden carp.

'I hadn't realised you were a woman of influence,' I said, impressed. Kate had a definite style that commanded respect. Elegantly chic in designer white, with fine porcelain skin and hair rolled back into a chignon, she was the epitome of sophistication. This was the sort of woman who could run the board-room, whip out and beat the boys in three rounds of tennis and return to the office without a hair out of place.

'I'm rather well known around these parts,' Kate replied, fully aware of her own power. 'Managing a disco tends to be high profile.'

'So tell me, how did you end up working here?' I asked, a tinge of envy creeping into my voice. 'Wouldn't it be pretty hard?'

'Oh, it depends on your connections. I have to admit I've been lucky. Came to Bali for a week's holiday and ended up staying.' Kate had the persona of a woman in love. Despite her independent veneer, her energy was concentrated elsewhere.

'All this because of a man?' I reflected.

'That's pretty astute of you,' Kate gasped, genuinely shocked. 'I don't usually give away any secrets, how did you figure that out?'

'Let's just say I'm a natural sensitive. Now tell me all.'

'I'm used to keeping things to myself,' Kate said, leaning back and crossing her long legs. Her sandal dangled casually off the sole of her foot, 'maybe after a few Strawberry Daiquiris ...'

'Where do I begin?' Kate asked, staring into her drink. 'In a nutshell, I came here and did something I vowed I'd never do, I committed the cardinal sin - *I fell in love.* I had a ten-year career plan and went and botched it all up. I'd never swerved off course in my life; I'm nearly thirty and I've never allowed emotion to get in the way of my ambitions before.'

'Aren't you being a little hard on yourself,' I replied, scooping into the avocado dip, 'one *can* combine business and pleasure.'

'I know, but I'm single-minded, driven in fact. I don't like feeling out of control. To make matters worse my lover is my *boss.* I fell for the man the first time I laid eyes on him and he arranged this job so we could be together. Can you imagine, I threw away a crack position in an advertising firm in Melbourne where I'd spent the last few years clawing my way up the corporate ladder, to be with him. Threw it all away on a whim.'

'Who wouldn't? Living on a tropical island, a job with bright lights and music, plus a man who loves you. It doesn't sound so bad.'

'Cliff's wonderful. He's rich, handsome and an absolute gentleman, and,' she added, switching into cool business mode, 'he gives me free reign to do what I want with the disco, besides he's far too busy running his other business interests. We've gone to great lengths to hide our relationship - at my insistence. I don't want my credibility destroyed, it's hard enough being a woman around here and getting the guys to respect you.'

'It sounds as if you've got it made, you're lucky. I left home with no particular goal in mind - except to escape. I knew it was time to go, all the doors were banging shut in my face, or perhaps I was closing them.'

'Ah, the end of an era and the beginning of a new one. Join the club. At least you were fortunate enough to recognise the need to move on, a lot of people go through the motions of life without the courage to change.'

'For me it would have taken infinitely more courage to stay. I couldn't handle the demands of conformity any more, my spirit was clamouring for release. I had a good job as a counsellor but I'd simply outgrown it. My relationship of three years was fine, Brad was a good man - in retrospect, too good. The spark, or maybe the challenge, wasn't there anymore. I can't believe it's been over a year since we split; time flies by and then it's lost forever. When my health started to suffer, reflecting the sorry state of my mind and spirit, I knew I had to make a move before it was too late.'

'So you hopped on a plane and came here.'

'Basically. I've always been something of a wanderer. I've travelled all over the world looking for a place to belong, and never found it. I've come close a couple of times, but the circumstances never gelled. I'm determined to finally make sense of it, I want to find out where I'm meant to be.'

'And you think Bali might just be the place ...'

'The wheels of destiny are turning, I'm sure a higher power compelled me to come here. As soon as I got off the plane it was all so familiar. That sharp blue sky, the white of the frangipani blossoms, the exotic scent in the air. I almost bent down and kissed the tarmac. Then when I saw the bedlam outside, I suppressed my instinct to judge. There's much more to this place than meets the eye, and I intend to find out exactly what it is.'

'Brave woman! I'm quite happy just skimming the surface, that deep stuff can get pretty heavy. The one thing I have learnt since I got here is how to have fun. Life shouldn't only be boring business luncheons, corporate meetings and deadlines. Let me propose a toast.' Kate clinked her glass loudly against mine. 'To life and the complete pursuit of happiness.'

'How far is Mojo's?' I asked, narrowly missing a tree branch that had been tossed into a gaping hole in the pavement. 'Can you imagine how many drunken Aussies have disappeared down there?' I asked, peering into the dark hole. 'There's probably still a few wandering around the sewers trying to figure out where the hell they are.'

'With a bit of luck they'll stay down there!' Taking purposeful strides, Kate skirted the bands of beggars blocking the way and leapt over the collapsed slabs of cement, barely batting an eye.

I followed her down a congested dark alley throbbing with music and low-life. Four or five bars competed for attention, megaphonic speakers spat out deafening octaves of Jimmy Barnes. By day Kuta was hot and ugly, by night it bordered on the supernatural. Sunlight had given it a hint of reality; its absence invited hallucination. Looking ahead I winced, fazed by the awesome scene. I had rammed straight into a human catastrophe.

Poised at the bar, clutching their prize schooners, a heaving barrage of manhood was all set to race for line honours in a drinking competition. *'Wayne from W.A.,'* an over-ripe man with a sagging belly bellowed into the microphone. The mob from Perth roared its approval. His opponent, *'Morrie from Mudgee,'* balanced his glass on his sweaty scalp awaiting starter's orders. He looked all set for victory until the hairy meatball on his left wrenched the mike from his hand. *'Norm from New South fuckin' Wales, watch out you bastards.'* With that, the race was on, the boys guzzling the beer down in a battle of wills. Norm won hands down.

'Can we get out of here?' I begged, trying to escape from the moving mass of insanity. 'It's like standing on the highway to Hell!'

Braving a thick pall of cigarette smoke, we pushed inside Mojo's as the beat of the heavy music pounded against the walls. Reeling from the impact of the flouro lights, I shimmied into the only empty booth and watched enthralled as the seething crowd danced and drank their way to oblivion.

Kate was in her element. I wondered if she gained some sort of perverse pleasure in torturing herself every night. 'Fascinating, isn't it,' she said, gazing into the bottomless pit, 'and what's more I love every sleazy inch of it. It's the antithesis of everything I've ever known.'

Suddenly a sharp crackle echoed through the speakers. 'Oh, shit,' Kate sighed, 'looks like there's a problem again. Here comes Jett and he doesn't look too happy.' The DJ climbed down from his musical tower and strode over. As he walked by every female head turned in awe. His was the arrogance of a thousand conquests and he wore it well. Dressed in black skin-tight trousers and a shirt peppered with the merest splash of rhinestone, he carved a path through the crowd on the strength of his aura alone. It was almost as impressive as the parting of the Dead Sea.

Seating himself strategically between us, Jett got involved in a heated discussion with Kate. Every now and again, he shot me a meaningful glance to let me know I wasn't forgotten. Formalities over with, he squeezed my thigh under the table and deposited his hand in my lap. 'Lose something, did we?' I asked, giving it back to him.

He laughed haughtily and swivelled around for a full-on stare. 'Black is so sensual,' he fingered my collar and rubbed the back of his hand along the nape of my neck, 'just like you.' His touch was smooth and well oiled, his manner equally slick. Jett was supremely handsome in a vampirish sort of way. 'Come up to the booth later on and see how I handle my knobs,' he said, flicking back his hair rakishly. 'We can get to know each other better.'

'Is he for real?' I asked Kate as soon as he was out of earshot.

'Jett's got an ego the size of this building, and then some. He's our top DJ and all the girls run after him, so he's left a trail of broken hearts behind. It's all an act really. Deep down he's got a heart of gold, looks can be deceptive.'

'You know it's strange but every second man I meet on this island turns me on. Half of them look like the last tribe of the Mohicans - I think it's awakening past life memories. I walked around for the last year back home with barely a twinge of desire but since I arrived, I've been on heat.'

'It does it to the best of us - all that smooth brown skin, those hunky bodies and steamy nights. You'll have to excuse me for a while, I've told Cliff a thousand times to invest in a new sound system but he always gets side-tracked. I better find him before Jett quits and really leaves us in the lurch.'

I spent the next hour getting slightly inebriated and looking up at Jett, pretending to stare at a spot on the ceiling. He was busy with the failing speakers and the battalion of young hopefuls who were shoving much more in his palm than a record request. Jett brushed them all off with the disinterest of a stuffed bear who has overdosed on the honey jar.

Much to my chagrin, my obsession did not go unnoticed. Jett caught me out. He stared back at me - a deep, searing look that said it all. Slowly and deliberately he changed the record, never once averting his gaze. The mood changed, the lights dimmed and all movement ground to a halt. The music melted into the walls.

'Baby, feel the heat ... I'm breathless with desire.'

Slow, sensual and erotic, the message pointed.

'Let me wrap my love around you ... baby, feel the heat.'

The trap set, Jett stalked over with the stealth of a black panther and refusing to be thwarted, dragged me back to his den. Locked in a tangle of cables and whirling lights, I sifted through the records. Jett manipulated the complex control panel while skilfully draping his body over mine. 'You're not like the others, something about you is so sexy ... you're really turning me on.'

'Jett, why do I get the feeling that you say that to every girl?'

'But *you're* different,' he said, breathing into my ear and coming in for the kill. With the soft wisp of his sigh, I could feel my resolve melt.

'Aren't we all?' I wriggled from his hold. 'Ah, my favourite, Santana.' Plucking the disc from the stack I threw it at him, hoping to stem the overflow of rancid passion. *'Black Magic Woman.'*

From the first twang, I knew I'd made a mistake. Jett was ecstatic, working himself up with every grind of the guitar. The smouldering heat generated between us was burning up the wires, his dark eyes slicing erotic highways through my heart. My knees melted as he pressed against me, the magnetism intensely carnal.

None of it made sense. Jett could have his pick of the young crop, and I should have known better. As much as I hated to admit it, I was flattered. It had been a long time between suitors, ages since I'd been singled out for attention and it felt good. Forget that he was a seasoned performer, forget that he'd probably got all his inspiration from a Fantale wrapper and practised his moves night after night - I'd deal with that later. Right now, I had come alive.

'Let's get out of here,' Jett said, unable to handle my erotic fantasies any longer. He too had a few of his own he was keen to try out. Signalling a friend to take over, he grabbed his leather jacket and led me towards the nearest exit. 'I'll show you just how serious I am.'

'Not so fast, I have to find Kate,' I protested, trying to let the effect of the alcohol wear off. Maybe I needed time to reconsider. A year or two.

'Don't worry about her, she knows you're in safe hands.'

Once outside, Jett snapped his fingers at one of the security guards.

From a darkened alcove, emerged a huge black and silver motor bike dripping every optional extra, including two gleaming chrome exhaust pipes that looked like they'd dropped off a Concord.

'Check out my Harley?' Jett beamed, wiping away the merest hint of a smear on the body. 'Great, isn't it?' He jumped onto the bike in an almost orgiastic ritual and motioned for me to follow.

'I must be mad!' Muttering mantras of protection, I flung myself headlong onto the enormous monster.

Jett revved up the huge engine and the bike roared into life. It unleashed its fury and hurtled down the crowded lane scattering people like fallen leaves in its wake. I clung on for dear life, burying my head in his jacket. 'Isn't this wild?' he roared above the din.

'Sensational! Can we get off soon?'

We screeched to a halt outside some shops in a side street. 'This is where I live,' Jett said, fixing his helmet to the bike. 'Come up for a drink.' He led the way up the decrepit staircase.

The place was a mess, a double mattress lay floundering on the bare floor amidst a stack of stale ashtrays and half-drunk cups of coffee. A rotating orb light cast warped patterns on the walls as the radio played softly to itself in the background.

'Coke all right?' Jett handed me a chilled bottle, flopped onto the lumpy mattress then inserted a *Songs of Seduction* tape into the deck. 'Come join me,' he said, patting the edge of the bed.

My mind became a battleground of conflicting thoughts, flashing from saint to sinner. Red light warning. *Wait for the romance, the love, the flowers and intimate promises.* Green light. *Life's too short, have a ball.*

In spite of my better judgement, I sat down beside him. Jett was not one to waste time. His lips crunched into mine. The first taste of him was enough to lift the alcoholic blur. I refocussed sharply and pulled away. Jett wasn't quite so impressive in the bright light. Did I detect a trace of boyish acne?

'Well, do you want to do it or not?' he asked absently picking his teeth with a toothpick. Spreadeagled on the bed, Jett's muscles were hot with purple fire, throbbing lustily in time to the music.

'I'll pass this time,' I replied, not completely won over by his romantic overture. I was used to men with a little more finesse.

'No worries, I could do with a night off.' Jett lit up a cigarette and stared into space. I found a chair a safe distance away and fell into a stupor. When I came to, Jett had passed out and was snoring loudly.

Seizing the opportunity, I grabbed my bag and tiptoed down the stairs.

The first rays of morning sun tinged the sky as I emerged onto the street. I hoped no-one would be up, but it was already a hive of activity. Hopelessly out of place, my black sequins crumpled and limp, my make-up smudged beyond recognition, I knew exactly how Debbie felt after a sordid night out with Shane. Luckily, I was able to find my way back to the hotel.

I tried sneaking through the entrance undetected. I didn't want news of my humiliation to go public. Instead I walked straight into the leering gaze of *that* security guard. Winking lecherously, he murmured something indecipherable under his breath. It was a sign.

I vowed to catch the first bus out of Kuta and go in search of the real Bali. I made a solemn pledge to concentrate less on the physical and more on the spiritual. That way I wouldn't get myself in trouble. Or so I thought.

CHAPTER TWO
Escape to Ubud

The road to Ubud flowed through a panorama of lush green fields fringed with towering palms. Packed into a small van between a sprightly old man and a heaving black pig with a bad case of wind, the trip took forever. The driver hurtled along the curvy road, screeching to a halt only to offload his many passengers and swap them for more.

It was a great relief when I was squeezed out near Ubud. Trailing a string of signposts, I followed one pointing to Mama's Guesthouse and hiked down the road for the longest fifty metres I'd ever experienced. There, set amid the rice fields, were three small thatched bungalows.

The young man working in the garden wiped his gritty hands against his sarong and walked over. Naked to the waist, his body was sleek brown and firm. 'Hello, my name's Nyoman,' he said, opening the gate. 'There's one room left if you'd like to take a look.'

The bamboo hut was simple yet comfortable. Nestled amongst a patch of red hibiscus, it lay hidden from the world outside. 'It's wonderful,' I said, drinking in the quiet beauty of the scene. The rice fields shimmered soft amber, reflecting the peaceful glow of the surroundings.

'It's quiet here,' Nyoman said softly, sensing my need. 'I'm sure you'll be happy. We don't provide meals but I'd be pleased to show you around, there's plenty of good restaurants to choose from.'

Later that evening I strolled through fields of long grass with Nyoman silently leading the way. Vivid rays of sun engulfed the sky with streams of golden-red as the day folded into night. A young boy in ragged clothes wandered by, leading a flock of well-fed ducks. They warbled happily as they waddled past in single file. Delicate doe-eyed cows, with tinkling wooden bells tied around their necks, grazed unperturbed by our presence.

'That's Laura's cafe,' Nyoman pointed to an open terrace laced with pink lotus, 'the food's delicious. Want to give it a try?'

Leaning against some large floral cushions, I stretched out on the rattan mat, mulling over what to order. Nyoman sat cross-legged, agile and poised. As he spoke to the waiter, I studied his face fully for the first time. Serene and composed, his was the beauty of an old soul - an old soul perfectly at ease in a young man's body. It was his hands that betrayed the secret. They were a study in timelessness, with fine bones and ecstatic sensitivity. Even as he talked, I found it difficult to remove my gaze.

'Ubud attracts a more cultured type,' Nyoman explained as the restaurant filled up with guests, mostly European. 'This is the centre of art, so those who come here are more serious about discovering the real Bali.'

'Tell me about the real Bali,' I asked, staring out into the still darkness. 'I'm sure most tourists barely scratch the surface.'

'They see what we allow them to see. That's why the culture remains strong, nothing can truly penetrate it.' Nyoman looked at me through eyes of antiquity. The eyes of a people who have seen much change but remain impervious to it all. 'Ours is a turbulent past with many kings and even more heroes, empires spanning centuries. The Dutch tried to defeat us earlier this century but failed. Like many before them, they underestimated the character of the people - their strength and determination. When the troops marched on the palace in Denpasar, they could not anticipate the outcome.'

'And what was that?' I asked, engrossed.

'*Puputan* ... death with honour. The king ordered the palace burnt then led a procession outside. Despite pleas from the Dutch, he ordered a priest to stab him in the heart. Then his wives, children, officials, servants, dressed in white and wearing their finest jewellery, rushed the troops, forcing them to open fire. Over four thousand died in one day alone. Mass suicide with dignity rather than enforced submission. When you can penetrate the rationale behind this, then you will begin to understand.'

After dinner, we walked back under the stars as I pondered Nyoman's words. A solitary bat ripped though the sky, charging it with mystery. From the distance, came the pervasive, steady sound of a single drumbeat. Tiny fireflies flickered around us, flashing translucent beams of light. I reached out, but they evaded my touch. The answer to Nyoman's question was equally elusive.

Determined to tap into the secrets that lay buried beneath the surface, I spent the next weeks exploring the area. Ancient villages, shielded by vast canopies of sacred banyan trees and guarded by feral dogs, stood curiously detached like gnarled fortresses. The people appeared as aloof as their surroundings, regarding my forays into their territory with disinterest.

Many villages specialised in their own unique artistic skills; painting, woodcarving and stonework - unparalleled workmanship, perfected over centuries of collective consciousness. Young children, barely able to hold their tools, sat immersed learning the gifts of their grandfathers. I spent countless hours perusing the local galleries stocked with a vast array of fine works.

Thus inspired I sought to uncover my own artistic side. With my easel set up in a secluded rice-field, I discovered more about myself than I expected. Not so much in the proliferation of talent which had lain dormant for so long, but more in the inexplicable connection that developed between myself and my environment. The familiarity was profound.

Standing alone in the shaded fields, hushed by the stillness of the air, I was overcome by an obvious peace. The profound sanctity that comes when the soul identifies inside itself a place of innate value, a land that awakens memories and reactions stored deep within the psyche. A land that inspires an instinct of belonging so strong, that once aroused it refuses to be denied.

Here in this sublime setting, with its lucid shadows and polished sunlight, the bond was absolute. High amongst the clouds, I'd catch a glimpse of the mountain, Agung, jutting into the heavens and the feeling would escalate. Feverishly I worked to capture its mystery onto canvas, hoping to pierce the enigma but it was an impossible task, no more feasible than counting the drops in an ocean. Such beauty was unfathomable.

'Time for a break.' Nyoman poured some hot tea from the thermos.

'Thanks,' I said, putting down my brush and wiping my hands with a cloth. 'How do you like my masterpiece?'

'A true work of art,' Nyoman smiled, wiping a dab of paint off my cheek. 'How are the dance classes going?'

'I've given up! I'm not the lithe classical type, and short of traction my fingers simply refuse to bend backwards. I've decided to concentrate on painting instead, but I'm having trouble capturing the magic of the mountain. Any suggestions?'

'You've set yourself an awesome task. Mount Agung is the holiest site in Bali. There's an old folk tale that says a god skimmed off the top of the Himalayas and hid it under the sea but the highest peak remained visible as Bali. Mount Agung, jutting out in all its glory, became home to the gods.'

'And they cast their blessings over the entire island. Nyoman, if you were given the chance, would you leave? There's a very different world out there, aren't you tempted to venture out and take a look?'

'We are taught that the world was created as a turtle. Bali rests on its back under a cover of perfumed sky. It is the jewel of the earth, its centre. I already have the best, why seek more? In any case, wherever we go our soul follows. I am at peace here and have no desire to go further.'

His words glimmered with truth. Perhaps if I had been born here, I would not venture beyond. The island exuded enough spiritual essence to endow its offspring with a certain contentment. If I stayed long enough I might imbibe the divine elixir and be similarly blessed.

'Oh, I nearly forgot the main reason I dropped round,' Nyoman said, taking an embossed envelope from his pocket. 'My friend, Agung, is getting married tomorrow. Would you like to come to the ceremony as my guest?'

With every gesture, the bond grew more intense.

Under an elaborate outdoor canopy, the guests filtered into the courtyard. Dressed in all their finery, most sat nibbling rice cakes and gossiped, none visibly interested in the proceedings.

'Weddings can be very long-winded affairs, many rites have to be completed before the ceremony begins,' Nyoman explained, handing me a bottle of tepid tea. In white tunic buttoned in gold, atop a burgundy sarong, he looked stunning. The true essence of his self shone through. 'Agung's high caste and he's marrying a woman of royal caste like himself.'

'Can the castes intermarry?'

'Yes, but it's not encouraged. In the past, it was essential to find a partner of equal status, so first cousins were often chosen to prevent dispute. This was even more vital for the girl, if she married below caste she lost her title, bringing discredit to the entire family. In one Regency, six of the nine princesses never married because no suitable men could be found. It wasn't unknown for couples to be exiled or put to death for breaking this code.'

'Do these distinctions still exist today?'

'Yes, but not as strictly. The majority of people are Sudra caste like myself. We are given the names Wayan, Made, Nyoman and Ketut according to birth order, regardless of sex.'

'So you're the third born in your family?'

'No, actually I'm the seventh. The names repeat but the parent selects a different surname for each child. The *triwangsa,* the three other castes, are believed to be descendants of the aristocrats that fled the spread of Islam in Java six hundred years ago. The Weisyas were the warriors; the Ksatrias, like Agung, the royal class. The Brahmana priests, addressed as *Ida Bagus*, are revered and still highly respected today, because they are the members of the highest caste.'

After an hour's wait, there was still no sign of movement. *'Jam karet,'* Nyoman smiled, noting my discomfort, 'rubber time.'

At last, a flash of gold - the bride had arrived. Bare-shouldered and wrapped in heavy bolts of rich brocade, her chest was so tightly bound that every breath was laboured. Deeply shadowed eyes, accented by lines of thick kohl, remained downcast as she took small, tentative steps forward. Her high cheekbones were strongly rouged, her lips red and full. Raven black hair swept back in a loose bun, was topped by an intricate headdress of golden flowers and filigree. She was a stunning picture of stylised beauty.

The bridegroom, looking every bit as impressive, emerged from behind a small building. His sarong was the deepest of purples, banded by a wide golden sash. Tucked within was a magnificent *kris* dagger, its jewelled handle glistening in the sun. Dramatic in effect, his face was heavily made up, his eyes accentuated and wide. On his head was a *destar*, a raised headband, the same vibrant indigo as his sarong. His was a feast of imagery.

The couple stood nervously waiting for the ceremony to begin. On a raised platform close-by, sat the *pedanda,* the high priest. Tiny, with a body gnarled by the ravages of time, his uncut hair lay buried beneath a layer of twisted cloth, forming a huge white turban on his head. Chanting methodically and ringing a small brass bell, he descended from his tower and splashed the rigid couple with holy water from a hollow coconut shell.

Walking slowly together in concentric rings around a small tree planted especially for the occasion, they showed no sign of emotion. The bride, balancing a bowl of rice on her head, broke through a strand of white yarn held in her path by the groom's relatives. Her husband gently wielding a twig, struck her several times on her back. She blushed visibly and looked to the ground, her lack of eye contact deliberately submissive.

The ceremony dragged on forever. Nyoman had gone to talk to some friends and disappeared into the crowd. Standing well out of the way, I backed into one of the decorations - a tree of pork fat. Globules, melting in the hot sun, ran down my back. Several ladies tittered at my stupidity.

'Need this?' Nyoman handed me a napkin. 'See why people often choose to elope rather than go through an elaborate ceremony.'

'Do I detect a hint of romance underneath that studied exterior?'

'Not quite, an elopement is well planned. The man runs off with his intended wife to a friend's house. Once word has been sent that the girl is unharmed, the village head having confirmed that she has gone of her own free will and that the couple are truly in love, a dowry must be presented by the groom's family before they can be married in a simple ceremony.'

'I knew love figured in there somewhere.'

'You Westerners are far too sentimental.'

'I've come bearing offerings.' Nyoman proudly deposited a large bunch of rambutans on the verandah table. 'Freshly picked! I risked life and limb climbing up the tree getting them for you.'

'Are you sure your sister didn't buy them at the market?' I peeled off the prickly red skin and bit into the juicy flesh.

'You're getting far too cynical lately,' he laughed, tossing aside my book. 'It's time for a break and I know just the place.'

Brushing aside a giant palm leaf, Nyoman guided me along a steep ledge that led to an isolated ravine. Carefully negotiating the slippery rocks, I slid my way across a massive boulder slicked in green moss. Up ahead, a sparkling waterfall tumbled out from the rocky chasm, swelling into a deep natural pool. We climbed down to the river and followed the flow.

'Our own private swimming pool,' Nyoman laughed, plunging straight into the crystal water. Feeling lazy, I stretched out on a rock to bask in the sun. Shafts of light filtered through the trees, the transparent beams warm and healing on my body. I dared not move and disturb the flow. The soothing sound of the waterfall added to the effect, sending me into a dream.

Snatches of thoughts surfaced in my memory like vibrant prisms, spurred into consciousness by the erotic flow of the senses ... the vivid emerald of the leaves glistening with tropical dew, the rich warm smell of the earth, the sensual taste of the breeze as it brushed my lips. Strong, crisp images lay buried under a thick layer of time, desperate to take form.

A small child staring into the eyes of a cobra.

'Come on in.' Nyoman stood tall against the sun, dripping cool droplets of water onto my skin. Stooping down, he swept his wet hair back and stared at me intently. I caught my breath at the familiar beauty of his eyes. He belonged in this sheltered grove, part of my memory, as if I'd painted him there a long time ago.

'I feel so calm in this enchanted glade,' I said, rubbing my hand over the burnished stone, 'so impenetrable and safe.'

'Maybe you belong here, you look Balinese,' Nyoman smiled, stroking my arm, 'dark with soft, golden skin.'

'That's part of it, but it goes deeper ... much deeper. Wherever I go, I'm hit by this acute sense of deja vu, like I've been here before. It's difficult to explain, but it's like I've just returned home after a long, hard voyage.'

'Who knows, you could have lived here before, we might have been friends. The Balinese believe in reincarnation - the reward for a good life is to be reborn in Bali. In paradise. Maybe it was time for you to come home.'

Veiled by a tapestry of verdant leaves and swaying palms, I stared up at the remnants of the sky. Memories flooded back in a torrent. 'I used to have a recurring dream when I was child. I was in the middle of a jungle, I can still hear the cry of the birds. A young girl, with long shimmering black hair, lost in a tangle of plants and vines ... searching ... for something.'

'Searching for what?' Nyoman's mind was lost in wonder.

'I'm not sure. I vaguely remember the remains of an ancient temple hidden within the shrubs, a heap of toppled grey stones and moss. Drawn on by an invisible force, I climbed down the crumbling steps until I was trapped in a hollow dark chamber. In the corner was a huge leathery snake, its eyes searing fire - they burnt holes straight through me. I was less scared than fascinated. Strange, I haven't thought about it for years.'

'Under the surface of this island lie many secrets,' Nyoman whispered. 'If you stay, you may uncover some of your own.' A solitary dragonfly landed on his hand, drawn by his incredible energy. It stood transfixed, as he brushed its gossamer wings. 'Mystic secrets ... *yours* ... if you dare.'

A day of secrets. A grey day with a heavy, humid pall. Innocently I strayed along the wrong path, the path to the monkey forest. Struck with an innate sense of foreboding, I should have followed my instincts to retreat.

The woods were dank and musty. Venturing slowly through the gateway of twisted tree trunks and dense foliage, I reached a vacant pocket of air. My trepidation increased with the drop in temperature. A lone monkey swooped down from a tree, screeching at the sight of me. It bared its fangs in warning before scrambling back into the thick scrub.

Drawn onwards, I rounded an obscure bend and stumbled onto the ruins of an old temple. A shiver ran down my spine. *The temple of my dream?* Ominous statues, coated in a carpet of moss, stood guard over the decaying grey walls. Strewn offerings lay stiff on the temple floor, fetid and stale among the dry leaves. I choked at the memory.

Against my better judgement, I took a step inside and was struck by an eerie sensation, a mild discomfort followed by a real dread. I shouldn't be here. The fear escalated as the shadows of the trees collapsed upon me, their weight smothering me. Enveloped in a giant thorny trap, there was no escape. I tried to scream but my words were trapped, victims of my vocal impotence.

The sudden clash of a gong reverberated in my head as chanting voices droned a warning. *'Leave ... leave.'* Soft silhouettes glimmered through the trees, ghostly hands forming within the leaves. The wind bristled, leaves rustling as a twig broke sharply. Without pausing to think, I backed through the temple gate and fled from the forest.

Stunned, I ran back to the bungalow. Nyoman was kneeling at the temple amid a cloud of billowing incense. Locked in prayer, his face was mute and intractable as if his spirit had departed to a far-off place. Breaking the silence, he chanted softly then opened his eyes. 'Are you alright?' His gentle voice eased my fear.

'Something frightened me in the forest ... ' I stuttered, unsure of what to say. 'It was probably only my imagination.' Dark fears tumbled through my brain, stirring a deep-rooted memory. Terrified, I pushed it further down. 'I'm convinced what I felt back there was evil, it made my skin crawl.'

'The powers of darkness are many,' Nyoman warned. 'Here we believe that good and evil are equally powerful, thus in prayer we honour both. Like the yin and yang, day and night, the moon and sun, the opposing forces are equal. See the statue guarding the gate over there? The black squares in the cloth wrapped around it represent the force of evil; the white, good. Theirs is a natural balance, one is powerless without the other and neither should be ignored: to do so would be highly dangerous.'

'That still doesn't explain what happened to me back there.'

'Today is *Kajeng Kliwon*. Every fourteen days in Bali, the dark spirits have free reign. The monkey forest is an ancient burial ground that is believed to be haunted. You may have disturbed some restless spirit, or they you. Perhaps it was not your imagination, after all.'

'Hi there, neighbour,' a voice called out from the next bungalow. 'I'm Gerry. Come on over and rescue me from this drudgery!'

I looked up from my book to be greeted by a splendidly round woman in her mid-fifties hanging out her washing on a makeshift line. I slunk through the dripping clothes and sat on a weathered cane chair on the verandah.

'As you can see, I've been travelling through Asia for quite a while,' she said, pushing aside the wash basket, 'on sabbatical. Now I'm so exhausted I'm staying put for a while. Besides I love Bali. My friend Vanessa's off buying half the island, she collects antiques.'

'You mean the 'made to order' ones down the road?'

'Probably,' Gerry laughed. 'Ah, here comes the lady herself.' A car door swung open and a tall tan woman in flowing beige silk got out lugging an armful of parcels.

'Give me a hand,' she called. 'You should see all the treasures I've uncovered today, it's been marvellous.'

'Looks like you've bought them all too,' Gerry sighed, wedged behind a giant wooden banana tree. 'Heaven knows where we're going to put all this. Why not join us later for a bite to eat?' Gerry asked, tugging at a heavy branch. 'I'll need a break after sorting through this lot. How about six?'

We took the long way, enjoying the mellow evening air. Strolling through the rice fields we walked for miles until hunger overcame us and we headed for a nearby cafe. Gerry ploughed through several courses of the local delicacies, while Vanessa nibbled on some lettuce leaves. I settled for the *nasi goreng*.

'Bali is such a unique culture,' Vanessa commented in a low, worldly tone. 'I did my thesis on the art forms of the Asian region. That's why I find this area so fascinating, such a superb blend of music and dance. In a category of its own.'

'I studied the history,' I replied, reminded of an earlier interest in the area. 'I would like the opportunity to see some of the other islands if I can ever get past the mystique of Bali.'

'Well you can certainly have your choice,' Gerry said, blowing on her hot coffee. 'Indonesia's the world's largest archipelago with over 13,000 islands inhabited by over 200 million people, all from such amazingly diverse backgrounds. Goodness knows we barely touched the surface, it was all so fascinating.'

'My, it gets dark so early,' Vanessa sighed, staring out into the night. Menacing clouds loomed overhead swamping the sky in black. 'I forgot the torch, we'd better buy some candles on the way back.'

Taking long, purposeful strides, Vanessa led the way back after dinner. Tired from the combined effect of good food and pleasant conversation, Gerry and I had trouble keeping up. 'I know a short cut,' Vanessa said, steering us towards the monkey forest. I was flooded with dire memories but chose to say nothing. There was no point in alarming the ladies.

Keeping closely behind them, I bristled with apprehension. The woods were dark and forbidding. The path was indistinct so I groped my way along until reaching a point where I could no longer see. The treetops merged into thick cover, obscuring any light from the moon.

'I think it's time to light the candles.' Gerry's voice wavered. A match flared then faded into the night. 'Darn it!' Another flash, the burnt smell of wood, then darkness. 'As soon as I light the damn thing, it blows out,' she exclaimed, the tension mounting in her voice.

Following the smouldering scent, I steadied her trembling hand and lit the candle. It flared, then sparked brightly before dissolving in a pool of melted wax on the forest floor. 'What the hell's going on?' Gerry stammered, scraping the wax from her skin.

'Cheap candles.' Despite frantic efforts to light the others, they refused to stay lit. The air was deathly still, yet the candle's flame would consistently falter then die out, as if someone was standing behind us blowing them out, sabotaging our every attempt.

'This is crazy!' Gerry grappled with the matches, scattering them in all directions. Desperate to retrieve them, she dropped the candles. They rolled between some rocks. 'I give up!'

'Oh, great! Now what?' Vanessa asked impatiently.

'Guess we'll have to make it in the dark,' I said, feeling the full weight of Gerry's hand on my arm. We marched on, clinging to each other, stumbling along the vague trail that disappeared into obscurity. 'This way,' Gerry said. 'I hope there's no ghosts in here.'

More darkness, then a scream pierced the air.

'Aaaah! Something horrible touched me,' Vanessa cried. 'It felt like ice. It tapped me on the shoulder. I'm getting out of here.'

'Don't panic,' I replied, wishing to placate myself more than anyone else. 'It was probably only a twig. Let's stay together.' There was no answer. 'Gerry? Vanessa?' Still no answer.

I had the terrible feeling I was lost and alone in the midst of a haunted forest. I willed myself to stay calm, fighting the sense of uneasiness forming in the pit of my stomach. Something was close by, something cold and unfamiliar. 'Who's there?' I called feverishly. 'I know someone's there.'

Fixed to the spot, I was too terrified to move. Dank breath wafted past in a hideous cloud. A grotesque force clawed at me, plunging me further into the darkness. Spurred on by a tremendous inner strength, I broke free from the insidious presence and fled through the bushes until I stumbled over the stump of an old tree. There I lay helplessly on a bed of fallen leaves, a chill wind hovering overhead. *Thump, thump, thump.* Louder with every step. Was someone coming or was it my heartbeat?

The wind gathered force, kicking up the leaves in its wake. Sucked up toward it, I clung onto the tree root and prayed. A howling protest, then total silence. The wind dropped suddenly, taking the terror with it.

With great trepidation, I opened my eyes. Mercifully, as if my prayers had been answered, a faint shaft of light shone up ahead. With every step, the glow intensified until I found my way out of the forest's dark womb and revelled in the soothing glow of the heavens.

'Are you OK?' a tall shadowy form called out. It was Vanessa. 'Did you see Gerry in there? I'm so worried, she hasn't come out yet.'

We waited and waited but still no sign of Gerry, so we rushed back to the guesthouse to get help. Arriving breathlessly, we were all set to bang on Nyoman's door when we noticed a light shining from Gerry's room. To our surprise there she was, passed out on the bed with a peaceful smile on her face. A large bottle of bourbon lay empty beside her.

'There was only one way out of the forest, wasn't there?'

In Ubud, among star-filled nights and balmy days, I had come close to finding true peace. Lost in introspection, in sanguine moments of creativity and quiet meditation, my stay empowered me. I had tapped into hidden reservoirs of myself and in so doing, identified a place of inner power.

My ghostly encounter in the forest forced me to face my strongest fears, leaving me with the stark realisation that something truly sinister did exist. On this mystical island, with its tremendous surge of energy and its transcendental undercurrent, I knew there was wisdom to be had. The wisdom that comes from real awareness, a mindfulness of the myriad unknown forces pulsing through the universe.

Taking respite in the rich green fields, I had replenished my strength and allowed myself to be. To do nothing more than to breathe, and so exist. Throughout my life I had been fired by a restless drive, now for the first time I was content in spiritual hibernation. In solitary contemplation I had passed a winter of my soul. Thus recharged I was ready to emerge; it was time to enter spring.

'I have to leave.' Splendid white herons flapped in the trees overhead. I lay in a field of wild grass, searching for the words.

'I know,' Nyoman answered, piercing through my thoughts.

'Please take me back one last time ... back to the waterfall.' I needed to imprint him and this place on my memory forever.

Without hesitation, I dived into the water. Ripples of energy coursed through my body as I submerged deeper and deeper into the cold, hard currents. Breaking through the rainbow jets of the waterfall, I let the pounding waters embed the moment in my mind.

'I'll miss you so much,' I said, hauling myself onto the rocks. Nyoman lay silent, staring at the sky. Over the weeks he had become more to me than a friend, he had become my anchor to the earth, connecting me to a fine thread of humanity; a reminder that wherever I went there was always someone. A person who, despite their particular upbringing or place in society, chose to walk along their own unique path. A person like myself.

'I'll miss you too,' he said, rolling nearer. 'You've become like a sister to me.' He brushed my cheek gently with the remains of a crushed flower. 'Let me tell you a story about one of our ancient kings, Udayana. He married a Javanese princess and they had a son, Airlangga, who became a great leader. Legend has it that the king exiled his wife into the jungle because she practised black magic. When he died, she came back as a witch, a Rangda, to seek revenge. She caused chaos until she was defeated by the power of a white magician who stole her secrets.'

'Nyoman, why are you telling me this?'

'After all that has happened, it would be wise to be prepared. Rangda's power still lives today, potent and real. You must learn to protect yourself.'

I shut my eyes tightly. Through the darkness came shadows of green, flecked with deadly gold. I was staring straight into the eyes of the cobra.

'So child, you dare to learn the secret. A secret locked away for so long, buried for an eternity. What gives you the right?' the snake hissed as the cool green plunged me into every twisted chasm of its body. *'Why will you succeed, when so many before you have failed?'*

'I don't know,' I gasped, mesmerised by its intense beauty. Its scales shimmered like burning flames of fury. *'Go back ...'* it warned, coiling into a deadly arch, *'... before there can be no turning back.'*

CHAPTER THREE
Love in Sanur

'Last I saw of you,' Kate said perusing the menu, 'you were heading off into the Kuta sunset with Jett. I thought he'd done away with you.'

'Not quite, I fled to Ubud to try and recover from the ordeal.'

'Well you certainly look rested, but then again there's only so much peace a person can stand! Now you've opted for the salubrious Ocean View Villas of Sanur.' Crisp blue water sprawled out to the horizon, a flotilla of fishing boats dotting the clear surface.

'What's that island over there?' I asked, pointing to a craggy peak, brooding mysterious and dark among the distant clouds.

'Nusa Penida,' Kate replied, 'it's an old penal colony that's supposed to be haunted by a fanged demon that hurtles over to Bali as a huge fire ball, usually at the end of the rainy season, exploding into a million sparks. The embers spread all over the island causing illness and lots of misfortune.'

'Remind me not to row out for a day trip.'

'Don't be too put off. Like many ancient cultures, Bali abounds in magical tales. It was one way of explaining occurrences outside the people's understanding at the time. They're only stories.'

'How can you be so sure? Most myths and legends are based on some measure of truth, that's why a common thread runs through so many different cultures. The supernatural presence on this island is downright tangible, it's a mystical powder keg waiting to explode.'

'Why do I get the feeling you're the one about to light the match! I'm steering clear, that's one area I always avoid. Ah at last, food! I'm starving.' A large sizzling pizza was plonked onto the table. Before we could plough into it, a horde of flies whipped up by the whiff of mozzarella attacked.

'Must be mango season,' Kate said, fighting off a particularly persistent one. Eating was a nightmare, a race between woman and fly to see which one would triumph. 'I give up,' Kate fumed, calling the waiter over. 'Waiter, can you get these flies to go away.'

'Sorry madam,' he responded curtly, clearing away the dishes, 'can't help, I don't speak fly.' We watched in amazement as he shuffled over to the kitchen, threw the plates onto the sink and began to ravage the cleaning woman. She let out a delighted squeal that echoed through the restaurant.

'Now I've seen everything! Let's go swim off lunch.'

'This is the life!' Spread out on a deckchair by the pool, surrounded by a wealth of tropical blooms, I sipped on a cocktail. Alas even the garden of Eden had it's snake. 'Oh no, Ketut's coming. Quick hide.'

'Hello miss,' he said, tapping me on the shoulder, 'what would you like - drink, towel, massage? How about I rub oil on your back?'

'No, that won't be necessary,' I replied, pulling away.

'You special woman,' he winked. 'I wait for you after work.'

'A secret admirer,' Kate grinned, peering over her sunglasses as he hosed the pool tiles. 'Lucky girl, your own private lifeguard!'

'He never leaves me alone,' I moaned, 'and the lines that man comes out with! Surely he doesn't think women fall for that stuff?'

'You'd be surprised, they've probably served him well in the past. They use the best lines in the business and we fall for them.'

'You can't really be serious, Ketut's hardly a catch.'

'For some simple young lass he's a perfect match. Yours is somewhere out there too,' she exclaimed. 'We just have to find him!'

'We're in the lobby,' Kate announced the next evening. 'I've told Cliff all about you,' she breathed into the in-house phone, 'and he's dying to come up.' I struggled into my dress, jerking up the zipper just in time.

'Pleased to meet you,' I said, opening the door.

Cliff brushed me aside and headed straight for the bar. 'Do you have any cognac?'

'No, but I've got ginger ale,' I said rifling around the fridge. Flustered, I handed him the can. He didn't bat an eye, peeling off the ring-top with studied precision. Cliff exuded money, down to his casual white sports coat, Giorgio scent and gold Rolex. He was not so much attractive as impressive - a vision of understated elegance.

'I'm sorry I can't stay,' he commented dryly. 'I've got a business meeting in Jakarta and I'm on my way to the airport.' He outlined his plans but I couldn't concentrate, I was too busy staring at his hair.

Perfectly groomed and streaked with silver, it was a glowing testimony to his style. I curbed my natural desire to turn on the fan full force to see if a single hair would dare move out of place. This man was so cool, he was almost frozen solid.

'What do you think?' Kate asked, as soon as he'd left.

'He reminds me of someone, I can't quite put my finger on it.'

'Don Johnson,' Kate smirked. 'Bali's answer to the man. The framed photo in his office, complete with autograph, is a dead give-away. They met once and he hasn't been the same since. Despite that, I still love him.'

'So, why the long face? Something's obviously bothering you.'

'I should've known I couldn't keep a secret from you.' Kate kicked off her shoes and propped her feet up on the bed. 'I haven't been entirely honest with you ... there's one small detail I overlooked.' She paused for a moment before blurting out the truth. 'Cliff's married and he's got a couple of kids. I didn't tell you before because you'd think I was a fool falling for the same old line - *Darling, I'm going to leave my wife and marry you.* I trust him to keep his word.'

'Look, I'm not in a position to judge anyone, but you could be heading for disaster. Married men tend to make a lot of promises they can't keep.'

'So you've been involved with a married man yourself?'

'No, but I've been married! That's one little secret I didn't tell you, so now we're even. It was too painful to remember.'

'Was your husband having an affair?'

'No, actually we were very much in love which made it all the worse. We came from different continents and he got homesick. I tried living with him in England but it didn't work, too cold and distant for me. He couldn't stick it out in Australia, so one day he upped and disappeared.'

'What do you mean? He couldn't just vanish into thin air?'

'Want to bet? He dropped me off to do the shopping, raced home, cleared out his belongings *and* the joint bank account, then left without so much as a note. By the time I got back, there was no reminder that he ever existed - only an empty closet and the groove in the bed where he used to lie. Five years gone from my life, erased in one day. I was devastated.'

'The miserable bastard! I bet you swore off men for life.'

'Almost, until I met Brad. He was a saint - he restored my faith in men. Trouble was, in my mind love equalled loss. Sure that it was only a matter of time before he left me too, I got in first, hurting us both a lot in the process. The fear backfired on me.'

'How we end up sabotaging ourselves,' Kate sighed, stubbing out her cigarette, 'but you can't really have decided never to fall in love again?'

'Of course not, I'm a romantic, but I don't care for all the pain.'

'Look, let's forget all this heavy stuff and concentrate on having fun! The Black Coral club is *the* hot spot around here, and I have the feeling tonight could just turn out to be your lucky night.'

In a feisty mood, Kate was ready for the daunting task of *bemo* bargaining, haggling over the cost of transport. The driver of the van was propped up against the wall, his arms crossed defiantly. '25,000 rupiah,' he barked, refusing to budge. 'Evening price, already late.'

'That's robbery,' Kate grimaced. 'Let's walk.'

'How much you pay?' he called, a hint of panic in his voice.

'10,000, that's my final price. Take it or leave it!' Kate shouted.

'OK, me bankrupt,' he mumbled, revving up his clapped-out old engine. Bobbing through the small doorway, we clambered inside.

The bemo catapulted down the road, swerving around corners to avoid the endless posse of aimless pedestrians and stray dogs. Tossed around in the back, I shouted out in protest but to no avail.

'Kate, perhaps next time you could negotiate a little higher.'

The van screeched to a halt outside the Black Coral club. The flashing neon light was like an oasis in the desert. Kate pushed past the doorman, plucking a stray leaf from her hair. The club was deserted except for a few guests scattered around the plush booths. 'Swinging place. We could always make a run for it,' she suggested.

'And what, risk another bemo drive? I'd rather die!'

'This way, please.' A waiter gestured for us to follow him to a corner spot. 'Other guests will be arriving soon, it's still early.'

While we scanned the drinks' list, two men raised their glasses in greeting. Relieved that some stray females had arrived to break the monotony, they were most amenable. 'Would you like a drink?' one asked in a pronounced European accent.

Before we could consider our options, one of the barmen came over. 'Hi, I'm Froggy,' he chuckled, bright in a yellow jacket and lop-sided grin. 'I show you a trick.' Folding a serviette, he twisted it into a shape closely resembling his own. 'A frog!' he exclaimed, bouncing the paper creature across the table. His rubber face, ready to explode from its pent-up mirth, burst into a wicked gale of laughter. Buckling over in hysteria, his stool collapsed under the sheer weight of his humour and sent Froggy flying.

'I wonder what he's been sniffing?' Kate said, winking at her dark admirer. That was all the encouragement he needed. He and his friend were over in a flash, scrambling over Froggy's heaving body.

'My name's Peter,' the blond one said squeezing my hand. 'This is my friend Klaus. We're out here on holiday from Switzerland.' We soon became engrossed in discussion, swapping stories about our travels. As more guests trickled in, the DJ roused from his inertia and switched into automatic mode. The music exploded like a deadly missile across the room.

'Would you like to dance?' Peter shouted, dragging me to my feet. As soon as we hit the dance-floor, Peter shed all his Teutonic inhibitions and went on the rampage. Inspired by the beat of a lusty Tina Turner number, he twirled me with such gusto that I nearly crashed into a cluster of silver palm trees. Meanwhile Kate, fighting off the over-zealous Klaus, glared daggers at a buxom redhead who had backed into her during a spirited version of the lambada. Giving up, she stalked off into the whirling lights.

Suddenly I was struck by the strangest sensation, the distinct impression that someone was watching me. Looking around hoping to tap the source, I spied a solitary figure. A man standing alone in the shadows, leaning against one of the mirrored pillars. Too far away to discern his features, I could feel his gaze burning holes in my body. Resentful of the intrusion, I immersed myself in the music but even buffeted by a human wall, I could not escape the look.

It was torture .... Able to stand no more, I headed off on a scouting mission. Pushing through the crowd, my view was marred by a busload of Italians. Negotiating my way through a mass of Fiorucci jeans and gesticulating limbs, I took sanctuary in the powder room to rethink my strategy. There was no need.

As soon as I stepped outside, the doorman was there waiting for me. 'Come,' he commanded, grabbing my arm and ushering me toward one of the bars. 'My friend want talk with you.'

'Hold on,' I protested. 'What friend?'

He refused to answer. Following dumbly behind him, he led me straight to one of the barmen. It was *that* man, the mysterious figure in the half light. The pull intensified, drawing me onward until I stood right in front of him. Only the cool marble of the bar separated us. There was no escaping it, the magnetism was even more intense at close range. His dark, penetrating eyes stared through me, riveting me to the spot. My heart missed a beat.

'Haven't we met before?' he murmured in a low, hypnotic voice. I suppressed my natural instinct to lean closer. His face was strikingly handsome, his proximity intoxicating.

'I'm sure I'd remember if we had.' Although his was only a line, I meant what I said. This was not a man you'd forget in a hurry.

'Will you dance with me?' The heat in his eyes was smouldering, melting through my resolve. 'I'll wait ... all night ...'

I tried to resist. With every ounce of strength, I fought my instinct to submit. The voice of reason echoed through my brain, intent on rescuing me from the golden trap. I responded with a million excuses, but in the end I gave in. After all, where was the harm? It was *only* a dance. As I spun around the floor in a garland of light, I was lost. Under his spell, trapped in those brooding eyes, there could be no turning back.

Years later, knowing what I do now, I doubt very much if I would have taken that first step onto the dance-floor and into his life.

'What a night,' Kate sighed, collapsing onto the bed. 'I'm exhausted. Those guys were pretty hot, I was almost tempted to invite them up.'

'I don't know what got into me,' I muttered. 'I must be mad.'

'What are you raving on about?' Kate asked baffled. 'Ooh, now I recall - the barman was kinda cute. No wonder you looked flushed.'

'I scribbled my name and room number on the back of a drink coaster like some love struck teenager. Now, at the very least he'll think I'm hard up, and at worst, a raving nymphomaniac!'

'He's probably back at work salivating, ticking off the seconds and preparing for a torrid night of lust. I can always catch a taxi back to Kuta, if you two want to be alone.'

'Don't be silly. I'm not even sure that I want him to come,' I sighed, throwing my arms up in exasperation. 'Why do I do these things to myself?'

'Because it sure beats watching telly.'

'I should ring the club and tell him not to come ... what was his name again?' The ice shot all over the floor as I tried to fix a drink. Crawling around picking it up, I whacked my head on the tabletop getting upright.

'Calm down before you self-destruct. I'm sure that was the last thing you were thinking about in the heat of the moment.'

'Now, what was it?' I asked, obsessed with remembering. 'I know he's named after a drink. Johnny Walker, Black Label? No ...'

'A Russian, Smirnoff? Gilbey - an English chappie.' I glared daggers at Kate. 'No, a Latin lover - Galliano, Lambrusco?'

'I've got it. Remy! He said he was smooth and mellow like the brandy.'

'Brother, what a line. The man's got style!'

'That's it! I've made a mistake. When he comes I'll pretend to be asleep or you could say he's got the wrong room or even the wrong hotel.' I spent the next hour inventing as many excuses as I could not to meet him. Another hour passed and still no call.

'See,' Kate admonished as she snuggled under the covers, 'all that worrying for nothing. He's probably not even going to turn up.'

'Maybe the club's closed late or his bike's broken down. I know, he's lost my number ... what does it matter, the hotel won't let him in anyway.'

'Make up your mind before you drive me insane.' Kate buried her head under the pillow. 'You can sure tell you're a Libran!'

'OK, as much as I'm ashamed to admit it, I desperately want him to come.' At that precise moment the phone rang. I jumped up and grabbed it, dropping the receiver in the process. Groping for it under the bed I heard his voice. It purred pure black velvet.

'I'm in the lobby,' he whispered.

'Oh, you're here,' I yawned, trying hard to sound disinterested. 'I'd forgotten. I'll be down in a few minutes.'

'That was easy,' Kate grinned, as I grabbed the key. 'Don't forget to ...' I didn't hear the rest of it, I was already halfway down the stairs.

The hotel was positioned right on the ocean-front, so we walked down to the beach. Taking off our shoes, we skimmed through the soft, white sand, finding a private spot sheltered by a string of palm trees. The leaves fluttered warnings in the breeze.

Neither of us spoke for the longest time, unsure of what to say. Lost in silence, entranced by the soft rippling of the waves, we stared out to sea. It reached into eternity, inky black and forbidding. Delicate lines of silver, etched by the moon's shadow, shimmered across the glassy surface, casting soft patterns into the night.

Remy's body pulsed close to mine. Scooping up some sand, he let the grains run through his fingers. Subtly, I scanned every detail of him searching for a clue. The muted contours of his face, the heady smell, his hazy silhouette, every slight nuance, nothing was missed as I sought to infiltrate the soul of the stranger beside me.

Unable to look away, I felt compelled to reach out to him but suppressed my natural instincts, convinced that he would dissolve with my first touch. What if he was a figment of my imagination? I might have created him with the intensity of my need.

Remy leaned over, sweeping back a strand of hair that had blown across my face. His touch was warm and strangely soothing. I have little recollection of what happened next. All that remains sketched in my mind is the salty taste of the sea, the feel of his hands gliding across my body and the untold pleasure of his lips. Having savoured it, I could never return to the place of my original innocence. Such was the price of passion.

'Right on time,' I said, looking at my watch. Pacing the verandah, I had checked it at least a hundred times before Remy arrived, certain he would not come. 'How did you manage to get time off work?'

'I had some days owing,' he smiled. In the daylight hours, in white trousers and a soft blue shirt, Remy was as handsome as I recalled but less intimidating. Gone was the dark mystique, replaced by a lingering magnetism. So marked that I still avoided looking at him completely, afraid I'd somehow be disappointed.

'I'm really looking forward to touring around the island but I'm not sure how I'll handle the motor bike.' Based on past performance with Jett, I wouldn't make it past the hotel gate.

'You'll get used to it,' Remy said, carrying my bag down the path. Under Kate's careful guidance, I'd hurled a few essentials together. I don't know who was more excited by the trip. Kate had egged me on ... 'a chance to get know each other, and the island.'

'Let me help,' Remy said, adjusting my helmet. His hand grazed my cheek and I shuddered inside. I looked down at the ground to avoid discovery. Surely I had left this vulnerability far behind. When it came to affairs of the heart, I still had a long way to go.

The road to Lovina wound north, cutting through dense forest and climaxing in a series of spectacular bends that spilled over the mountain. The bike clung to the road with the same ferocity with which I held onto Remy. His body was rugged and hot, his scent mingled erotically with the wind.

Exhilarated by the speed, spurred on by the rush, I willed him to go faster, never once wanting to look back. My body, unable to keep pace with my mind, forced us to stop many times along the way. Remy never once complained, sitting patiently by the side of the road gazing into the valley.

'I never tire of it,' he mused. 'The fields are as beautiful as in my childhood. It's not far to Bedugul, we can have lunch on the lake.'

A misty haze swallowed the lake, making if difficult to see further than a few metres. The air felt damp and cool; rain was imminent.

Impressive Hindu thatched towers jutted out from the water, framed by flowering shrubs. 'The temple dates back to the seventeenth century,' Remy explained. 'It's dedicated to Dewi Danau, the goddess of the lake. People come to make offerings to her and ensure an abundant supply of water. Over there is a Buddhist stupa.'

'So your religion is not strictly derived from Indian Hinduism?'

'No, we worship the same gods - the trinity of Brahma, Wisnu and Siwa - the creator, the preserver and the dissolver of life, but we believe they are all manifestations of our own supreme god, Ida Sanghyang Widi. Our country is ruled by a belief in one God but what makes our religion so unique is the fundamental belief in animism, the force of the spirits.'

'I've experienced a little of that already.' I immersed myself in the beauty of the lake, 'it's so tranquil here ... I miss the peace. My world seems under siege from noise, I crave the silence of yours.'

'Don't be so sure,' Remy interrupted, 'everything's not always what it seems.' The loud buzz of a speedboat zooming past echoed his words. 'My house is so busy at times it's difficult to find space.'

'I gather you don't live on your own?'

'That's a Western disease, it's unnatural for us. Here we believe in safety in numbers; it might have something to do with those spirits we were talking about. Besides I'm used to a large family - my mother had eleven children and my father's second wife has ten.'

'What?' It made my family shrink in comparison. 'So your parents are divorced?'

'No, my father's still married to both wives. In our religion, a man can have as many wives as he wants as long as the first wife gives permission. Some of the kings had hundreds, not to mention a string of concubines.'

'Polygamy is beyond my comprehension, so alien to my culture it's almost inconceivable. Isn't jealousy a problem?'

'Not in our house, both women get along well. It *can* get a bit hectic at times, but I couldn't imagine living by myself, it would get so lonely.'

'It does, at times ...'

'Well, I guess I'll have to adopt you.' Remy put his arm around me protectively. 'We'd better be on our way, it looks like rain.'

Halfway down the mountain, the heavens opened. Huge black clouds dumped water onto the road, drenching us in the downpour. Impossible to stop, the bends too dangerous, we drove slowly until coming to a shelter, an open bamboo hut on the side of a steep ridge.

'You said you wanted adventure.' Remy helped me off the bike. Soaked, my hair was matted and limp, my clothes stuck together in a sodden mess. On Remy 'wet' looked good, his t-shirt clung to his body, accentuating his masculinity.

'Let's find something to change into.' We hunted through the bags. The top layer was saturated but we were able to salvage a few dry clothes at the bottom. I didn't want to appear a prude but I wasn't about to strip off in the middle of the road. Remy, a true gentleman, found a sarong, strung it up across a pole and looked the other way.

'You shouldn't be so self-conscious.' He lit a cigarette. 'You're really quite beautiful, you know.' I felt myself redden, not so much for the compliment but more for Remy's uncanny awareness of my discomfort. There went my last defence, the pretence of being worldly. Physically I'd stayed concealed, emotionally I was exposed.

'Even wet?' I asked, wringing out my hair.

'Much more so, I can see you more clearly now.' Turning my face towards him, he looked into my eyes. His were more exquisite than I'd imagined, full of liquid light and kindness. Wrapping his sweater around me, he drew me closer, shielding me from the storm.

I hoped the rain would never end but ignoring my pleas, the clouds shrank and were replaced by drifts of blue. Reluctantly, we broke apart and continued the journey cruising through pockets of crisp dry air until we reached the coast.

'We made it,' Remy said, with the first sight of the black sands of Lovina. 'Let's find a place before it gets dark.'

After settling into a small bungalow by the sea, we sat on the warm sands savouring the last shadows of sunset. I leaned my weary body against Remy's, calmed by his warmth and the intrinsic beauty of the scene. The ocean was the palest gold, reflecting the fading embers of the setting sun. The sky, bleached of its colour, merged with the horizon, its substance absorbed by the endless sea. The air was still, disturbed only by the soft wail from a distant mosque, heralding the onset of night.

'The god of the underworld, Kala, created the earth and the ocean,' Remy said, immersed in the colours of dusk. 'Above them, lives the god Iswara in the middle sky, then hidden among the clouds is Semara, the god of love.' He looked at me longingly, until embarrassed by his sentiment, he diverted his gaze to the heavens. 'In the Perfumed Sky, scented with rare flowers, live the snakes, the falling stars. Higher is the heaven of our ancestors, and then higher still is the home of the great gods who protect us.'

Remy touched a nerve. I stared up into the sky, pondering the forces that had sent this man to me. A single white star carved a path through the darkness, as a chorus of crickets mourned the death of day.

'My grandfather taught me about the beauty of the night,' Remy whispered, 'how the breeze spills its secrets into the wind. If you listen well you can hear the spirit of the wind.'

'Your grandfather sounds like a wise man.'

'My grandfather is a *balian,* what you'd call a shaman - a healer. When I was young, he came to my house and asked for a child to raise in the path of wisdom. I was chosen and so blessed.'

'You mean your parents just gave you to him?'

'Of course, they considered it an honour. He's well known for his powers and many people come from afar to seek his help. I realise I'm not ready yet to use the knowledge I've learnt, I'm still young and working in a nightclub doesn't help. But one day I will ... one day when the time's right.'

I sat mystified, too tired to fully comprehend. Through the countless questions, one thought pushed to the surface - the nagging certainty that our meeting was no mere coincidence. Something higher was at work here.

That night, we lay in bed exhausted and in spite of all our expectations, fell asleep in each others' arms, safe in our little hut by the sea. Calmed by the gentle lapping of the waves, comforted by the feeling that life was going exactly according to plan, I drifted into a beautiful dream. One that I hoped would last forever.

The hot springs, hidden deep within the jungle, nestled like a jewel in the mountainside. The sound of gushing water lured us through the emerald greenery to the secluded pools. Hot sulphuric steam rose off the surface in shallow clouds, evaporating into the afternoon heat.

Remy waded into the thick water till he stood under the mythical stone dragons lining the walls. Volcanic jets spewed out healing water from their spouts. 'This is the elixir of the gods,' Remy called, the white foam gushing over him. Cleansed, his energy appeared more vibrant, his body pulsated at an even finer frequency. His was a genuine lightness of being.

Drawn towards him, I stepped down the slippery steps lined with moss. 'The water comes from deep within the earth, from Mount Agung,' he said, holding me under the rainbow jet. 'It's holy, it can heal anything.' His chest, wet and raw, glistened with crystal beads.

'So can this,' he added, branding my lips with his. They scorched a passage straight to my heart.

Helpless I fell deeper under his spell. 'Should we be doing this here?' I backed away, fearful of incurring the wrath of the gods.

'What better place?' Luring me back, he wrapped me in a steamy embrace. A tremor racked my body. I looked up into the mouth of the serpent. Its stony jaws snapped open. *'Trapped,'* it hissed, its sinister voice echoing through the surging water. *'Will love blind your way?'* My emotions spun dangerously out of control, as turbulent as the raging pool.

'I need some time to think.' Dragging myself out of the water, I found a quiet place amid the ferns. 'I've got some things to sort out.'

'Like what?' Remy asked, squatting down on the grass.

'I don't know,' I admitted, unsure of the true dilemma. 'About love, life and the whole damned thing. Have you ever been in love?'

He paused in reflection. 'I'm not sure I really know what it is. People get married here for many different reasons, least of all love.'

'Maybe it's better that way - far less complicated.'

'You don't really believe that,' Remy said, squeezing my hand. He knew more about me than I dared admit. 'You're too much of an idealist.'

'How come you've never married?' I asked, enamoured by the strong contours of his face. His cheekbones were high, his jaw solid. Remy was undeniably attractive. It seemed inconceivable that he hadn't been snapped up in the club by some love-struck tourist or local girl in the village. A man of his age, in a culture so obsessed with partnership and bearing children, would be an easy target.

Remy mulled over his reply, 'I've got other priorities, I decided a long time ago that love wasn't important in my life, there's so much left to do. Or maybe, I just haven't found the right woman - *yet.*'

With dawn's early light, a fishing boat was waiting on the edge of the beach to take us in search of dolphins. 'I can't believe this is our last day together,' I said, climbing into the boat. It floundered in the tide.

Our time had passed too quickly, a passionate interlude spent in close exploration of each other, transcending our own personal boundaries. I had let Remy get closer than I'd intended and now fought the thought of separation. There had to be more.

'Don't worry,' Remy reassured, 'this is only the beginning.'

Out to sea, I willed the dolphins to appear. A small group burst through the waves as if tuned into my thoughts. Chanting a morning song, they frolicked from the ocean's depths. Bewitched, I watched them cavort in the surf, aware of an intrinsic connection to these mystical beings.

Remy grabbed his snorkelling gear and dived in after them but they disappeared from view. Despite the temptation to follow I stayed put, locked in by an inherent distrust of the ocean, a remnant of an unknown trauma. My own dark shadow rippling across the waves anchored me there, an unwilling captive of my fear.

'Come on in,' Remy shouted, surfacing for air. 'You should see the view down there, it's spectacular.'

'I can see from here,' I replied, peering into the clear blue water. Small fluorescent fish swam past, darting into bright bands of rainbow coral. Despite the overt beauty, an uneasy feeling crept over me. I had the distinct impression that something sinister lay hidden far beneath the ocean bed.

'You sure you're not Balinese?' Remy said, clinging to the side of the boat. 'People here are afraid of the ocean, they think it's full of terrible monsters. Don't tell me you're superstitious?'

Back on dry land, I treated myself to a long massage. While my body unwound, my mind staged a private war. Fear was a powerful adversary. As much as I'd wanted to dive into the water, I couldn't. Some intangible force blocked my way, a deep inner voice sounding warnings. Was this an obstacle of my own creation?

Remy was reading quietly on the verandah. Looking up from his book, he flashed me a smile. I knew I was heading for a fall, my thin shell of protection was splitting apart. Fighting an overwhelming feeling to run, I rebelled. I made a secret vow to face my inner foes and do battle. There could be no real beginning, without an end.

As the sky darkened and the sea assumed the colour of silky oil we waded in, drifting closer together. Oblivious to the world around us, Remy and

I made love one last time, under the cover of dark. The danger of discovery made it all the more urgent, its consummation ultimately more satisfying.

'Say you'll never leave,' Remy begged. His hands caressed my body, coaxing a response, urging me on.

'Yes,' I vowed, aware that I was making promises that I may never keep. Remy didn't care, he wanted to hear the words. 'I'll stay.'

'It's crazy, I know we've just met but I feel I've known you forever,' Remy confessed as I floated in his arms. 'I've never felt like this before.' An ominous yellow ring circled the moon. 'And I'm not sure I want to ...' Remy too, had internal demons yet to grapple.

CHAPTER FOUR
A Place of the Soul

'A whisky on the rocks and *you* on the sand,' a garish woman in her fifties ordered, winking at the barman. Blowing smoke rings into the air, she looked me up and down then introduced herself. 'My name's Joyce, seen you down here quite a bit. Let me buy you a drink.'

Flamboyant in sequins and weighed down by enough gold to sink a ship, Joyce was a human tour de force, not so much for her flashy looks, but the grandiose way in which she flaunted them. Gloria Swanson in the round, hers was an image honed and perfected over many years.

'Tonic water!' she snapped when my drink arrived. 'Is that all you're having, dearie?' Puffing on her gilt cigarette holder, she looked horrified. 'Not even a shot of gin? Ah well, to each their own.'

Snapping open her gold purse, she let a large wad of money tumble onto the counter. Slowly peeling off the top layer, she handed the barman a crisp note. 'Another drink for the lady, I'll have a double whisky and one for yourself too, sweetie.' He acknowledged her with a scant smile, not so easily bought.

'Let me guess,' Joyce said, 'you're here nearly every night ... the Black Coral club is a pretty hot place but I reckon in your case there's more to it, and if I'm not wrong the attraction is over there.' She pointed to Remy. 'He's the best thing behind the bar, except for the booze. Fancied him myself until I realised he was taken.'

'Sting's next on my list,' she boasted, casually grazing the barman's arm with hers. Picking up the vibes, Sting sensibly retreated to the end of the bar. Sophisticated and worldly, it was clear from his manner that he had repelled many such a proposition in his time. Joyce was not one to give up the fight so easily and persevered, staring hard at him from a distance.

I recognised *that* look. I'd seen it many times before. Lonely women, in need of company and respite from a dreary life, would drift into the club. Most hoped for a distraction, a holiday fling, but for others the need was greater, the look more desperate.

I couldn't pretend that it didn't bother me. I glanced over to Remy's bar where a bunch of leggy beauties with peroxide hair were poring over Remy as he regaled them with witty conversation. Convinced they were all nymphomaniacs, I had to fight off a pang of jealousy. Putting the emotion aside, I could understand the attraction.

Remy was a charismatic man, exuding animal magnetism. In the club's bright lights and music, Remy came alive. Guests flocked to his bar unable to resist his vibrant spark and the compelling lure of his smile. Gone was the man I had come to know as quiet and introspective; in his place was a remarkable individual, possessing a bold, exciting energy. The problem was, I didn't want to share him. In the throes of a new relationship, I wanted Remy all to myself. This time, Joyce picked up the look in my eyes.

'Hey, what's got you worried?' she asked.

'You know what they say about holiday romances, they tend to fizzle out.' My voice wavered, 'who knows if it will last ...'

'Don't be silly,' Joyce said, patting my hand. 'Look, you two have been together for a while now and Remy's not a sleaze like some of the guys around here. Don't worry, dearie, you're the only one with a bit of class in the joint - he'd be a fool to look elsewhere.'

'Thanks for noticing,' I said, warming to her. Apart from being sweet, Joyce was blessed with good judgement. 'It's been two months now, so I guess I should be optimistic. I've found a nice bungalow on the beach and Remy's there every night - so far, so good.'

'See, sucked in like the rest of us,' Joyce smiled. 'You've fallen under the spell, I wish you luck. Heaven knows us women deserve it. One word of warning - I've been in these parts long enough to know what goes on. Enjoy yourself, but as they say around here - *hati hati,* be careful. Things aren't always what they seem to be on this island.'

Like her words, there was a hardened edge to Joyce. Carved out of pure bedrock by the pressures of a tough life, she sparkled like a rough diamond. Brazenly crass under a flashy blond perm, her telltale wrinkles were camouflaged by a thick layer of powder, her lips animated and overfull in red. Her boldest feature was the mole on her cheek, accentuated by pencil rather than concealed. Joyce was proud of her flaws.

'I've spent most of my time on the road,' Joyce reminisced, staring into her glass. 'I did the carnival circuit up in Queensland, it took me round to most of the small towns. Started off doing the rides, ended up owning the lot! They said it couldn't be done, goes to show you shouldn't listen to that bullcrap. Seen more than most in my time, but I can't figure out this place. That's why I stay, I love a challenge!'

'Sounds like you've led an interesting life.' As she continued, I got swept away in the richness of her tales. Joyce had gotten where she was through grit and determination, snubbing convention and breaking some tough barriers along the way. 'So now you're having a break?'

'Yeah, a permanent break, but that's another story ... now, enough about me - tell me, how did you snare the elusive Remy?'

'I'm sure there's nothing you don't already know.' This woman didn't miss a trick, she was a goldmine waiting to be tapped.

'Oh no,' Joyce moaned, distracted by the sound of a stampede. 'It's Pub Crawl night. Quick, take cover.' A busload of Aussies descended upon us like a pack of sharks on a feeding frenzy, spilling over each other in their fervour to get to the beer.

'A schooner of ice-cold beer mate, and none of that local crap,' a strapping six-foot rugby player shouted, elbowing us out of the way. 'Fair crack of the whip, look at the head on it!'

'Yeah, Lance, its bigger than the one Noeline gives ya after footie practice,' his mate grunted, swaying drunkenly by his side.

'Now I know why I left home!' Knocked off her seat by the mighty Lance, Joyce shoved him aside. 'Move it buddy!' she yelled, wrestling to heave her ample behind back up. 'Bloody morons.'

Lance, undaunted by the chaos he'd created, jumped onto the lounge intent on creating some more. Clutching his glass, he twisted upright and with one mighty lunge landed on his head. Swaying precariously, he guzzled his beer as the foam dribbled down his chin.

'Get it down ya, ya mongrel,' stocky Kevin shouted, as the rest of the team offered support. 'Good one Bluey, a true champion!'

Wayan, the security guard, stepped in and dragged him upright, nearly wiping out half the bar on the downswing. Lance jerked up his jocks and mopped his sweaty face with his singlet. 'We're only having a bit of fun. Give this guy a beer,' he said whacking Wayan on the back. 'Good on ya mate, get that inta ya.'

'Ever think of becoming a nun?' Joyce asked, shaking her head in disbelief. 'A life of celibacy looks like a viable option from here.'

'Surely there must be a few good ones left out there.'

'Are you kidding?' Right on cue, Wild One, the DJ, appeared out of thin air and slunk down between us. Perverse to a fault, his mere proximity was enough to bring on a severe case of thrush. Perched on the precipice of his own madness, he rarely deigned to make contact with the outside world.

'To what do we owe this unexpected pleasure?' Joyce asked, as he grabbed her whisky. 'Hands off!' she snapped, seizing it back.

'I'm bored,' he confessed, fingering his mane of long black hair. Striking in appearance, Wild One's appeal was enhanced by a dark mystique and brooding, depraved eyes. Women flocked to him in droves, spurred on by his blatant contempt of them and the inherent danger of a liaison. Burnt out by all the attention, he'd lost his inner spark. 'Life is so tedious ... I've had to put on a long play.'

'Let me guess, *Bananarama's Greatest Hits*,' Joyce giggled. 'No, I've got it, the theme from *Hawaii 5-0*. A true classic, Wildy.'

The first twang spurred Lance and the boys into action. Splayed onto the dance-floor, legs wrapped around each other in mock canoe formation, they were going crazy, paddling invisible oars in a frenzy to get to the mainland. I hoped they'd hit a tidal wave before sighting Honolulu.

'Why are we here?' Wild One demanded abruptly.

'That's a tricky one,' I replied. 'Do you mean *here,* as in the club or are we talking more large scale, as *per* the planet?'

'Can we have some time to come up with the answer?' Joyce asked, puffing hard on her cigarette. 'It bears some thought.'

'The universe is ours for the taking,' he continued, staring at us as if *we* were mad. 'Can't you see that? How can you be so blind?'

At that precise moment the disc came to an abrupt halt and saved us. Wild One ran back to his booth to fill the void with an ancient blast of Pink Floyd. Everyone reeled in horror at the brusque change in mood.

'Definitely a case of "beam me up, Scotty". All those years of heavy metal and poisoned mushrooms have caught up with him.'

'The problem is that us sane people are in the minority in this riff-raff. Look at this lot, there's not a collective brain between them!'

The club was carpeted with a bevy of young beauties, all dressed to kill. Each adopted a different fashion statement depending on which edition of *Dolly* they'd just read. Spandex minis and boob tubes abounded in a startling array of fluoro shades.

'A pack of flaming galahs,' Joyce muttered. 'Thank God some have the guts to stand out,' she added, eying the lass propped up at the bar next to her. A platinum blonde with interesting black roots, nubile Donna stood resplendent, encased in a gold lamé dress apparently spun onto her body. Her black fishnet stockings, gloves and gold stilettos were set off by a startling display of rhinestone accessories. 'At least she's visually entertaining.'

'She could mellow with age.' Lounging in the next booth, sipping on a sparkling mineral water, was an unremarkable matron stuffed into a little striped Carla Zampatti number. 'She'd prefer to be on a yacht cruising the Caribbean with some rich octogenarian.'

'Not my style,' Joyce huffed. 'There's a woman of my own heart!' Lusty Lucia from Naples was seated opposite surrounded by a group of young admirers, holding them spellbound with her witty repartee. Defying the laws of gravity, her strapless fuschia silk dress stayed stiffly upright, unlike her multiple chins and breasts which sagged nastily. As she plunged further into her bottle of vino blanco, her jokes became more bawdy, her laughter more pronounced. Her bright maraschino cherry lips strained under the pressure, causing a crack in her make-up. A network of fine time lines shot across her face, coating it in a web of antiquity.

'On second thoughts,' Joyce despaired, 'it's time for me to hit the sack. If I don't get my beauty sleep, I might end up looking like that!' I'm at Swaying Palms hotel, Room 24. Drop round any time.'

'Joyce, I hope I didn't wake you.' A few weeks had passed since our first meeting, but I'd only just taken up the invite. My timing was lousy. Rubbing her eyes, Joyce tried to focus on me through layers of caked mascara. 'I'm sorry, I thought you'd be up by now.'

'Come on in,' she muttered, hiding a few empty bottles under the lounge and throwing on her peach satin dressing gown. 'My God, is that the time? I guess it must have been quite a night!'

'I can always come back later if this isn't a good time.'

'Nonsense, this is as good as it gets. Let me get some breakfast into me and I'll be right as rain. One pot of black coffee, and make it a big one,' she shouted to the room-boy. 'Let's sit out here and relax.'

The room was on the first floor and looked out over the hotel gardens. A few people lay on deckchairs around the swimming pool, but most preferred to avoid the intensity of the midday sun, sitting in the comfort of their shaded balconies. Huge pots of bougainvillea tumbled out over the roof, glazing the hotel in soft pastel tones.

'Nice here, isn't it?' Joyce said, pouring the coffee. 'I'm a long-term guest, so I get a special rate. I've been here nearly six months.'

'It's very peaceful. My place isn't quite as fancy, but it's on the beach. A friend of Remy owns it, so I got it dirt cheap.' While I envied Joyce her comfort, I wouldn't compromise my privacy for anything. My room afforded me precious time alone with Remy.

'I'm a Taurean, I prefer the finer things in life,' Joyce said, emptying the sugar bowl into her coffee. 'This island agrees with me.'

'Tell me about it.' My eyes drank in the absolute blueness of the sky, the pink and mauve display of flowers, the heady fragrance of the air. 'I left behind a concrete tomb back home, smog grey and streaked with graffiti. Trains jammed with people with vacant eyes, their souls sucked from their bodies a long time ago. I didn't want to end up like that!'

'Why do you think I'm here, I've always been a free spirit,' Joyce said, lighting up her first cigarette of the day. 'Tell me, if it wasn't for Remy, would you have ended up staying here this long?'

'Tricky question,' I hesitated. 'Let's just say he's part of the package deal, he makes me happier than I've been in a long time.'

'Funny thing about men, they're either the source of your salvation or the path to your ruin. There doesn't seem to be any in-between.' Joyce looked forlorn, immersed in unpleasant memories.

'So what inspired you to stay so long?' As usual there was a man involved, but in Joyce's case she was getting away from him.

'That miserable, gutless husband of mine,' she seethed, locked in bitter memory, 'I've got him to blame for ending up in this paradise. We'd planned our second honeymoon after twenty-five years of marriage, our first trip overseas together. The day before we left, I found out Bill was having an affair with my best friend, Sylvia. She did our accounts.'

'That's apparently not all she did.'

'I thought I'd never get over it, I couldn't believe the two people I trusted most would betray me. I withdrew, wouldn't go out of the house for months, but life goes on,' she added, flicking some ash off her lap. 'I woke up one morning and decided not to throw away any more of my life on that bastard. Packed my bags and came alone, smartest thing I've ever done.'

'No regrets?' Despite her bravado, Joyce was not happy.

'A few. With all that new-found freedom, I got a bit carried away. God, when I think back to the first time,' she coughed, years of heavy smoking catching up with her, 'I shudder. Got all dolled up, more glam than I'd been for ages, and went out on the prowl. There was this hunk hanging around the club with the most obscenely gorgeous body I'd ever seen.'

'Pity they're not endowed with the brains to go with the brawn.'

'Darling, let me tell you, the last thing I was interested in was his mind! He was at least twenty years younger than me so when he suggested a romantic interlude on the beach I thought I'd died and gone to heaven.'

'Did you get what you bargained for?'

'Not quite,' she admitted. 'One look at those waves and there was no holding me back. I ripped off my dress and took the plunge. I felt so daring, I'd never done anything like it before in my life. Anyway, when I got out of the water, lover boy was nowhere in sight - neither were my clothes! I ran along the beach in a panic.'

'I wish I'd been a fly on a coconut tree.'

'Well you might laugh, but I wasn't at the time. I was convinced that the guy had set me up and made off with all my money. Then I heard a noise coming from behind the fishing boat so I figured he was hiding, trying to play a joke on me. I crept up with arms outstretched whispering sweet nothings, crashing straight into an old fisherman fixing his nets. I'm not sure which one of us jumped the highest!'

'The poor old codger was hoping for a quiet night on the beach with the fish, the last thing he'd expect was a naked water nymph!'

'He shone his torch and got such a start that I thought he was going to cark it there and then. With the seaweed wrapped round my silky white body, he probably thought I was a sea monster come to wreak havoc. The last I saw of him, he was heading for the hills!'

'Then what happened?' I asked, having great difficulty keeping a straight face. 'I hope you didn't turn up at the hotel in the buff.'

'No, thank God. I'd swum out so far I'd misjudged the distance, my guy was way down the beach freaking out, thinking I'd drowned.'

'Tell me, did you ever get to consummate this relationship?'

'Sort of. We rode off on his bike to this really seedy joint where you pay five dollars an hour and get handed a towel and a fan,' she said, unashamed of exposing her foibles to the world. 'It was a real hole in the wall, one grotty double bed and a bare light bulb. Lover boy wasn't one for hanging about, he tore off his clothes and jumped straight on top of me.'

'That sounds very romantic,' I said, cracking up.

'He begged me to stroke his hair,' she smirked. 'No sooner had I touched it and he was gone. In, out and over. Didn't even take off his shoes! The best part of it,' Joyce laughed, holding her belly, 'was when he rolled off and asked, "Was it good for you, darling?" I nearly died, I didn't even know he'd begun! My graphic introduction to a life of sin. He almost made Bill look good! My first reaction was to run back home, but I figured I still had a lot to learn. After all, practice makes perfect!'

'Tell me, in any of these conquests did you ever come across anyone special? A person that raised more than a flicker of interest?'

'You mean a pearl amongst the swine, like Remy - not even close! I envy you that bond. I had it once, with Bill ... but that was so long ago. If I was being totally honest, I'd have to say this has been one of the hardest times of my life. I'm not used to my own company, it can get so lonely,' the humour drained from her face. 'Sometimes I feel *so* alone I take solace in this,' Joyce said, grabbing a drained vodka bottle. 'It helps numb the pain,' she groaned, 'but it doesn't make it go away. You want to hear the worst part - I'd take that bastard back in a minute ... that's if he'd have me.'

'Don't sell yourself short. You're an exceptional woman, and Bill's an idiot to have lost you.' Joyce looked at me, the spark returning to her eyes. 'You know, relationships aren't always what they're cracked up to be. Remy's so caught up in his own life that mine suffers in the process. It's not his fault, but I spend a lot of my time sitting around waiting for him.'

'It's easy to get bored around here - jobs are scarce, and work permits impossible to get. If you want to stay sane you'd better develop some new interests, or try becoming a larger part of his life.'

'Every time I bring up the subject he comes up with an excuse.'

'Listen, I reckon if you're good enough to sleep with, you're good enough to meet the folks. You should start putting your foot down,' Joyce insisted. '*Galungan*'s coming up soon, Bali's answer to Christmas, it's the perfect opportunity to pay the family a little visit.'

When I got back to my bungalow I was surprised to find Remy stretched out on the bed flipping through some magazines. Propped up on a pile of pillows he looked exhausted, all the late nights catching up with him.

'I had a few hours free so I thought I'd come here for a rest.' I lay down beside him. 'A token of my affection,' he said, handing me a beautiful white gardenia. 'It reminded me of you, sweet and pure.'

This was a good time to make my move. 'Remy, you know that I'm happy when we're together, but you're gone so much of the time.'

'I have so many other commitments,' he sighed. 'A Balinese has obligations that take precedence over everything else - duties to the family, the community, and above all to our religion. There are five basic principles in our religion - a belief in one supreme God; an acceptance of the soul; the concepts of karma and reincarnation; and the quest for *moksha,* the blessed release from the cycle of existence. That's why we work hard at our faith in this lifetime and why I'm busy every second day. Just imagine, there are over twenty thousand village temples on this island, plus countless festivals.'

'So far there's been a special day to honour trees, animals and learning. The last one you had was for metal, when you blessed your motorbike.' Religious ceremonies placed constant demands both on time and finances. Much wealth was poured into the offerings, the richer the devotee, the more elaborate the offering.

'Not to mention our life cycle rituals, the temple anniversaries, and don't forget the phases of the moon. *Purnama,* for the full moon, *Tilem* for the dark moon. *Kajeng Kliwon* for the evil spirits, *Galungan* for the light - and many, many more.'

'Remy, I don't pretend to have an insight into your religion, but everyone seems to pray fanatically without any real understanding of why. As if, dare I say, they're motivated more by fear than by faith.'

'On this mystical island, would you be the first to defy the gods? Our forefathers, aware of the awesome power surrounding them, were wary not to incur their wrath. They devised an intricate system of offerings to appease an invisible world of gods and demons. Over the centuries they absorbed elements of the many religions that crossed onto these shores - the Hinduism of the Majapahit empire, the Vishnuite cult of the underworld, the mystical Brahmanic world of cabbalistic symbols and the discipline of Mahayana Buddhism. Even some satanic practices from Tantrism were included, with their blood sacrifices and black magic.'

'No wonder the energy flow around here is so potent.' So many times I'd been struck by the island's power but had never succeeded in penetrating its source - the accumulated vibration of some of the world's most archaic religions in a dynamic mix of doctrines.

'People here do not need, nor care to know the meaning of their prayer. The religion is not one of reflection or ecstatic insight, but rather one of ritual. By creating beautiful offerings, the gods are kept happy and so impart their blessings on the island. The common priests are facilitators of this process, with little understanding of what they say or do. As stated by one, "I do not know and I would not dare to understand."'

'So who does have access to the knowledge?'

'Wisdom is the domain of the high priests. They are the guardians of the sacred lore and keepers of the history of our people. Only they can prepare the holy water essential to our ceremonies. Balinese religion is called *Agama Tirta*, the Religion of Holy Water.'

'So, the high priests act as intermediaries for the gods?'

'No, that is more the task of the medium. My grandfather is one, that's how he carries out much of his healing. Within a trance state he communicates with the gods and partakes of their essence. I too have slipped into the trance state but feel uncomfortable losing control of my body. It's part of my initiation to learn, but the time is not yet right.' Despite our closeness, Remy was still an enigma.

'Can you understand how important it is for me to learn more about your culture,' I argued. 'I can't possibly begin to understand who you are without getting an insight into the forces that created you.'

'It's complicated, there are some things you don't understand,' his voice trailed into silence. After the longest time spent in reflection, Remy spoke again. 'Galungan is our celebration of the triumph of the forces of good over evil. During a ten day period our ancestors are invited down to earth to bless us with happiness and peace. I will take you home to meet my family then.'

The important day finally arrived. For a week the villages had been a hive of activity. Women chatted away happily under shaded canopies, making elaborate decorations. Fingers worked at cutting stacks of young coconut leaves and weaving them into intricate designs. Piles of fruit and flowers were stacked into ornate pyramids, splendid offerings for the gods.

'Come Lia, you help,' Komang, one of the waitresses called from the hotel restaurant as I was passing by. The girls had been so preoccupied with making the offerings, they had neglected most of their other duties. The beauty of their creations was compensation enough. 'I show you how.'

Bending one of the supple leaves in half, Komang cut through it with a few deft movements, carving it into an intricate shape. Taking a sliver of bamboo, she skewered the leaf, producing a small flat-bottomed basket. 'Now, you try.' I managed to demolish the leaf in a matter of seconds.

Komang giggled then spread out a number of small baskets on the bamboo mat. She filled each with a little boiled rice, dried fish and banana, sprinkling some petals and fine leaves on top as a final touch. 'Now they are ready to put on the altar to send to the gods, the smell of the incense will wake up heaven. These ones,' she added filling some baskets with rotting food, 'are for the evil *bhutas* so they don't get jealous and cause trouble. We leave them on the ground for the dogs to eat.' Equating dogs with demons, I could now understand the local contempt for the animals.

'Where husband?' Komang asked, feigning disinterest. The staff gossip, she loved to keep tabs on everyone. 'I no see him today.'

'Remy left early. Now I must go and try to find Joyce.'

'I no see Miss Joyce for long time, she go away?'

'No, but I haven't seen her at the club for nearly a week.'

'Oh,' Komang enthused, her cheeks blushing, 'she find new boyfriend, good for Miss Joyce. She ripe woman, need boyfriend.'

'Komang, keep up your English classes, won't you?' I wasn't sure whether she meant 'mature' or 'ready for the plucking', but either way I was sure Komang was closer to the truth than she realised.

'There you are!' I spotted Joyce sprawled out on a deckchair around the pool at Swaying Palms. Buried under a copy of *Hollywood Wives*, she was snoring blissfully. 'Be careful or you'll be burnt to a crisp.'

'What's that,' she stirred groggily. 'Oh God, I was out of it!'

'Where have you been lately? I've missed you at the club.'

'I'm harbouring a little secret.' Her eyes lit up with delight. 'I'll unveil *it* to the world when the time is right.'

'It's a man,' I gasped, 'you sly fox.' Joyce's cheeks were flushed with the bloom of meaningful sex. 'Tell me, don't leave out a word.'

'Nothing you can say or do will induce me to talk.' She lay back adamantly, her lips pursed. 'It's still early days yet and I'm not jinxing myself ... suffice to say, I think I've hit the jackpot.'

'More, more,' I begged. Despite my entreaties, Joyce remained clammed tight even though I could tell she was dying to spill the beans. A few more hours in the sun and I knew she would crack.

'Joycie, I didn't recognise you under there,' a shrill voice cried.

'Oh hello there. Madge and her husband Len are in the room next to mine. Madge was kind enough to help me the other night when I locked myself out of the room in my nightie.'

'I'm not even going to ask about that one.'

'I'm sure it was all perfectly innocent,' Madge said, valiantly trying to defend Joyce's virtue. It was a lost cause. Perched on the edge of the chair, Madge was a picture of gentility in traditional Balinese costume.

'We're off to the temple to join in the festivities. Would you girls like to come along?'

'That's very kind,' Joyce replied, 'but I'm being picked up soon.'

'Ah, here comes my Len now, and doesn't he look dashing!' A portly man strutted down the stairs showing off his elaborate outfit.

'Indeed,' he replied, sucking in his stomach. 'What's that you're drinking Joyce?' Len asked, perhaps feeling a bit dry.

Caught out, Joyce dragged the plastic container out from under the table. 'A present for Galungan, *arak* - rice wine. My friend brought me some special brew from his village. Would you like to try it?'

'If it's the custom,' Madge said, 'I'll have a tipple.' One sniff of the deadly brew and she keeled sideways. Len took a large gulp, almost choking. Just as he was about to empty his glass onto the plant, a shaggy looking creature plodded towards us on platform thongs.

'Hi there, folks. I'm ya neighbour, Wanda from Wodonga. Wow, is that arak?' she asked, whipping the bottle out of Len's hand. 'Do youse mind if I have one? Me head's banging like a dunny door.'

We all cringed simultaneously, while Joyce hid under her hat vowing never to drink again. Helping herself to a large beaker of arak, Wanda fell into the chair with a massive thud and propped her feet on the table. Lighting up a cigarette, she coughed violently and picked out gritty grains of tobacco from her teeth. 'I hope we didn't make too much of a racket last night. I met Icky on the beach two days ago and we're in love. Can ya believe it, the guy's a spunk!'

'We're very happy for you, dear,' Madge said, searching for a means of escape. 'If you'll just excuse us we're off to the temple ...'

'I'm gonna work double shifts down at the Central,' Wanda boasted 'so I can bring Icky out to Aussie. He's already said he wants to marry me. I can hardly wait to tell my mum, she'll be rapt.'

'Lucky woman,' Len said, mumbling into his beard. 'Now, we must get going, don't want to be late for the ceremony.'

'Come to think of it,' I said, running after them, 'I do have a few hours to kill. Maybe I should absorb some of the local colour.'

'That's right, dear,' Madge agreed. 'One must grasp the opportunity, after all Galungan comes but once a year.'

'Twice ... here the year is only 210 days long.' I left Joyce in the clutches of the awesome Wanda. An early Galungan present.

Once outside, we followed a steady stream of people towards the temple.

Festooned with swaying bamboo poles, *penjors,* laden with fruit, rice and other symbols of fertility, the streets looked gay and colourful, lending a brilliant backdrop to the festive day.

'So gala!' Madge cried, 'as grand as the Wangaratta Show day.'

Bands of women superb in embossed lace and batik swarmed past us, carrying offerings that soared up to the sky. Huge ornamental pyramids, embellished with lush fruit and flowers, were balanced expertly on their heads. Despite the immense weight, they walked with incredible aplomb, their backs erect, their heads held high, bearing their bounty to the gods proudly. It was a labour of love.

Crammed inside the temple forecourt, Madge, overcome by the heat and the growing crowd, had a panic attack. Len saved the day by plucking her to safety, redeeming himself in her eyes forever. His status ensured, he whisked Madge back to the room to recover with a good lie down, then headed off for a relaxing game of golf.

Inspired by the parade of sumptuous fashions at the temple, I rushed back to get ready. Determined to create a good impression for my first meeting with the 'in-laws', I enlisted the aid of Komang. After a few adjustments she was satisfied - the fold of my sarong fell exactly at the front, its pastel tones augmenting the lilac lace of my blouse. *'Cantik,* very pretty,' Komang enthused. 'Husband lucky man.'

I sat on the lounge, careful not to crease my outfit. Attempting to read my book, I was too nervous to concentrate. Every few minutes I got up to check myself in the mirror. Nothing out of place. Half an hour passed, then an hour. Remy was late, but then again the whole island seemed to have inherited a flagrant disregard for time.

At last he strode into the room. 'You look lovely,' he said, erasing any trace of annoyance. Words were a panacea for the soul.

Encased within the rigid confines of my sarong, I was obliged to ride side-saddle on the bike. Buffeted by the strong wind, I feared everything was about to unravel. An endless stream of bikes whizzed past bearing a bevy of elegant ladies. Without a hair out of place, they held onto grand floral offerings while juggling several children.

We came to a halt in a small side-lane cluttered with houses. Walking down the narrow pathway, we passed under an arched gateway leading to a central courtyard flanked by a hotchpotch of rooms. From their hanging bamboo cages, a chorus of exotic birds loudly announced our arrival. I hovered behind Remy.

Everyone turned to stare. A raised eyebrow or two then the curiosity passed, and they all resumed their previous activity. Remy disappeared into a room while I sat down on the steps, hoping somebody would come over for a chat. No-one did; all preferred to look from afar at the odd Western woman perched on the verandah.

Mercifully, Remy soon returned. A sullen-faced woman walked behind him. She shot me a dour look before placing some tea and rice cakes on the table. One last glare and she retreated into the shadows.

'Don't worry,' Remy said, easing the blow. 'That's my maiden aunt, she's not used to strangers. You'll grow on her with time.'

'You've certainly got a large family.' I tried to keep track of all the people wandering past, 'are you sure you know who they all are?'

'This is only some of them, that's my father over there,' he said pointing to a wrinkled man crouched in the corner, cradling a large rooster. Several men were gathered around, meticulously examining the bird. 'There's a cockfight later on. My father's been preparing for ages, hoping his rooster will win. He feeds it its own special mix of grain every day and never puts it down - see how he's massaging it?'

'I should be so lucky! Now, where's your mother?' She obviously wasn't in the running when the rooster was around.

'See those women over there?' He gestured to two elderly women stooped on the opposite porch. 'They're my father's wives.'

'But, which one's your mother?' I asked, perplexed that he didn't deem to discriminate between the two.

'The one smiling at you.' An old woman, her teeth saturated red from the remnants of betel, was beaming at me. 'She likes you.'

'I'd really like to talk to her, but my Indonesian's lousy.'

'Wouldn't do you much good anyway. Like most old people, my parents only speak Balinese, they never went to school.'

Set in the midst of the courtyard, encircled by a grey slabbed wall, stood the family temple bedecked in all its finery. The base of each shrine was girdled with white cloth, the sides flanked by yellow fringed umbrellas. The compound emanated a very potent energy.

'That's my temple,' Remy said, pointing to a small one. 'I pray there twice a day.' Mindful of my belief that God resided in the heart, and was present in every living thing, I was wary of his attachment.

'If I wish to retain my race,' he explained, 'I am linked eternally with the temples of my ancestors. One can only be born a Balinese, there can be no converts. If a woman marries outside her faith, she leaves her own family gods forever and worships those of her husband from that time on. She loses the right to be Balinese, just like a man who changes his religion.'

Dense incense clouds billowed from the temple, which was laden with the leftover traces of prayer - scattered flowers, an empty coconut husk, grains of saffron rice. Yet it was the auric imprint of spirits that dominated, even though there was no visible remnant to suggest their presence. 'I don't see any images of the gods in your temples. You don't worship statues or idols?'

'The shrines remain empty to create a space for the ancestral gods to visit. The temples are a temporary residence for their spirits.'

The roar of a crowd interrupted our talk. We followed the feverish sound down a series of alleyways to a vacant plot of land. A large group of men was gathered there, sweating with excitement. Several proud cocks were strutting impatiently under upturned bamboo baskets, waiting for the fight. Remy's father was standing close by, clutching his black rooster tightly to his chest.

'I don't think I want to watch, it's so barbaric.'

'Cockfighting is part of our tradition. A blood sacrifice is necessary in any ceremony to appease the appetite of the demons.'

The first round was imminent, the betting furious. The men were in chaos, flinging money onto the ground. A fine copper haze enveloped the scene, particles of dust tinging the evening air. Slowly the birds were removed from their baskets, straining for the skirmish. The atmosphere was tense, the arena hushed. Then the fight began.

The roosters, set free, unleashed their savage fury. The crowd erupted into a frenzy as a violent wave of energy shot through the air. The birds circled each other menacingly, their claws studded with metal spurs. Then one attacked. The smaller tawny bird was no match for its darker opponent, its flesh shredded to pieces in moments.

'I have to go.' Running back to the house, I found a dark corner and hid. After some time, people began to trickle back. Remy's father was euphoric, parading his winning bird proudly. Victory had somehow confirmed his masculinity, the triumphant cock a timeless symbol of man's unflagging virility and valour.

By way of celebration, a feast was laid out. The women had outdone themselves. Steaming bowls of rice, vegetables and noodles, were spread around huge chunks of suckling pig fresh from the spit. 'Help yourself,' Remy said, plunging a knife into the pork. He cut me off a slab, before piling a mountain of meat onto his plate. 'Would you like some *lawar*?' he asked, grabbing a plate laden with a red, congealed mass. 'It's made from boiled pork. The heart, stomach and blood of the pig are mixed with seasoning. It's delicious.'

'I'll pass,' I said, trying not to gag. After some hunting, a fork was found for me while everyone else hoed into the food with their fingers. Hunched over their plates, they downed the delicacies then went back for more. Very few words were exchanged, this was a time for eating, not for social pleasantries or banal conversation.

As soon as we had finished, Remy motioned that we were leaving. I looked around in a futile attempt to extend my thanks to his family. No-one seemed interested so I gave up; these people were definitely not into niceties. Slipping out the gate, I vowed that I would never push Remy to take me anywhere ever again.

'Ten days after *Galungan*, at the festival of *Kuningan*,' Remy said, 'it is believed that the souls of our ancestors leave Bali and return to heaven. All my family are going to the temple on *Pulau Serangan*, Turtle Island, to pray. Would you like to come?' An unexpected invitation, but with what intent?

I was taken by surprise, my presence had left an impression on the family after all. More to the point, I knew Remy had deeper concerns. Nearly six months had passed and my time in Bali was coming to an end, my visa running out. Aware there was little to return to and nowhere else to go, my choice was a relatively simple one. Remy had assumed a much more significant role in my life than I'd intended, deep in my heart I couldn't bear to be parted from him.

'Of course I'll come.' I didn't relish a return engagement with the family, but I'd pressured so hard to establish the ties I couldn't backtrack now. Maybe the 'in-laws' would grow on me with time.

'I've brought my sister, Kadek, to look after you.' Remy hovered at the door. 'I have to go and find a boat to take us to Turtle Island.'

The young girl lingered outside, too shy to enter. No more than fourteen, she was exceptionally pretty, her long dark hair laced with white frangipani. Slender in pale blue lace *kebaya* and woven sarong, she was the epitome of youthful beauty. Smiling through the softest brown eyes, Kadek gently took my hand and led me through the garden to the roadside.

A battered bemo was parked under a tree, the family jammed inside. 'Mum' in the front broke into a spontaneous cackle as I passed by, whacking my arm in greeting. Hoisted into the back by the relatives, I dodged a mountain of offerings and squeezed in next to my 'favourite aunt.' Sour as always, the festivities of the day had done little to lighten her mood. I diverted my gaze out the window rather than face her relentless scrutiny.

Lurching down the bumpy road, the driver insisted on hitting every pothole along the way. Coughing through a thick layer of dust, I held on tight to the railing as he careened round the corners. Fortunately, the trip was short, the road coming to an abrupt end in a glade of banana trees. Masses of people were gathered there, waiting for boats to take them across to the island.

Up ahead, Remy was negotiating with a boatman. Once a price was agreed upon, we headed off in an orderly line along the path to the beach. Remy led the way. Even though his brothers were present they deferred to him, in honour of his undisputed power. I sensed this was due to the link with his grandfather, or to spiritual authority he'd either earned or had thrust upon him.

'Come,' Kadek said, helping me up a steep ridge of burning sand. Over the wide blue horizon, a flotilla of small fishing boats bobbed on the water, their sails flapping colourfully in the wind.

One by one, baskets and people were loaded aboard until our small craft was ready to set sail. The wiry boatman took charge, negotiating his way through the reef. As Sanur receded from view, the waves grew bigger, lapping against the sides of the boat and showering us in a fine salty spray.

Remy stood on the boat's prow staring out to sea, the wind lashing the strong contours of his body. I willed him to look at me. Sensing our connection, he turned slowly. Our eyes locked. For a split second, the ocean, the people and the vibrant red sail of the boat receded from view. Together we reached a clandestine place of the soul, a forbidden sanctuary that was ours alone. For a single moment in time we were as one.

The sense of an intruder tore us apart. Kadek's questioning eyes blazed a path through our private world. Remy and I disengaged. Immersed in the ocean's glassy depths I gazed far within, pondering what mysterious quirk of fate had led me to this mythical island and to this man. To a link that transcended the bounds of time and space, triggering deep-rooted memories of a life once lived. A life so rich and profound in meaning, it confounded the imagination.

With a rough jolt we landed at Turtle Island, a sandbank anchoring us a few metres from shore. In the rush to disembark, the boat pitched to one side. Hitching up my sarong ungraciously, I jumped over the side and waded through the clear water onto dry land.

'Keep up,' Remy called out, 'there's so many people here, we may get separated.' Quickening our pace, we pushed past the milling hordes heading towards the temple. Along the way, I searched for the legendary turtle but saw only a few apathetic specimens lolling about in a murky green pond.

As we neared the temple, the activity became more hectic. Kadek, scared of losing me, kept a tight grip and led me through the two ornate carved gateways flanking the temple entrance. The inner courtyard was packed with hundreds of devotees kneeling in prayer.

'Over here,' Remy motioned, clearing a space by his side. He placed a fresh pink bloom behind my ear as I crouched down next to him. High temple pagodas towered into the violet haze, replete with the musky scent of ripe jasmine. The tinkling of bells embraced the silence with sound, one single transcendent tone amplifying the ethereal magnificence. Moved by the intense pulse of the prayer, I slipped into a holy vibration.

'Do as I do,' Remy whispered, easing me into the vision. Picking up some petals from a silver platter, he pressed his palms together and placed them on his forehead. I traced his movements exactly. Three times I followed his hands in prayer. The spell heightened with every motion.

An ancient priest, furled in white, circulated among the throng dowsing them with holy water. Scooping a little from his wooden bowl, he poured it into the upturned palms of each devotee. Then he bent over me. The water drenched my head, the cool moistness trickling into my hand. I took a sip. The taste was healing, the flavour strangely aromatic.

All at once I felt released, yet strangely the bond between Remy and myself tightened. The energy surged all around, drawing us closer in its mystical net. The priest had somehow given us his blessing, sanctified our union. Through tranquil eyes and an open heart, I felt the subtle imprint of Remy's hand on mine. A touch that was sublime in its intimacy and karmic innuendo.

Now it was clear. I was where I belonged, with a man whose presence had been ordained long before I was born. At last I had come back ... back to the spiritual place of my soul.

CHAPTER FIVE
Island of Magic

'Len's got a dreadful case of Bali-belly and these tickets will go to waste,' Madge pleaded. 'I do so want to absorb some of the local culture but I'm not accustomed to going out alone, say you'll come.'

As long as I'd been in Bali I'd only seen one dance, the *legong,* performed at a local restaurant. Colourful as it was, it was too commercial for my liking. The culture had a rich tradition of mystical dance, the 'trance' state a major component of many performances. Wanting to judge the authenticity of the experience for myself, I accepted her offer gladly.

'Super. The car will be waiting in front of the hotel at six.'

After a short drive, we reached the outdoor venue. The car-park was full of mini-buses and frantic tour guides shouting instructions in every conceivable tongue. A flock of Japanese tourists waddled past following a red flag, while a Taiwanese group, hell-bent on finding the best seats, nearly annihilated us trying to get inside. We took shelter behind some Swiss.

'Some people have no manners,' Madge huffed, hurling all out of her way to secure front row seats. Flipping back the brim of her hat defiantly, she chuckled, 'If I can handle Franklins on a Saturday, I can cope with anything. Look out world, Mighty Madge has arrived!'

As the sky dimmed, an ominous gong sounded and a hush fell upon the audience. A troop of men spilled silently onto the stage. Squatting on the ground in a tight circle around a burning oil lamp, they began to chant. A low monotonous hum, building into a hypnotic drone, *'chak ... chak ... chak ...'* escalating in speed until the air throbbed with the tense vibration.

'It's the *kecak* dance - they're supposed to be monkeys,' Madge fingered her program nervously. 'A little too loud for my liking.'

Waving their arms, the men swayed in unison. Undulating like a giant thrashing snake trapped in its own death-grip, the moving band of sound pulsated, crushing the imaginary demon with a single blow.

Two young girls floated onto the stage, their eyes locked shut. No more than eight years old, they were wrapped in ribbons of gold. Ethereal in movement, their virgin bodies were possessed by the spirits of celestial goddesses. Detached vessels, the nymphs danced in trance to music intended only for their ears. Untrained, they performed each movement with skill and the utmost precision, as if choreographed by a higher source.

'How strange,' Madge said, as her grip on my elbow tightened, 'and I don't mind telling you, a wee bit frightening.'

She wasn't prepared for what was to follow. Hot coals were spread onto the stage, the burning embers smouldering a vibrant red glow. A solitary dancer, more horse than man, leapt into the ashes, kicking at the hostile heat with his bare feet. The spirit possessing his body rendered it senseless, oblivious to all physical pain.

Stronger than the burning cinders, he challenged the fire to a test of strength – stomping on the heat over and over until it was vanquished. One last crackle and it petered into submission. The equine might reigned supreme, the spirit of the fire lost. A look of triumph flooded the dancer's face, until his eyes flickered open and focused on the dying ashes. His pupils, tense and dilated, were tinged with the glower of madness, a frightening legacy of his excursion into the twilight zone.

'My, what a peculiar people,' Madge shuddered, totally out of her depth, 'dare I say they all seem a little possessed.' Wrapping her cardigan firmly around her shoulders, she headed for the nearest exit.

'How did it go last night?' Joyce asked, rubbing on her suntan lotion. 'Madge didn't seem too impressed.' The hotel pool had been taken over by a posse of sun-starved Dutch grabbing the last of the deckchairs. Undeterred, I spread my towel out onto the ground.

'I think it was all a bit much for the poor dear, but I found the show fascinating. I've been trying to figure out if they were really in a trance or were doing it only for the crowd's benefit.'

'Anywhere else I'd say they were bunging it on, but here,' Joyce said, leaning closer, 'I've heard too much to doubt it. Look at poor Jean who was out here last year on holiday. She went touring with some friends up north and they came across an old temple. You know how it's forbidden to enter a temple if you're menstruating because you're *sebel,* impure, and will pollute the holiness of the temple, well it was Jean's time of the month so she was hesitant to go in but was too embarrassed to protest. Once inside she felt someone push her, then she went faint and passed out.'

'That's awful. Why would anyone want to do that?'

'No-one did ... physically. When she opened her eyes, she saw a band of children staring down at her, grinning maliciously. She was terrified, especially when nobody else could see them. They continued to circle and taunt her until she was forced to leave.'

'Maybe she had concussion and conjured them up.'

'Who knows? On the way back, she had a nasty turn and they had to stop on the roadside. As she lay there people appeared like ghosts from the fields and put frangipanis on her head. That night she'd recovered enough to visit some friends at the Dark Sands hotel.'

'Bad move! That place positively exudes evil.'

'Poor Jean found out the hard way. She'd walked down to the beach to look at the ocean, when she felt someone push her again. She passed out and when she came to, she literally saw stars! Both her ankles had swollen up like watermelons. Jean was forced to fly back to America after her 'accident.' Following a full medical examination and X-rays, they found every ligament in her ankles had been torn. The doctors were at a complete loss, of course. When one brave man suggested 'sinister' implications, he was laughed at.'

'Let's face it, our society has no understanding of these forces. There's a complete distrust of anything mystical, a leftover mentality from the witch trials of the middle ages when all metaphysical knowledge was feared, then ostensibly wiped out.'

'Strange how the supernatural often surfaces in literature and films but it's never outrightly acknowledged as existing. Here people accept these forces because magic runs rampant. If a doctor can't find a cure for an illness, he admits the problem stems from forces beyond his control and sends the patient to a *dukun,* a magic man who specialises in the removal of spells. He swings either way, he's also known to cast a few spells too ...'

'Did you know,' I added, 'that a lot of the locals avoid coming here to Sanur because it's considered *angker* - haunted.'

Joyce jumped as the bushes visibly flickered. Lily, the hotel's resident cat strolled out casually, her kinky tail angled like a broken antenna.

'I'm sure any self-respecting ghost would have been driven out long ago by the tour buses tearing down the highway.'

'Sunbaking, ladies?' I looked up to see the polite face of Gusti, the manager of Swaying Palms. Joyce, in a rare display of modesty, grabbed her towel and smothered her breasts. Gusti smiled charmingly as he took shelter under the umbrella. 'Be careful, this tropical sun can be fierce.'

'Gusti, you're a learned man,' I asked, eager to know more. 'Can you clarify something for us?'

'Certainly, how can I help?' Gusti had the proud stature of many Balinese combined with a natural elegance and noble stance.

'We're having a discussion about magic,' Joyce said trying to raise the subject carefully, 'perhaps you could give us a few clues.'

'Sorry, I'm very busy now,' Gusti replied, looking very uneasy. 'Perhaps we can talk later, I should be getting on with my rounds.'

'Come on, Gusti,' Joyce prompted, 'whenever I touch on the subject, people clam up on me - it's *so* frustrating.'

'Nobody wishes to provoke the powers that be; it is not an area broached lightly. People here are very superstitious and with good reason. They live with unexplained phenomena every day. Some encounters are mild, others devastating. Take 1963 for example. It was during the most sacred of all ceremonies, *Eka Dasa Rudra*, a massive exorcism which takes place once every hundred years where Rudra, the evil god, must be cast off the island. This is an awesome task that involves many elaborate preparations. Every type of animal in Bali, over sixty different species, is needed for the sacrificial rites.'

'Don't tell me you slaughter them?' Joyce gasped.

'It is considered an offering to the gods. The priests chant a sacred mantra to send the animal's soul to heaven for a better reincarnation next time. To ensure the purity of the rite, only a sacred kris knife made by the Pande clan of weapon-makers can be used.'

'So, what happened in 1963?' I asked, aware that it prefaced a period of time when many upheavals racked the country.

'Evil forces had taken control. There had been many bad omens - a plague of rats, crop failure, famine - the natural balance destroyed. Pressure was placed on the priests to fix a date for the ceremony, but there were many disputes regarding its accuracy. In spite of the controversy, it went ahead. On that very day, Mount Agung erupted.'

'What an incredible coincidence.'

'No mere coincidence ... Besakih, the mother temple of Bali, lies on the rim of Mount Agung within a ridge of deep valleys. Hundreds of people were kneeling inside in prayer as the rumblings began. Unsure whether the gods were angry or simply accepting their gifts, they remained rooted to the spot. Then with a mighty roar, an explosion sent rivers of lava down the valley. No-one moved, even though there was time to escape. Flames leapt into the sky, the temple roof-tops were set alight by hot ash, but miraculously the main sanctuaries and the people praying inside were spared.'

'Amazing - the sheer magnitude of divine intervention.'

'Still, it was a terrifying time, I remember it most vividly. My village lay far away, but even there, dense clouds of smoke and huge boulders poured from the sky. Then a veil of total darkness as a layer of thick ash fell upon the earth - it was as if the sky had caught fire. Thousands of people perished and one fifth of the island was destroyed. Perhaps now you can appreciate our tie with the gods. We respect their power, appeasing them daily to prevent any more catastrophes.'

'I don't blame you!' Joyce said, 'a few months back there was a minor tremor. Woke up to find my bed shaking, scared the life out of me. I sure wouldn't be taking any chances under the circumstances.'

'Cooee girls,' Joyce yelled across the sand, 'don't get sunburnt!' Since her niece, Annie, had arrived from Brisbane with a friend on holiday, Joyce had been clucking over them like an old hen watching over her brood. She'd nearly driven the two girls insane. 'Do you think they'll be alright? They've never been outside Australia before.'

'I'm sure they'll be fine.' Annie, a picture of health and vitality, looked like she'd been lifting weights in her spare time. Her friend Helen, ensconced in her novel, looked infinitely more vulnerable, as if she still believed in fairy stories, and that one day she'd find her Prince Charming. I hoped she realised there weren't many princes left on this island.

In perfect illustration, a bunch of beach boys strutted past, flexing their muscles and kicking up sand. Their presence barely raised a flutter. Annie was locked into her headphones, while Helen sat staring out to sea, lost in her fantasy world. She had fallen victim to the island's magic. Meanwhile, the lads were becoming vexed, all their best moves failing to impress. Giving up in disgust, they stood in front of the Watersport shed discussing tactics. I knew they'd be back, the bait was too tempting.

'Feel like a drink?' The sweat was pouring down Joyce's cheeks in tiny rouged rivulets. 'This humidity will be the end of me.'

'Damn powerboats,' I said, sitting under a huge white umbrella at the beachside cafe. 'It's impossible to find a bit of peace around here. One cold Aqua, please - lots of ice,' I called to the waiter.

'Make mine a double,' Joyce added, winking as he approached. Old habits died hard. 'Hey, isn't that Henny down there on the back of the jet ski? I thought in her profession, she only came out at night.'

'The only sport that woman's into is a spot of man-hunting at the club. By the looks of it she's hanging onto last night's catch.'

'And doesn't Olaf just love it!' Joyce gulped down her water and chuckled. 'I don't know what Henny's holding onto but Olaf's certainly got his foot on the pedal. He'd better slow down or ...' Horrified, we looked on as the jet-ski did a couple of spectacular wheelies before shooting into the air like a metal monster on the rampage. Cutting through the waves, it dumped Henny into the ocean with a bang. Olaf jumped in after her, heaving her onboard before guiding the sputtering machine back to shore.

A squadron of staff ran down the beach. Olaf barely had time to get Henny to dry land before the boys pushed them aside and ran to the aid of the boat. Lovingly stroking the surface searching for any sign of damage, they caressed the hull before one of the lads took it out for a test spin. It purred over the water and they all breathed a huge sigh of relief.

As for poor Henny, she was reeling about on her last legs, collapsing under the combined weight of her solid gold chains and recent ordeal. Olaf was clinging on helplessly, not sure which part of her to catch first. Back at the bar he pumped her full of cocktails, the rose coming back to her cheeks as she drained the decanter dry.

'Now I've seen everything,' Joyce groaned. 'Nothing like getting your priorities right! Well, the trauma seems to have passed.'

The boys, relieved that the boat was safe, were kicking a football around the sand, skilfully manoeuvring it so that it would land in Annie's lap. Touchdown! Annie winced visibly as the ball whacked her in the stomach. Helen was wrested from her novel, sprayed with a fine layer of sand. The boys loped over apologetically to wipe down her legs. Icky was being particularly attentive.

'Game, set and match.' Joyce snorted. 'Bali one, Australia nil!'

Later that evening I went down to Swaying Palms hoping to collect some mail. My bungalow was so small and out of the way that it didn't even have an address, let alone a postal facility. Visitors had to be given careful instructions: 'Turn left at the roundabout, down the lane, past the pigs on the right, watch out for the vicious black dog then veer hard at the roosters.'

I was sifting through a large batch of letters when Joyce swept into the lobby, resplendent in white and reeking of Poison. 'Wow, aren't *we* dressed to kill? Who's the lucky guy?'

'Wouldn't you just love to know!' In spite of all my wild attempts to crack her secret over the weeks, she was not breathing a word. The woman had the resolve of an FBI agent. 'Wander down to the club later on and you might just find out. I promised the girls we'd go out to dinner first - the way they've been carrying on lately, I thought they needed a chaperone.'

'By the looks of you Auntie, you're the one who needs watching!' Annie crept up behind Joyce and gave her a giant hug. The girls looked fabulous in crisp white linen outfits, perfectly designed to show off their sleek figures and newly acquired tans.

'It looks like rain.' Joyce stared out at the dark clouds. 'We'd better get a move on before the storm hits. See you down at the club.'

When they'd gone, Ketut, the receptionist, extricated himself from behind the desk and plopped down on the faded lounge. I was hoping for a little lively conversation, but he was glued to the television. A gruesome scene flashed across the screen. Young children were being carried on stretchers, their frail bodies writhing in pain. Doctors stood over them trying to alleviate their suffering but with little success. The spasms continued as their limbs quivered uncontrollably, their eyes wide and glassy.

'What's happening?' I asked, horrified. 'An earthquake?'

'No, it's Sulawesi.'

He turned up the volume, '... a school-group went camping near a sacred mountain, and whilst there, many of the children fell into a trance. Since their return some students have slipped back into the hypnotic state, and the school has been in chaos. The community is so worried they've asked for help from all the island's dukuns to release the spirits trapped inside the children.'

'What spirits?' I asked, distressed by the harrowed looks. What manner of entity would take possession of helpless children?

'The mountain was haunted and the group disturbed its sacred guardians. The same thing happened here in Bali in the eighties. Over forty children from one village went into trance, crying that they'd seen the witch Rangda, a horrible woman with long red hair and a hideous face. Two of the young girls were possessed by spirits that commanded them to dance. As soon as the music began, they performed the legong dance even though they had never been trained in its steps. Then many other children joined in.'

'Did they ever discover a reason for their behaviour?'

'When the children did not respond to traditional or mystical methods, a high priest was consulted. He said a small temple in the school grounds was built on a 'spirit rock' and so offended the gods. A purification ceremony was held and a new temple built. After that all attacks stopped.'

Although my rational mind fought for a logical explanation, a part of me, having experienced them first-hand, conceded the power of these forces. Many a night I'd walk along the deserted roads of Sanur aware of a lingering presence. Constantly I would look over my shoulder trying to catch it out, but I'd see nothing. Yet the sensation remained ... something singularly unpleasant was trailing me. I quickened my pace and never looked back.

'What the hell?' Ketut's face went deathly pale, convinced that the spirits of the thunder gods had come to wreak havoc. There in the pouring rain stood three dismal grey apparitions. As they started to advance, Ketut slunk further down into the couch. On the verge of apoplexy, he burst into gales of laughter as a wave of recognition hit.

'If you don't shut up, I'll slide over there and deck you,' Joyce threatened, wiping bits of gravel from her lips. Thoroughly drenched, she stood huddled with the girls in a pool of water on the lobby floor. Their once beautiful classic ensembles were caked in a layer of thick brown sludge. 'Those dense bastards! We were walking in the middle of the road 'cause it seemed safer, what with all those piles of earth dumped everywhere. It started raining, so we waded through the flood when a car roared past ... that's when we jumped out of the way and fell straight into a ditch.'

'Can you imagine, those bloody idiots dug a six foot trench along the road,' Annie raged, 'that was the same level as the footpath.'

'It was full of water,' Helen laughed. 'We jumped onto it or *into* it, to be more precise! We went straight down, right up to our heads. You should have heard the choice phrases as we pulled Joycie out.'

'I could hazard a guess,' I replied.

'Oh no you couldn't,' she gasped. 'I invented a few new ones!'

'Now Auntie, you must admit, it has its funny side. We must have looked a sight hauling you out of that hole - every time we yanked you up, you slid further in. We thought you were a goner!'

'Come to think of it, did you see the face on that old fella as we ran down the road past him in the pouring rain.'

'Even the dogs took one look and scattered down the lane!'

'How about we go back to the room and start again,' Joyce sighed. 'This time, don't wear white!'

Barefoot and hovering under a giant umbrella, I made a run for it in the swirling gale. Dodging the huge piles of dirt, I reached the club in record time. Wayan heaved open the door and helped me inside, slamming it shut before the wind could suck us out and deposit us in the closest coconut tree.

It was still early and the club was empty. Remy was playing cards with the rest of the staff and by the familiar ring of his laughter, he was ahead. Thinking it better not to interrupt his winning streak, I made a beeline for Sting. Less gregarious than the rest, he was sitting alone in the corner booth, flicking through a newspaper.

'Sting, can I talk to you for a minute? I saw something tonight that defies explanation.' Drifting into a cool alpine cloud, I sat down beside him. Loofahed to perfection, Sting had the capacity to make anyone within close proximity feel dirty. Instinctively I itched away a layer of auric grime. 'Do you believe in spirits?'

'Pretty heavy duty stuff, isn't it?' He put down the newspaper. 'I'd be lying if I said I didn't believe in it, most do. But we don't talk about it openly, you never know *what* might be lurking around.'

'Have you felt it personally?' I wanted more than hearsay.

'I'll tell you something that happened when I was young but promise me you'll never repeat it, it's not something I'm particularly proud of.' He took a deep breath, 'I once met a magic man who told me I could have any woman I wanted. He gave me a mantra to repeat, then taught me how to blow smoke in a woman's face so she would find me irresistible.'

'Just like Casablanca!' I gasped. 'Sting, you're a handsome man, I bet you'd have that effect on women, anyway.'

'You miss the point, I went to a bank and picked out one of the tellers and did what he said. That night she came to my house and we made love. She kept coming every night after that, the problem was that she was married and became obsessed with me. Her neighbours told me she was going mad, muttering my name and keeling over.'

'So what did you do?' I asked, intrigued as to why one human being would want to control another.

'I went back to the magic man and begged him to remove the spell. He agreed and she soon recovered, thank God. Since then I've learnt my lesson. I'll never dabble in any of that stuff again.'

‘Do others use magic?’ Alarmed, I suddenly felt vulnerable.

‘Yes, of course. There are lots of different methods that can be used. *Lengis colek*, touch oil, is common. Just a few drops on the girl’s forehead and she’s yours. I have a friend who uses magic teeth, they’re very potent.’

‘Excuse me, magic teeth? Now I’ve heard everything.’

‘Don’t laugh. He picked up the spell in Lombok. If he smiles at a girl, she’s a goner. I mean this guy’s really ugly but he’s always got a string of beautiful women trailing him. The only catch is that he’s got to go back every year to renew it, otherwise he loses his powers.’

‘This is all pretty fantastic stuff.’ I shook my head in disbelief. ‘So you can bring magic here from other places and it still works?’

‘Once it crosses water, it’s rendered useless but there are ways around it. My friend smuggled his over from Lombok inside a freshly sealed coconut. Another way is inside a chicken’s stomach.’

‘Are we talking dead or alive here? Either option’s disgusting.’

‘It doesn’t matter. When you get home, you slit it open and your potion is alive and kicking.’

‘Unlike the poor rooster! This place is weird.’ In a giant cosmic affirmation, a convoy of rotund German tycoons took over the bar, acting like a Lufftwaffer reunion party. Sting jumped up just in time to stop them ripping the top off a Schnapps bottle with their teeth.

Appearing out of thin air, a horde of killer sirens breathing flames of *Love is Dead, but it’s Yours for a Price* lipstick, descended upon them. Tugging at their overtight minis in fake leopard skin with matching muffs, they straddled the bar much to the delight of Gunter and the gang. So roused, they were ready to burst into a stirring rendition of *‘Munich the Motherland,’* using one of the dangling lovelies as a human glockenspiel. I was sure Gunter was hiding a pair of leather alpine shorts under his executive attire, but didn’t dare ask.

Interestingly, the sweetie who was now mounting Gunter in a reverse missionary position, had what appeared to be a three day growth. Knotty hands were stroking Gunter’s throat, the ruby red talons set to become permanently embedded in his jutting Adam’s apple. Gunter lunged for the silicone implant, as untold lusty fantasies flashed through his brain. Poised to plunge into the forbidden zone, Gunter was due to get more than he bargained for.

‘You keep strange company,’ Joyce said, shimmying onto the bar stool next to me and draping her legs around the cold chrome. Gunter was momentarily diverted by the squelch of wrapping flesh, but Juicy Lucy tightened her death grip and he succumbed willingly.

'Which rock did these people crawl out from,' Joyce sighed, fiddling with the neckline of her black dress. Her accessories were more understated than usual, her air mildly enigmatic. She looked almost sophisticated.

'Joyce, you've changed!' I gasped, disturbed by the difference. Where was that blatant temptress, the brassy babe I knew and loved.

'You noticed,' she replied, checking herself in her compact. Even her lipstick was subdued, her eye-shadow beige instead of gaudy green. 'I'm adopting a new image, it's time to tone down.'

'Don't you dare!' I pleaded, hoping it was only a menopausal stage she was going through. 'You're wonderful the way you are.'

'It's what *he* wants,' she said coyly. This didn't sound like my Joyce. Just as I was ready to have her committed, a hefty set of arms emerged out of the smoke and folded themselves around her breasts. 'Meet Sly,' she fluttered. The rest of the man materialised from the shadows - very much his namesake. Attractive in an underhanded sort of way, I felt an immediate distrust. Hooking one leg over Joyce's thigh as if he was staking some sort of territorial claim, he seemed all set to peg the Yukon.

Joyce burrowed into him with such ferocity that I feared she'd tunnel straight through his body and into the bar like a berserk beaver. The woman was smitten. 'Not bad,' I whispered in her ear, offering the only words of encouragement I could. They appeared hopelessly mismatched, not so much for the difference in age, but for the obvious gap in integrity.

'Oh, I was wondering what had happened to the girls,' Joyce said, distracted from her euphoria. Annie, fabulous in aqua, was standing at another bar flirting outrageously with a rugged hunk in bone-crushing jeans. I was sure he had spray-painted them on while he was doing his surfboard, such was the rigidity of his parts.

Meanwhile, Helen was being stalked by a hairy, bronzed boofhead. Embarrassed by the attention, she tried to get past but his pectorals blocked her way. Fudge, the local beach boy flavour of the month, stared at her with a look guaranteed to turn the strongest will to putty, then held out his hand. 'Dance!' he commanded.

Thrusting aside all inhibitions, Helen tripped over her feet in her haste to get at him. She had dreamed of this from the moment she was conceived and followed him onto the sterile dance-floor like an over-ripe ovum going in for the final scrum. Fudge grunted in appreciation, his hips groaning lustfully to the beat of the music.

Back at the bar, Annie was doing alright for herself too. Raunchy Randy was coming in for the kill. His hot loins pressed against her willing thighs. She was clutching onto the counter hanging onto the last of her senses. 'Wanna do it?' he dribbled into her Drambuie. A dangling dreadlock wound around her earring, trapping her in its deadly embrace. Rising silently, she followed him into the night.

'The girls seem to be having a good time,' I coughed.

'Too good,' Joyce huffed, catching the rabid scent of Randy as he swept by. 'What is it about this place that makes everyone go potty? Do they spray the planes with love potion when they land here? *Bali High?*'

'At least they don't disinfect you the way they do in Oz. I feel like I've got a case of foot and mouth every time I go back home.'

'It's better than a case of terminal crotch rot, no wonder the planes need fumigating! This place is crammed with over-sexed women who left any trace of morality back home on the floor of the departure lounge! Just take a look on the dance-floor.'

A brood of females were lined up, kicking their way through a stirring rendition of the *Bus Stop*. Rotating their buttocks in perfect time, they competed to outshine one another in micro shorts and flounce tops. Apart from differing degrees of perm, it was hard to tell them apart.

'I think it's time to leave,' Joyce snarled. Sly's eyeballs were dilated with delight as he scanned the offerings. Irate, Joyce snapped him up along with her handbag and shoved him out the door.

Feeling adrift, I needed to talk to Remy and assure myself of his allegiance. I fought the tortuous crowd to get to his bar. Remy was busy mixing the drinks while Froggy was entertaining the troops, juggling the cocktail shaker high into the air. It spun out of control and hurtled across the bar straight into the lap of a comely lass, spilling her martini down her dress. Remy ran to her aid, mopping her chest with a soiled tea-towel.

During the mishap the olive was mislaid somewhere down Moira's front. Remy was being overly helpful in retrieving it and the search appeared to spark a common bond. By the ethereal look on Moira's face, their kinship had achieved biblical proportions. Grovelling in such a deep abyss had drawn them together, as profound a mission as the quest for the Holy Grail.

I moved closer hoping to get a better look. Moira was eyeing off Remy like a vulture deliberating over dinner. It was clear from the glint in her eye that she had every intention of picking his bones clean. Everything about Moira reeked desert, down to her pungent perfume *l'eau de Cactus*.

Her coarse skin was pure mud brick, her teased brittle hair baked on a vacuous brain confirmed she was tumbleweed in motion. Lighting up a Camel cigarette, she took long meaningful drags, searching for a line of conversation.

'You people have such an awesome country,' she droned, her eyes curiously lizard-like. 'We've always wanted to come to Bali, haven't we Mandy?' Her friend was too preoccupied to answer, stacking a pile of martini glasses into a precarious glass pyramid.

'Then you like Indonesia?' Remy asked, trying to be sociable.

'Oh,' Moira gasped, 'never been there, bit too far from home.'

'I'm not game,' Mandy said, rousing from a self-inflicted coma.

'But this *is* Indonesia,' Remy groaned, not believing his ears.

'It is?' Mandy bounced to an upright position, shocked. 'That bloody travel agent told us we were going to Bali. Never mind,' she warbled, 'cause the guys here sure are hot. You're pretty spunky too.'

'Yeah, want to come back to our room when you finish work?' Moira pouted, plunging her neckline to even more perilous depths.

'He's busy,' I flared, deciding now was the perfect time for a little direct intervention. Three heads swivelled around in unison.

'Who the fuck's that?' Mandy yelped. Moira looked crestfallen as Remy ran down the bar. 'God, you're a stupid bitch, I told you not to talk too much. It puts them off if they think you're clever.'

'What's wrong?' Remy asked, looking concerned.

'I need to talk to you.' It sounded a genuine enough excuse.

Aware of the boss's cutting stare, Remy was tense. 'You know he doesn't like it if we stand around chatting. Can't it wait?'

'I guess it will have to,' I answered, backing away. I could feel all my insecurities welling to the surface. 'Better get back to work, gotta keep the customers satisfied! I'll see you later on.'

Depressed, I went back to the bungalow and lay in bed, unable to sleep. Persistent thoughts flashed through my mind. The fragile face of Helen, young and gullible. Ignoring all the warning signs, her mind clouded by romance, she had fallen into the trap. Fudge was a user, a manipulator of the worst kind. Like many before her, her heart would not only be broken, it would be mutilated. All her fanciful notions of life dissolved in one crushing blow.

Annie was more resilient and would give Randy a run for his money. With any luck she'd enjoy the experience, then have enough nous to give him the flick. Even if she did, I knew it would have little impact. These guys were too thick-skinned, so lacking in conscience, that no amount of rejection would make the slightest dent.

And now indomitable Joyce had succumbed, sacrificing her personality to win Sly's approval. It should have been the other way round. She was by far the stronger partner, if only she'd realise it.

I tossed and turned. If Joyce had so easily fallen victim, then what about me? Perhaps it had already happened and I wasn't aware of it. Parts of myself had been swallowed up in an effort to keep Remy happy. Resolved not to interfere I gave him free reign, sublimating my own emotions in the process. At work I kept a distance, pretending not to notice or be hurt when girls flirted with him. Increasingly, I felt I was trying to stuff a cork into a volcano; explosion was imminent.

I was Venus in Scorpio. I loved with a bold intensity, with a possessive drive that bordered on the manic. Remy unwittingly fuelled my insecurities. He was more than happy for me to do my own thing so he could be free to get on with his. I interpreted his encouragement as rejection - an indifference to our relationship.

The sound of a motor-bike ... Remy had arrived. Automatically, I looked at the clock - 2.15. Right on time. No time for deviations or unholy alliances. As much as I tried, I still didn't trust him fully.

'You awake?' he whispered in the darkness, before lying down and wrapping his body around mine. I pretended to be asleep. My thoughts were too destructive; he didn't deserve the mental onslaught.

Gradually he fell asleep, his soft breath caressing the hairs on the back of my neck. I was frightened to turn and face him. My love for him was so real, so potent that I knew it had the power to propel me to great heights. I shuddered, aware that the same force could turn against me and plunge me into the living hell of my worst fears.

A deadly snake twirled, coiling through the tortured recesses of my mind. *'Falling deeper down ... down into the bottomless pit.'*

The cruel eyes tormented me, transforming my mind into a treacherous minefield. I only needed to stumble, to trip over the wire and detonate it. My dread lay in the knowledge that only I could activate the lethal time bomb ticking inside my head.

CHAPTER SIX

Burning Flames

'Grandfather, grandfather!' a voice cried out in the dark.

'What is it?' I asked, woken from my sleep. Remy, pale and haunted, lay thrashing in the bed. 'Remy, what's wrong? Wake up.'

'Grandfather,' he repeated, tiny beads of sweat dotting his forehead. His body trembled as he struggled to get up. 'I have to go.'

'Calm down, it was only a dream. You know how much you've been worrying lately - your grandfather's so sick, it's understandable.' For weeks now his condition had worsened, he was old and plagued with fever, it was only a matter of time before he chose release.

'No, no ... you don't understand. I saw the sacred bull. A long procession of people carrying the body for cremation. I must go.'

Jumping out of bed, Remy dressed in a panic. I did my best to placate his fears, but it was useless, my words fell on deaf ears. Suddenly there was a knock on the door. Remy froze. Mustering all his courage, he slowly opened it. A stranger stood outside. Although he said nothing, the message was clear.

'My grandfather's dead, isn't he?' The man merely nodded.

Remy tore off on his bike half-mad, the engine fading into the distance. I sat on the bed staring at the wall, wanting so much to be with him in his hour of need. It was impossible, for while all my thoughts revolved around Remy, my distress was the furthest thing from his mind.

'Don't worry,' Sting said, a trace of real sympathy creeping into his voice. Hours stretched into days and still no word. 'With death, many rituals must take place before the cremation can go ahead.'

'It's only a matter of time,' Ben added. Of all the staff I liked Ben the most. He was a caring soul, whenever I had a problem I would go to him. He helped me understand a man's point of view and eased me through the cultural gap. 'Remy's grandfather was a great man with special powers, thus many people will need to be informed so they can pay their final respects.'

'I didn't realise it would take so long, or be so complicated.'

'Be thankful he wasn't a high priest. Last time a priest died in my village, the cremation couldn't take place for more than a month. A number of rites must be completed; the body must be cleansed, then provided with tools for a stronger rebirth. Mirrors on the eyes to make them bright, a gold ring on the teeth for strength, jasmine flowers on the nose for fragrant breath and steel for the bones. Then the body is wrapped in white cloth and guarded by the village men to prevent evil spirits from capturing the soul.'

'And then the ceremony can take place?'

'No, if the family doesn't have enough money the body is buried first. The spirit may grow restless trapped beneath the ground so when a rich or influential person is cremated, many poorer people will exhume the bodies of their relatives and include them at little cost, for the price of the offerings. Last year, during the priest's ceremony, over sixty bodies were burnt.'

At any other time, I would have found Ben's words fascinating, but right now I was aware of the large knot forming in my stomach. Anxiety was taking its toll. Ben gave me a gentle hug, but all the reassurance in the world could provide little comfort.

'Hi, there stranger.' I spun round, recognising the silky voice.

'Kate, I don't believe it!' With incredible regularity, when life was one big void, someone came along to fill it.

'Sorry I haven't been around much lately but we've been flat out at Mojo's what with the revamp, not to mention the drama of the divorce. I've been pressuring Cliff to get it over and done with,' she said, knocking back a martini, 'so we can put it behind us and get on with the rest of our lives.'

'So is there a fairytale ending to this ongoing saga?'

'I certainly hope so! I do have my qualms though,' she said, fiddling with her pearls. 'Cliff's fighting for custody of the children, but I'm not prepared for a ready-made family. I don't even know if I want one of my own. It's never been high on my list of priorities.'

'I'm sure you'll manage, you always do.'

'I'm selfish, I don't pretend to be otherwise. Cliff's so busy as it is, I hardly get any quality time with him.' I was in complete empathy. 'Besides I'm downright ambitious, not the earth-mother type at all. Can you really see me with a troop of kids?'

'If they were dressed in Armani, with a string of maids in tow.'

Kate's brow tensed, 'I've never failed in life at anything, motherhood's daunting.' A gulp of her martini and Kate's face was flooded with its natural optimism. 'This is ridiculous, everyone else can do it so why can't I?' Another swig and she was sold on the idea.

In the midst of our discussion, a couple of sloppy drunks sashayed over. 'Scuse us, ladies,' Merv drooled, 'mind if me and me mate join you?' Kate ignored them, having the admirable capacity to cut off from the vulgarities of life. Merv got the gist of the knockback and retreated from the fray, while his friend Bart, totally sloshed, slid comatose onto the floor.

'Where's Remy?' Kate asked, using Bart as a human beanbag. I filled her in. 'Don't worry,' she advised, 'the men around here have a million obligations designed to separate them from their spouse, particularly if she's a Western one. You'll get used to it after a while.'

'I don't like being relegated to the bottom of the pecking order.'

'Accept it or die on this island! You know it's funny but you've never told me whether you really do *love* Remy. You've hinted at it, joked about it, but you've never come outright and said it. Well?'

'Tell me what love is,' I challenged, refusing to say something I might live to regret, 'then I'll reply. Until then my lips are sealed.'

'Did someone mention *love*,' a familiar voice trilled. Joyce had arrived. 'Why don't you girls consult a real expert?'

'Have you met Kate before?'

'Once, but those fabulous legs have left a lasting impression on a mind plagued by cellulite! Meet Linda. She's a friend of my daughter, Faith. Isn't she a stunner?' The young woman had eyes of perfect translucent emerald. Suddenly brown seemed so ordinary.

'Don't mind Joyce,' Linda smiled, embarrassed by the truth. Sweeping aside the merest wisp of corn-gold hair, she held us captive with her presence. Perfect teeth, alabaster skin, the nose of a Grecian goddess, set off by a divine body. So much perfection was unnatural.

'Sometimes beauty can be such a curse,' Linda said, flicking away a group of admirers gathering nearby. 'So shallow.'

'Let me try it,' Joyce said, 'I might land myself a rich sheik. Then again they like them curvaceous, with the odd love handle or two!' She tugged at some excess flesh that had popped out from beneath her sweater. 'I'm set for life. Now, what was the question again?'

'The million dollar one, what is love? Between us we cover every angle on the subject. Kate's the pampered mistress, you've screwed everything that isn't nailed down on the island, and me, I chase phantom lovers that could be figments of my imagination. What about you, Linda?'

'My marriage is just *perfect,*' she crooned, wrapping her tongue around the word for emphasis. 'Are you ladies in love?'

'I miss him a lot,' I replied, 'have a tight knot in my stomach ...'

'And,' Joyce interrupted, 'she wants to belt any woman who looks at him sideways. Hooked like the rest of us! Ah, now who's this?' A stringy woman with hairy armpits had infiltrated our group.

'So you're Remy's girlfriend,' she slobbered, reeking of cheap gin. 'I'm Gwen.' She continued to stare at me, hoping that her mere presence would elicit a reaction. Pasty and gaunt, she steadied herself against the bar then leant over and whispered. 'All the staff here are married, *all* of them.' She toasted her glass then waved good-bye. 'Don't say you weren't warned!'

'Stupid bitch,' Kate fumed. 'What's her problem?' I had to hold back Joyce from marching off and turning her into a human pretzel.

'I don't know what's going on, but I have every intention of finding out.' I collared Froggy on his way out of the men's room. 'Froggy, tell me the truth. *'Is Remy married? And no bullshit either.'*

'What,' he protested, zipping up his fly, 'why ask stupid question? If Remy married, he at home every night making babies.'

My next target was Sting. He was astute so I had to use a more sophisticated approach. *'Is Remy married? And no bullshit either.'*

'Don't be ridiculous. Who told you that?'

'Some quasi-skeletal being called Gwen.'

'That figures. I bet she was having trouble standing up at the time. Her brain died long ago from alcohol poisoning, ignore her.'

One last try. Ben. If anyone was honest, it was him. 'Lia, you have to remember this is a nightclub. A lot of love-starved women come here looking for men. Remy's attractive, Gwen's been after him for ages but he's not interested. I guess she's got it in for you.'

'What's the verdict?' the gang asked when I rushed back.

'Not guilty!'

'He's the only one then!' Joyce snarled. Obviously the bloom was already starting to fade from Sly's rose.

'Thanks for inviting me, it's nice to be in a real home for a change.'

'It's not much but its mine,' Linda smiled, full of the glow of young love. 'We've only got a mattress on the floor so far, but the bed's coming. As soon as my husband, Ace, can find some work. Has your guy showed up yet? You must be frantic with worry.'

'I got word he'll be off for a week, so I'll have to be patient until its over.' Speaking without any trace of emotion, I hid my desolation, unwilling to admit it to myself let alone to a hopeful young woman in the throes of love. She'd only married recently; my disillusionment shouldn't be allowed to cloud her happiness.

'Would you like to see our wedding photos?' Linda rustled through her suitcase. Her precious album was wrapped in silk. Crouched on the floor, she turned each page lovingly, pausing to reflect on the memory. 'It's not exactly the wedding I'd dreamed of ...'

'You look lovely,' I countered. Although not a traditional ceremony, the charm was still there. Linda had worn a plain white sheath for the service, stunning in its simplicity. A chiffon scarf draped over her head accentuated her own veiled innocence. The groom in contrast, in dark suit and velvet fez, looked surly and slightly sinister. The marriage was definitely a union of opposites.

'I met Ace five years ago, my first time in Bali,' Linda sighed. 'Since then I've been here seven times to see him, and on the last visit he took me home to Java to meet his folks. That's when he proposed.'

'His family looks nice. Yours didn't make it for the wedding?' There was a noticeable absence of Westerners in the photos.

Linda's face dropped, she shrugged her shoulders in dismay. 'They didn't approve. I was always Daddy's golden-haired little girl and he expected me to marry some bright young lawyer and live in the suburbs. As far as they're concerned, Ace has no future and I've thrown away my life. It hurt me they didn't come for the wedding.'

'Old prejudices die hard. One day they'll come round,' I said, not fully convinced myself. 'Perhaps when you have children.'

'No chance. If you heard what my father said about *brown* babies,' she flinched. 'Ace's family treat me well but they're a long way off in Java. Sometimes I feel so lonely. Ace is gone most of the day looking for work. I listen to the radio and read a bit, but I'm running out of English books.'

'I've got a few spares, I'll drop them down for you next time.' I knew exactly how Linda felt. Isolation was a great adversary, an elusive partner couldn't begin to fill the gap caused by its impact.

Walking back to my bungalow along the beach, I contemplated the implications of the things we'd discussed. Without a qualm, Linda had left behind everything she valued to start a new life in a foreign land. All for a man she had met for fleeting moments on holiday, when her spirit was open and accepting. Love blossomed in letters, through the romance of distance and longing. Was the reality as appealing? I hoped so, for all our sakes.

I sat down on the warm sand, engrossed in the calm blue of the sea. Lost in the roll of the waves, my mind wandered. Love had brought so many of us here, but was it the *real* reason we stayed? I inhaled the salty air, recharging my lungs with energy.

More precisely, was it the island itself? The earth pulsated with a potent surge of energy. The coconut palms rustled mysteriously, guarding the secret well. The place held a fatal fascination, an allure that enticed one to stay. Blinded by the mystique, the truth was harder to bear. Life here was difficult, splintering the strongest of souls.

Yet oddly we all chose to stay. Perhaps for all the wrong reasons. A rejection of an unfulfilled life left behind, or an identity outgrown. Were we all lost souls, starved for a little love? Hopeless romantics believing there should be more to life than TV dinners and empty rooms? It hardly mattered. In all cases, these men offered hope. A chance to discard the brittle shell of what once had been and replace it with the dream of what might yet be.

Ultimately, they represented a way out.

The next few days dragged by and I handled Remy's absence badly. Ensconced on the balcony of my room I couldn't relax; a random line in a book would evoke a response, awaken a memory in my brain. All around couples sat together happily. There was no disruption to their lives and I felt cheated.

For once in my life, I strove to reinvent the pattern. Maturity spoke in words of wisdom, trying to reassure me. He won't be like the others, he *will* come back. There is a chance of happiness. But with every thought, the internal saboteur reared it's ugly head, plaguing me with insecurity and doubts. Why should *he* be different? He's just like all the rest.

Out of control, I slept badly, my nights immersed in vivid dreams. Constant flashes of a past life so lucid that it made the present one fade into insignificance, enticing me into a shock of repressed memories.

Swept back to an ancient time, I floated through shimmering corridors dressed in lustrous silk. A man wandered through these shadowy portals every night, leaving heavy footprints in my mind. A dark, lingering soul, with eyes of richest ebony. Even though the form was blurred, there was no mistaking those eyes. Remy. Calling to me, beckoning me onwards. Drawn by the force of his voice I followed him through a dimly lit passage until we came to the edge of a void.

In a horrific blaze, a huge wall of flames erupted, blocking my path. Remy's eyes locked into mine, urging me beyond. Without fear, I braved the billowing smoke and stepped into the fire. Burning orange, it engulfed me in a huge swirling inferno until I felt myself implode, then dissolve into an ashen grey haze. A dazzling white light followed by a profound sense of peace. My fate was sealed. Remy took my hand; nothing could ever separate us again.

'Sorry I didn't get the chance to drop round last night to say good-bye to the girls. How did the farewell go?'

'A little *too* good,' Joyce replied, holding on badly to last night's hangover. 'Thank God, they made it to the plane on time. Annie was fine, she's made of hardy stock like me. It's Helen I'm worried about. Fudge was at the airport promising his undying love.'

'I hope you didn't disillusion the poor girl by telling her he'd be whipping off to the Arrivals hall as soon as she'd boarded, waiting for the next planeload of young hopefuls to get here.'

'Of course not!' Joyce lit up her first cigarette for the day. 'We all need our dream, whatever it might be. Let's hope hers doesn't turn into a nightmare. By the way, you look terrible, what's *your* excuse?'

'I haven't slept properly in a week, and it's all Remy's fault!'

'Don't tell me he still hasn't shown up! Don't worry, men have a nasty habit of turning up again - usually when you least expect it.'

'I know, it's more that I'm angry with myself for reacting like this. My emotions should have mellowed with age.'

'Don't be so sure.' Joyce plonked onto the lounge. 'Being older doesn't insulate us from the pain, it's only supposed to help us deal with it better. You know how it is around here, no phones or mail. Remy's probably sick with worry because he can't contact you.'

'Do you really think so?' Joyce had a remarkable capacity to put everything in perspective. 'Being separated from him is agony.'

'That's normal, we all miss our mates - such as they are!'

'But this goes beyond the usual. Every time I shut my eyes, I drift off into another time to a fascinating place - it's like viewing life through a peacock's feather, I'm sure I'm tapping into a past life.'

As I painted in the details, Joyce's appetite peaked. 'Let's see,' she pulled some books off the shelf, 'there could be clues in here.'

'This life I see is around five hundred years ago, I know it's here in Bali.' Joyce's eyebrows rose questioningly, but she thought better of it. She'd seen my intuition at work often enough not to doubt its accuracy.

'In the fourteenth century the great general, Gajah Mada of Java, came to Bali and defeated the supernatural king, Bedaulu, claiming Bali as part of his empire. Two hundred years later it faded from sight, the aristocracy of Java fleeing to Bali and establishing a royal court near Klungkung. Seven other kingdoms followed.'

'The only thing I know with certainty was that Remy and I were lovers somewhere on this island. I know this must all sound batty!'

'Listen, I've been accused of being nuts so many times in my life that nothing fazes me. What about this fire you keep seeing?'

The strangest sensation flooded my body. Without thinking, I blurted out my truth. 'I died for Remy.' There was no question.

Joyce flicked through the pages, intent on solving the puzzle. Tired from many sleepless nights, I couldn't concentrate, but Joyce's mind was razor sharp. 'Read this,' she cried, holding the book open.

'The Burning of Widows,' I read, tracing each word slowly. 'After the death of the rajah, his wives and concubines would be burned alive with him. Jumping off a bamboo platform into his funeral pyre, they would release a small white dove. Flying away, it symbolised their escaping spirit.'

'That's amazing,' Joyce gasped, 'so they did practise suttee here. Apparently, it was common practice until the end of the last century when it was stamped out by the Dutch. Can you imagine, if Remy was one of the kings I'd be connected to royalty!'

'Knowing my luck, I would have been one of his concubines!' A sobering chill racked my body. 'What does this all mean?'

'I don't know, but I've got a good idea who might.'

'This man comes highly recommended,' Joyce argued. 'He's supposed to be one of the top psychics around these parts.'

'I don't have a good feeling about this.' The vacant lot was littered with rubbish. Several mangy dogs rummaged through the scraps while the driver tried to make sense of the scribbled map.

'This must be the place.' The car came to a halt outside a small house. It stood alone, behind a clump of thick bronze bamboo. We crept up the overgrown path then hesitated. The door creaked open.

The front room was airless, painted a dull flaky grey. Only a solitary picture of a swan broke the monotony. An aged, wrinkled man, as pallid as his surroundings, emerged from behind the plum curtains. 'Welcome, I'm Kenyo,' he said, stroking the scant remains of his white beard with his bony fingers. His eyes were enigmatic, an ancient storehouse of long lost secrets.

He ushered us through the curtain into a dusty room strewn with books. Comfortably seated around the ebony table, Kenyo produced a pack of cards. Worn from use, each was marked by a symbol, abstract yet strangely evocative. He handed them to Joyce. 'Please shuffle,' Kenyo advised, 'and concentrate on what has brought you here today.'

Joyce, stony-faced, took her time, determined to give nothing away. Kenyo spread the pack out on the table, examining each card carefully. 'Many problems have blotted your past, you guard your hurt well, but one day it will turn against you like a cancer. Yes, your husband betrayed you,' he said, rubbing his hand along the card studded with swords. 'Your heart is bruised but finding these young men is not the solution.' Joyce bit her lip unconsciously.

'I don't know what you mean,' she replied in an effort to hide the truth. Kenyo shook his head, turning over the last card. *Death.*

'Beware, you will be plunged into chaos and pay a heavy price. What you believe to be the solution will ultimately become the problem.' Joyce's eyes reddened as she swallowed hard. 'Heed my advice, stay strong. Two men will fight to control your spirit but neither must be allowed to succeed.'

Having left his mark, Kenyo turned his attention to me. 'Don't worry, he'll soon come back.' I was caught unaware. 'A word of advice - if you choose to, you will suffer his loss greatly. If you accept the separation and wait patiently for his return, then you will not suffer at all. Bear in mind, our reaction never influences the outcome of an event, all it can affect is our capacity to cope.'

Kenyo handed me the pack of cards. I held onto them tightly, not wanting him to gain access to my soul so easily. Fanning out the shuffled cards, he began writing on a sheet of paper. 'Understand,' he said, not looking up, 'that love can be both uplifting and perverse.'

'I don't understand.' I was prepared to defend our union to the death. 'My love for Remy is so strong, it can't be wrong.'

'Such a connection is as profound as it is dangerous,' Kenyo warned. His heavily hooded eyes flickered with compassion. 'When you surrender your boundaries, you begin to lose your sense of self. You think as one, breathe his breath, identify with his life - not with your own. Your very existence becomes dependent on his. In the end nothing of you will remain, you will simply cease to exist in your original form.'

'What about the dreams,' I choked, 'what do they mean?'

'Ah yes, the dreams, strong memories of the past.' He turned over some cards. '*The steely knight ... lovers ...* many years ago. Five hundred to be precise, during the time of the Majapahits. You have waited so long to be reunited. Be careful, the link between you is absolute. Your love was so fierce that you jumped into the flames to be with him, followed him to the grave through tongues of fire.'

Alarm bells rang in my head as my mind switched to alert.

'Make sure you don't repeat your mistakes in this lifetime,' Kenyo snapped. 'Don't let love lead to your destruction. Your karma is strong, so I can't dissuade you from your chosen course, but be aware of one thing. When you died, you reincarnated to the West but he stayed locked in the East, unwilling to move beyond. Thus he will never fully understand and accept you, and you will find his limited awareness a burden.'

I rose unsteadily to leave. Joyce was already at the door.

'One more thing,' he said gravely, 'you will need to see me again. When the time comes, I will be here waiting for you.'

We walked quickly down the path to escape. The cracks in my armour had widened, in danger of splitting apart. Were Remy and I linked on such a deep level that it could lead to my ultimate demise? I could not even begin to fathom the implications of Kenyo's words.

When I reached the gate something held me back. Compelled, I turned around. Kenyo was standing at the window staring at me. His eyes piercing with wisdom. In the shadows of my mind, I knew he was right. Destiny would lead me back to his door once more.

The day of the cremation finally arrived. 'Stand back,' Ben urged, with the sound of the first gong. The beating became more frantic as the funeral procession neared. People jostled for position, the road was jammed. Charged with excitement, the mood was frenetic. Cymbals clashed defiantly, metal drums beat wild and hard.

Through the mayhem, I searched for Remy, but my view was blocked by the swarming crowd. A long line of women in deathly black slithered towards us like an endless winding snake. Above their heads they carried offerings for the soul to take on its long journey, food and gifts to use along the way. Some held a long ribbon of white cloth, a shroud covered by cabbalistic symbols drawn by the priest to ensure the dead man's entry into heaven.

Another clash of cymbals and a volley of men hurtled forwards balancing a heavy tower on their backs. Whipping themselves into a frenzy, they spun the tower around recklessly, trying to trick any evil spirit that might be lurking close-by, hoping to whisk the corpse away.

'Bhutas can only see in straight lines,' Ben explained, 'they're easily confused. Look closely at the tower, it's designed like our vision of the cosmos. The base of winged serpents depicts the underworld, the platform is the world of man; the flowers and leaves its forests. The coffin is placed on this level. The tiered roofs jutting into the sky represents the heavens.'

Made from bamboo and wood, the tower was painted white and decorated with brightly coloured wool and fringed in tinsel and gold. It looked quite beautiful. I marvelled at a culture that was so infinitely creative, so intent on reproducing the beauty of the gods. 'Why five towers, Ben?'

'The towers must always be an odd number, one for a commoner, then rising upwards in status, to eleven for kings. These days for practical purposes, the height is restricted - no higher than the electricity lines.'

A bull, carved from rich wood and adorned with mirrors, followed close behind the tower, carried on the shoulders of a group of men. Sweaty and tired, they were on the verge of collapse. Not so the bull - it stood proud and aloof, ready to transport the soul to the after-life.

Everyone was in an uproar, laughing and joking. 'To the Balinese,' Ben said, 'the cremation is a joyous time, the soul is about to find release. The body is only a shell, most of the soul's energy is concentrated in the head. That's why it's considered holy and should never be touched.'

We followed the procession down to the beach. The cremation site was nestled under the palms, close to the sand. Sitting in the shade of a giant gnarled tree, I searched through the faces until I found him. Remy stood next to the priest watching the fire being prepared. Outwardly joyful, his face betrayed a deeper emotion - a fierce sadness. I had to restrain my natural impulse to walk straight over to him and take him in my arms.

The coffin was handed down from the tower and the body placed inside the bull. Ritual items were placed around the corpse, rich silks, brocades and ancient coins - a ransom to Yama, the lord of hell, to allow the soul to pass undisturbed. The priest stooped over the body, splashing it with copious amounts of holy water.

Suddenly a hush fell upon the crowd. Mirrored glass decorating the bull's hide glinted in the afternoon sun, reflecting the sacred moment. Set alight, the bull ignited in fury. Pumped with kerosene, the flames shot high into the sky. Everyone stood back, scorched by the force of the blaze. A sharp crackle whipped through the air, followed by the smell of charred flesh. The wooden bull groaned, collapsing into embers emitting a fine layer of floating black ash. An extraordinary look of peace flooded Remy's face.

'The soul has now departed,' Ben smiled, 'and its remains must now be cast into the ocean. Cleansed by all four elements - earth, fire, air and water, it will go on to *swarga,* heaven, a place of infinite bliss. After some time it will be reborn, usually within the same family. If a virtuous life has been led, the spirit may be reborn into a higher caste. A priest would aspire to be freed from the cycle of births and go beyond.'

As the fire subsided, the ashes and fragments of charred bone were collected in a hollow coconut shell. After blessings by the priest, they were wrapped in a white cloth and placed onto a tray of offerings, then carried out to sea. Remy waded through the water following the priest. Reaching the reef, they stopped and whispered a silent prayer to the spirit of the sea to guide the soul safely. In one last symbolic gesture, the ashes were flung into the ocean. The tide sent the soul of Remy's grandfather to its final resting place.

'Don't worry,' Ben said. 'Now Remy is free to come back to you.' He had found release, and I too would be liberated in the process.

CHAPTER SEVEN
Twisted Karma

'Breathtaking!' The ancient temple clung to the steep crumbling rock, fierce waves lashing its sides. Guarded from intrusion by the elements, Tanah Lot's mysterious secrets lay safely protected within its walls.

Remy stood perched on the cliff face, surrounded by a surging wall of ocean. Deep sapphire blue, the water rippled across the sand smothering it in a stream of endless waves. A salty mist formed as a strong gust of wind whipped by, echoing loudly through the chasm. The crisp scent of the sea blew hard against the sky.

'Can you hear the voices?' Remy asked. Another blast of wind sucked through the hollow rock. Leaning into it, I tried to decipher the sound. 'Whenever the wind blows I hear my grandfather talking to me, his spirit calls out, whispering his deepest secrets.'

'I'm sorry you weren't with your grandfather when he died, I know how important that final contact was for you.'

'You don't understand. He chose to leave quietly, not wanting his family to suffer. I was the only one who didn't cry,' he said proudly. 'A display of sorrow would have been selfish and kept his soul earthbound, now he is free to ascend to heaven untroubled.'

'Remy, I *can* hear the voices.' I needed to share my innermost thoughts with him. 'I know they're out there.' Throughout my life I had been aware of a strong spiritual presence. My ancestors may have left the earthly plane, but they had never forsaken me. At times I was blessed by their touch - a light brush to the cheek, a gentle caress or a guiding word. These were my greatest source of comfort.

'We are so very much alike,' Remy sighed. 'It's so strange - sometimes I feel like a brother watching over you, then a caring father reaching out to you with advice. And when you lie in my arms I know for certain I can be neither, for the passion between us is so intense. There are many beams of light connecting us on all levels, from the physical to the sublime.'

'Perhaps you are my soul mate, our strong link the result of many past lives shared, how we react now our own immediate choice.'

'Yes, but isn't that choice moulded by events of the past? If I loved you before, how could I ever contemplate leaving you again?'

'It's more complex than that; we could have unfinished karma to sort out. Maybe that's one of the reasons I came back to Bali.'

Grounding myself, I tuned into the vibration of the earth. It resonated at the same frequency as me, as if my energy intersected at a magnetic place and time a point where my soul felt most at peace. A point where I was spiritually conceived and destined to be.

'When I was born,' I explained, 'the Sun and Neptune were in the sky together in a mystical union. If I overlay my birth chart onto a world map, these two planets intersect on the earth's surface exactly over Bali. Somehow I'm linked with this small island on the most fundamental of levels. Can you imagine the odds? Bali's only a tiny speck in the ocean.'

'So you really believe you were drawn back here to complete something from before, and that I'm part of this vast cosmic puzzle?'

'Yes. I always felt something higher was at work when we met, for what purpose I'm not yet sure. One thing I am certain of - if I were ever to leave this place, an essential part of me would go missing.'

'While we were apart,' Remy confessed, 'I'd gaze out at the sky every night but the stars had lost their brightness without you. I thought if I spoke loud enough you'd hear me - that distance could not separate us. All my life, people have looked up to me for spiritual guidance. Now for the first time in my life I need someone and I am lost, what can I do ... I love you.'

We walked along the windy path in the hot sun, arms linked, taking shelter under a fleshy mangrove tree. Guardian to an old temple hidden within its branches, the tree hung onto the earth by the merest sliver of root in a tenacious bid for survival. Remy wrapped me in his arms as we leant against its knotted bark, absorbing the tree's timeless energy. Amid the slate-grey clouds, a single ray of light radiated silver from the heavens. It filled the sky, flooding us in a beam of quintessential love. Never before had I felt so close to the infinite. There could be no greater peace.

'In my time, I've been to many places and seen much beauty. It is one thing to recognise the beauty, and another to belong to it. I *belong* here,' I stated resolutely. 'At last I've come home to my heart.'

As the late sun streaked the sky with copper, we climbed down the steep steps that led to the beach. With the heat leached from the day, hordes of tourists converged upon the hallowed site with as much reverence as a pack of mindless seagulls. Priests, haughtily benign, drifted through the crowds selling holy water and blessings. The masses surged closer seeking absolution. I ignored the violation and turned to the temple.

Hauntingly beautiful, its thatched towers silhouetted bitter gold against the sunset. The resonant sound of a gong announced a procession advancing over the rocks. Young girls bedecked in rich brocade, trailed bolts of pure white cloth studded with mystical symbols. Shielded by fringed umbrellas, others followed bearing lavish offerings to the gods. It was a visual feast, set against the magnificent backdrop of crashing waves and the brilliant face of heaven.

'Over here,' Remy called. 'Come see the cave before dark.'

Concealed beyond the sand was a small niche carved into the rocks. An old priest, crouching inside, held up a candle to light the seeping walls. Hidden deep within a crevice, a coiled snake lay inert, its scaly skin gleaming zinc glaze in the flickering light. Slowly it turned, slithering round till its eyes were transfixed, the black pupils a heinous dark slit.

'Run ... while you have the chance. Or stay ... if you dare!'

Gripped by its spell, I was powerless to resist. Beneath the inspiring beauty of nature, under the deceptive layer of calm, lurked an insidious hostile force: a consummate evil mirrored in the snake's eye. Little did I know that the snake was poised to strike, the venom aimed straight at my heart.

The next day I was lying in bed, Remy's body draped around mine. I was drifting in a half-dream, when I was woken by a sound - the grind of footsteps on the pebble path leading to our bungalow. Someone was outside. Automatically I wrapped the sheet around me.

My eyes focused slowly on a shadow hovering near the window. The unfamiliar face of a Balinese woman peered through the darkened glass. Assuming she had confused rooms I got up, careful not to disturb Remy. Inadvertently I bumped him awake. He stirred, then rolled over in the bed.

I crept over to the door and reached for the knob. Just as I turned it, Remy bolted across the room at lightning speed, grabbing it from me. Pushing me aside, he tried to force the door shut with his full body weight. The woman had gained a foothold; anger had increased her strength. Muttering obscenities, she pushed harder, the door buckling and yielding to the force of her wrath.

'Get into the bathroom,' Remy screamed at me. 'Lock the door!'

There was no time for argument. Bolting myself inside, I peeked out through a wide crack in the wood, watching the drama unfold. Remy unable to gain control, flung open the door and stepped directly into the line of fire. The woman became hysterical. Flailing her arms in all directions, she attacked everything in her path. The coffee table was hurled sideways, landing in pieces among the shrubs. Picking up several pot plants, she flung them against the wall. One ricocheted against the window, shattering it and spraying shards of glass all over the verandah.

With nothing left to smash, she turned to Remy. Pummelling her fists against his chest, she lashed out in a barrage of fury. He stood stone-like, refusing to flinch or to restrain her, choosing instead to accept the full force of her rage. Her frenzy abated, she collapsed in a heaving mass in his arms.

I looked on dispassionately, like a voyeur in someone else's nightmare. Innately, I knew I was involved, but didn't want to know how. Ignorance provided some measure of safety from the truth.

'You can come out now,' Remy called. I tiptoed out. 'Pass me my trousers.' Wading through the broken glass, I handed them to him through the fractured window. As soon as she caught sight of me, the woman screamed a volley of obscure, meaningless words.

'Remy, what's going on?' The full impact had yet to hit.

'I can't explain now, I've got to get her away from here.' Hastily putting on his clothes, he pinned down the woman's arms to prevent her from causing more damage. She remained dagger-eyed as Remy grabbed his helmet from the debris and led her away. She turned and shot me one last hostile glare before they sped off.

An old man emerged from one of the huts to clear away the splintered remains. I begged him to explain what was happening, but he stared at me blankly and continued to sweep, unable or unwilling to answer. My whole body went numb. I touched my face to gauge whether I'd been crying. Sifting through the slivered fragments of glass, I saw a reflection of myself. Jagged pieces of my soul lay bleeding on the ground. I clung hard to the remains.

Inwardly I screamed, silent tears welling in my throat. My fists formed tight balls by my side. Why me, God? Things were going well for once in my life, why did it have to be challenged? My life was on an even keel, everything was going fine. Or at least it was yesterday - but that seemed an eternity ago.

*

Many hours passed and Remy did not return, the anguish becoming unbearable. In a short space of time my life took on a feverish spin, a roller-coaster of dread whirling me through a gamut of feelings. First a frantic kind of worry; why hadn't Remy come back, was he in danger? Then a creeping anxiety took hold. Who was that woman, how did she fit into my life? Then the anger mounted, had Remy lied to me? Anger exploded into rage. How dare he do *this* to me?

Night fell and still no sign of Remy. Curbing the urge to run, I walked slowly down the road towards the club ignoring the wild beating of my heart. Sensing my mood, the staff were wise enough to make themselves scarce. Then I saw him. Wallowing in the deep hole he had created, Remy sat alone staring at the mirrored orb rotating from the ceiling.

'I'm sorry,' he said, refusing to look at me. His eyes followed the beam of coloured light. 'I couldn't face you with the truth.'

'What truth? For God's sake tell me, this is tearing me apart.'

Sitting bolt upright, Remy grabbed me. 'Lia I lied - that woman was once - my wife.' He waited for a reaction, there was none.

'Go on,' I said, determined not to show any trace of emotion. Most had been drained by the trauma of the day.

'We've been divorced for more than a year but she won't leave me alone, she simply refuses to accept that it's over. It's been hell trying to keep our relationship a secret so she wouldn't find out and make a scene. I knew this would all blow up in my face one day.'

'You never told me you'd been married,' I said exasperated by his lies. 'Why couldn't you tell me? I told you the truth about my life.'

'I got married for all the wrong reasons, she was pregnant and I had no choice. There was no love involved, only necessity. How it lasted for two years I'll never know.' Remy looked on the verge of tears. 'Our child died in its sleep when it was five months old - it was a tragedy neither of us got over. I'd blotted the whole thing from my mind - I couldn't even begin to bring myself to talk about it.'

'I'm sorry,' I said, feeling almost selfish in my righteousness.

'My wife never got over the shock and the marriage deteriorated from there. All we did in the end was fight - it was a disaster. The final parting was traumatic, but she never let go. When she found out about you, it was the last straw.' Remy looked gaunt, his face strained with pressure. 'I told her today that she must accept the inevitable - it's over between us.'

'Remy, I understand it was a very difficult chapter of your life,' I said, filled with compassion for his pain, 'but we all have episodes in our life we'd rather forget about. What I can't understand is why you couldn't trust me with the truth. It hurts to find out this way.'

'There were so many times I wanted to, but I didn't want to hurt you. Those times you accused me of being withdrawn and distant - you can never imagine what a burden it was to hide it for so long. The bottom line is that I was scared of losing you.'

'Love runs a lot deeper than that, it can withstand many things but not dishonesty.'

Full of remorse, Remy kissed me gently on the lips. My heart opened up to him, but my mind snapped shut. A relationship riddled with secrets stood no chance of survival. If Remy had lied about one thing so integral to his life there was a strong chance that other aspects of his shadow self remained covered. I needed to talk things through with someone I could trust, so despite Remy's pleas, I went outside and hailed a cab.

'Come on up!' Kate bellowed above the roar of the speakers. Hanging over the top balcony, she pointed to the stairs. Pushing past a crush of drunken Aussies in torn singlets and grotty headbands, clutching their 'stubbie' beers like sacrificial icons, I made it to the top. 'What a surprise, you don't usually slum it around these parts anymore.'

'I needed to talk to you urgently.' Kate was nobody's fool, one look at my face and she whisked me into Cliff's private office.

'Cliff's downstairs playing pool,' she said, ushering me through the locked door, 'so we can have some privacy.' My first time granted the privilege of entry, I was bedazzled. Like the last bastion of a once great Empire, the dark timber walls were lined with perverse relics of a bygone era - coiled cobras, buffalo horns and stuffed animal heads. Everywhere I looked, glassy eyes bulged out at me. I backed away from the onslaught straight into the autographed photo of Don Johnson, hanging in pride of place above the desk.

'Cliff's certainly got strange taste.'

'Tell me about it,' Kate laughed. 'Can you imagine trying to get amorous with that hanging over your head?' I wasn't sure whether she was referring to the snap of Donny or the stunned bison head but I decided to keep my mouth shut. 'Would you like a drink?'

Pressing the intercom button she ordered two Southern Comforts and a bucket of ice. A barman arrived bearing a tray which he placed on the carved antique table before backing out deferentially.

'Good view,' Kate said, gesturing to the huge windows looking down over the disco. 'One way glass, so we can keep an eye on everyone. If that doesn't suffice we've got this video system as well.' Switching on the screen, the cameras zoomed into action scanning the activity below, including some intimate canoodling on the balcony.

'I hope you haven't got one of these connected in the ladies loo.' Safely perched in my eagle's nest, all sound muffled, I scanned the warped collection of humanity dancing below in the airless vacuum. 'Oh, I see Jett's not here,' I remarked, spotting a new face in the DJ's booth.

'He's long gone, he took up one of the countless airline tickets he'd been offered by his long list of would-be girlfriends. We go through DJs like dishcloths around here, such is the need out there in the free world. It's a sad fact that many ladies have to pay for intimacy these days. Speaking of intimacy, what's Remy been getting up to this time?'

Sinking down in the plush tan leather lounge, I took a hefty gulp of my drink hoping to get deathly drunk so my brain would have a reason to vacate my body. Then I went through every excruciating detail blow by blow, until Kate sighed in exasperation.

'Men! Look, on the Richter scale of male deviants Remy scores about a seven. So he's got a psychopathic ex-wife lurking about in the background waiting to blow your brains out ... at Remy's age he's bound to have a few skeletons in the closet. So he lied to you, name one man who hasn't. OK,' she admitted, muffling my objections, 'it was a real whopper but in the grand scheme of things, it means they really care when they have to get so inventive with their excuses. Look, I don't condone Remy's behaviour for a minute, but the bottom line is: what are you going to do about it? You love the schmuck too much to lose him, you know you're going to find a reason to excuse his behaviour so you can love him some more, so why not get it over and done with and save yourself the strain? You want my advice - grab your things, move into Swaying Palms where security can keep an eye on you and Joyce can be your resident confidante. As for Remy, exercise the good old Christian ethic of forgiveness!'

I was settling into my new room at Swaying Palms hotel when there was a knock on the door. 'Hello I'm Made, driver for hotel,' the tall, gangly man beamed. 'We leave now, take things before wife can kill you!' he added cordially, as if inviting me to a Sunday school picnic.

'I beg your pardon?'

'Take everything before you dead,' he repeated slowly as if he was talking to a fool who had somehow failed to grasp his words.

'Are there *any* secrets on this island?'

Made's humming placated my frayed nerves as we drove towards the bungalow. I'd put off going back since the debacle, but I needed my things so I was forced to return to the scene of the crime. As we got closer, my stomach churned. Once the place of sweet memories, it now elicited only bitter emotion, marred forever by the recent drama.

Reaching the driveway, Made slowed down to negotiate the narrow lane. He wiped a cloth across the dusty windscreen, peering out uneasily before jerking to a halt. The rigid form of a hostile woman with arms crossed stood guard at the entrance, checking every car that drove by. There was no mistaking *that* face.

I dived straight under the dashboard. Made, astute enough to connect my nose-dive with the stern form up ahead, lurched the car into reverse. We swerved out of the drive and shot down the road, leaving behind a cloud of dust and flying feathers along the way.

'Strong woman,' Made muttered, the sweat running off his forehead. I wasn't sure which of us he was referring to.

Back at the hotel, I sat in my room working out how long I could last without changing my clothes, then contemplated buying a whole new wardrobe at Remy's expense. On his budget, my prospects weren't good. Joyce, outraged at the indignity, stepped in and saved the day.

'I can't believe the balls on that man,' Joyce huffed, 'leaving you to clean up his mess. Remy is old enough to know better, his life needs a major overhaul but he shouldn't wreck yours while he's at it.'

'Tell me about it, I don't even have any clothes to wear.'

'I've got something that will fit,' Joyce said, sorting out a battle plan. 'Us well-endowed women must stick together. By the way, how exactly does one forget to mention a wife?'

'Quite easily, it would seem. Now he's gone to temple, either to pray for redemption or because it's the only safe place for him.'

'Wimp!' Joyce seethed. 'Anyway, who needs a man when there's a good woman around. You lay low, I'll go get your things.'

'Are you sure? I don't want your blood on my conscience.'

'I love a good drama,' Joyce argued, fuzzing up her perm. 'Wifey needs to let go of the past and get on with life, just like I had to. We women need to be made of stronger stuff to survive.'

Joyce set off on her mission, dragging Made along as her reluctant partner in crime. I waited anxiously by the pool, dying for some news. Mission accomplished, they returned triumphant several hours later. Joyce, thriving on the excitement, looked particularly elated.

'You should have seen me,' she chortled, 'darting around your room like a mad woman, stuffing everything into your bags.'

'Any sight of her?' I asked, hoping she had faded out of sight.

'You betcha! Made picked her out, standing at the crossroads like Medusa, scanning every passerby. I glared daggers at her when we drove past. One look at my face and she turned away in fright.'

'Joyce, you're a wonder. I owe you one.'

Midnight found me waiting at the club. Kate had telephoned making arrangements to meet; she was anxious for an update. From the tone in her voice, it was obvious that Cliff's impending divorce was weighing more heavily on her mind than she dared admit.

I stood at the entrance so she couldn't slip by and get sucked into the heaving mass of people inside. Positioning myself discreetly among the tropical ferns, I backed straight into Ben who was moping amongst the palm trees, pretending to be a human frond. Over the past weeks, he'd become withdrawn. Thrust together in this plastic paradise was the opportune time to find out what was troubling him.

'Ben, it can't be that bad.' No response. 'Don't you think it would be better if you talked about it?' He looked beyond help.

'I've got myself into such a mess.' He twisted his wedding ring, 'You know how much I love my wife and child. Well, several months ago when my wife was at work I did something I regret ... I slept with our babysitter and now she's pregnant. In Bali every child must have a father, so I must marry her. Her family agrees with our choice.'

'Oh Ben, I'm so sorry.' What was it about human nature that attracted disaster? 'What a tragedy to break up your family.'

'Oh no, I'm not going to get a divorce,' Ben protested, offended by the suggestion. 'My wife's a Catholic – besides, I love her too much for that. As for Kerti, the Balinese are polygamous so there is no problem. I can work something out so I can keep them both.'

'Ben, you know your wife will never agree to that!' Ben's wife was a modern woman, not the type to share her husband lightly.

'She doesn't need to know,' Ben argued. 'Kerti's happy to be my second wife. I'll see her when my wife's at work.'

'How long do you think you can keep up the deception?'

'What she doesn't know won't hurt her - or affect us.' There was no point in discussing it further, Ben had made up his mind.

'I know you,' a frizzy blond shrieked. Ben seized the moment to exit. 'You were here last time,' she gabbled, poking me with a bony finger. 'You're really boring! I'm the infamous Val. Darling, I met you last year when I was up here on hols. Had a ball, brought me hubby along this time. Oh well, never let that stop me before!'

'How enterprising, now if you'll excuse me ...'

'Speaking of hubby,' she said grabbing me with hands of steel, 'let me introduce you to Barry. I'm sure you two will get on a treat.'

Val waved at her husband to come over and join us. A synthetic man with slicked back silver hair, Barry glided towards us like a hungry piranha. Smoothing down the hairs of his perfectly groomed moustache he stared at me, silently undressing me with his cool grey eyes.

'This is Barry,' Val enthused. Standing side by side in matching white jumpsuits, they looked like an ad for an obsolete range of hairdressing products. 'We've been married seventeen years,' she smiled smugly. 'The only reason I stay is 'cause he's good in bed and is a whiz with a vibrator!'

I nearly choked on my iced water. 'Sorry, I must be going.'

'Nonsense, be a good girl and keep Barry company. Listen luv, this place is swarming with men,' Val whispered in my ear. 'Be a sport and take Barry off me hands.' Val vaulted off, attacking the first available male and having groped his rear end, thrust both hands in his pockets. 'Where d'ya come from, sweetie,' she bellowed, 'and where we goin' when this joint closes?' The poor unsuspecting victim of Val's ardour spilled his glass of beer and looked as if he was about to succumb to an imminent coronary.

Meanwhile, Barry had sleazed closer to me, rubbing his leg against mine. 'Well, well, what have we got here?' he crooned in a nauseating baritone. He'd doubtless spent many hours in front of a mirror honing his tone. I wished for his sake that I could have been impressed. 'How's about we go somewhere alone where we can really enjoy ourselves,' he grinned, his gold tooth glinting in the disco lights. 'My hotel room's got mirrored walls.'

'No thanks,' I answered tersely. 'I'm waiting for my husband.'

'No problem, honey. Bring him along, Val will just love that.'

'Oh there you are.' Kate appeared, chic in smooth black satin. Barry started to drool in reckless anticipation, but one razor sharp glare from Kate had him quickly retreating into the bleachers. Within seconds he'd roped in an exuberantly rotund redhead, infinitely more his style. Puffing on her cigarette, Narelle hung onto Barry's every word. From the smile on her face, she thought the drought had broken and she was set for the night.

Val was also making good progress. Sitting midst a group of Danish men, she was regaling them with a round of bawdy jokes. She cleared the booth in record time. Springing up like a hungry barracuda, she headed towards her next prey - a busload of Arabs.

'Ah,' I smiled at Kate, 'at last Val's met her match!'

'I don't want to know,' she replied, spraying a fine mist of Chanel on her wrists as if the very scent would dispel the debauchery around her. 'I have my own worries. Ever since Cliff's wife has been served with divorce papers, I keep waiting for her to show up.'

'And what, gouge your eyeballs out with an ice pick? Good luck! My lady is small time compared to Cliff's wife. We're talking big bikkies here and I don't think she's about to give up one measly shekel without a fight.'

'Come to think of it, you're right. How about we go down to the Hyatt for a coffee, I need to be on neutral ground right now.'

Wayan opened the door for us, took one look outside and slammed it shut. Several security guards barged through, grabbed hold of Kate and shoved her inside the Ladies. I got thrown in as an afterthought.

'Lock the door!' they shouted, hurrying outside.

'What going on?' Kate yelled through the marble walls.

'I haven't got a clue,' I answered, 'but I'm going to find out. I refuse to remain captive in a toilet cubicle. Stay put till I come back.'

Sidling through the lobby, I hid behind a clump of potted palms. Pushing aside a plastic leaf to get a better look, I spied a worldly woman dripping wealth and position, surrounded by a bevy of amply built bodyguards. They were busy sweeping a path for her through the crowd. She was intent on finding someone. With a haughty air, she scoured each face relentlessly, her eyes dark like a raven's. Her sinister entourage was equally threatening, hell-bent on their mission. They were out for blood. Everyone stood aside as they walked past, repelled by their negative intentions.

'Uh-oh, Cliff's wife has just hit town.' I beat a path back to the loo. 'Whatever you do, Kate, don't come out! Develop a severe case of constipation and stay put.' The svelte Swede at the sink looked at me as if I'd escaped from an asylum. Screwing her face up in disgust, Ingrid scrawled on her bright cerise lipstick, then fled.

'What's going on?' a muffled voice called from behind the door.

'I'll tell you later. For now, trust me and don't utter a word unless you've got a death wish. I'm going out to see if the coast is clear.' One step out the door and Wayan seized my arm and thrust me back inside. 'You've got the wrong woman,' I protested.

'No Lia,' he whispered urgently. 'Remy's wife outside, she like to find you and make trouble. Stay here till I tell you come out.'

'I don't believe this!' I lashed out at the cold marble walls.

'I hope nobody wants to go to the toilet,' a timid voice called.

We both started to giggle. There were so many things I wanted to say, but it was difficult addressing a toilet bowl. Locked inside for an eternity, we whispered to each other through imaginary gaps in the wall. Eventually Wayan's reassuring voice lured us to freedom.

'All wives go home. You come out now, ladies.'

Kate emerged looking like a livid chicken with all its feathers ruffled. 'Wait till I find Cliff! I swear I'll kill him. He's a dead man!'

'Right now, help me with Remy. I'm fed up with this drama.'

We neared his bar then stopped dead in our tracks. Remy's face was purple with rage, his pupils dilated. He was throwing the drinks onto the bar in an unparalleled fury. 'This may not be quite the right time,' I said, backing away. 'Perhaps later, in a few years, when he's calmed down.'

Wayan raced up behind us, relating the evening's events in gory detail. 'Big fight outside. Remy very angry, scream at wife to leave you alone. Him love you very much. You lucky woman!'

'Very lucky!' I slumped down on the seat, Kate flopping down beside me. 'Now what?' I mumbled.

'Tahiti looks nice this time of year!'

CHAPTER EIGHT
Day of Silence

'What a beautiful outlook.' The ocean view from the upper floor of Kate's thatched cottage was sublime. 'It's in a perfect position.'

'We chose Legian because it's so convenient, but unfortunately it's flush with all these weirdos. The beach is packed with European trendies in sequined G-strings, juggling balls and standing on their heads in preposterous yoga positions. It's one giant tropical circus.'

'At least you're insulated from it up here.' A vast expanse of lawn separated Kate's house from the beach, the abundant garden forming a natural barrier. Open-plan in design, the house was a blaze of colour. Bright, bold cushions, vibrant tasselled lamps and a mass of scatter rugs highlighted the golden weave of the walls and floor.

'It will do until we get married and build our own.' Kate was upwardly mobile. She expected the best out of life and always got it.

Cliff ambled into the room wrapped in a white terry towelling beach robe. 'Would you like a drink?' he asked, heading for the bar.

'Remember your promise,' Kate said, keeping a careful check of his movements. He put the bottle of gin back on the shelf and opened a can of juice, making a concerted effort to mend his ways.

'Don't forget the meeting tonight, Kate. We'll have dinner around seven then be on our way. I'm going for a dip in the spa now,' he said, ambling out the door. 'Make yourself at home, Lia.'

'Are you sure Cliff doesn't mind me staying over?'

'Not at all, he enjoys your company. With everything that's happened lately, you need time out. Besides, Remy has to learn to appreciate your worth - it worked for me going up to Candi Dasa.'

'Absence made the heart grow fonder?'

'Definitely.' A fluffy grey lump scooted across the floor after a wayward ball, tumbling straight into the maid. 'Isn't he adorable? Cliff bought me this gorgeous puppy as a peace offering. I adore him but I did want a furry white one like the dog I saw up at Candi Dasa.'

'I didn't think there were any such animals on this island.'

'Exactly, that's why the whole episode up there was really weird. I was walking back to my hotel one night after dinner when I was struck by a terrible sensation. Sheer dread, I didn't want to go any further. Then this beautiful dog jumped out from nowhere, its fur silky white in the moonlight. It looked exactly like a wolf with the most incredibly clear blue eyes I'd ever seen - they radiated pure light. I'll never forget them as long as I live.'

'Sure you weren't drunk at the time? The dogs here are vile.'

'This one was special,' Kate insisted. 'Every time I took a step it would circle me protectively. Then the bushes up ahead started shaking and to my horror, I realised that two men were hiding there. Luckily they ran away, thanks to my furry friend's barking. The dog disappeared, but by the time I got back to the hotel I was astounded to find him waiting outside my room. When I opened the sliding door to give him some food, he vanished right before my eyes. It really shook me up, I truly believe he was my guardian angel.'

'At last you acknowledge the powers that be.' Kate was too much of a pragmatist to confess to spiritual beliefs. Her priorities were more material; she had little reason to stray onto higher ground.

Stylish in a sleek gold swimsuit, Kate lay on a deckchair by the pool, adjusting the angle of her sunglasses to avoid the intense sun. Her body was slender and smooth bronze, a fortune spent on unwanted body hair wasting away forever on some beauty therapist's floor.

'I could do with some interesting company around here for a change,' Kate said. 'Cliff's forever immersed in his business journals.'

Exhausted, Cliff was down the bottom of the garden splayed out on a rattan hammock. By the tilt of the magazine, it was evident that Cliff was dozing blissfully underneath the crumpled pages.

'The stress of the divorce is really getting to him. He's nutted out an agreement with his wife; they get joint custody of the kids and split the property. She's satisfied with the money - the love between them died a long time ago.'

'Thankfully Remy's wife has dropped out of the picture, but I'm left with other issues. Remy's something of an enigma. There are parts of himself that he keeps covered up, a mysterious shadow side.'

'Cliff told me about Remy's grandfather. He was a well-known healer and mystic. One day Remy will follow in his footsteps. Can you imagine how much pressure that places on him? There must be issues he hasn't the courage to face himself, let alone confide in you.'

'I understand that. I have my own shadow self too, a psychic side I've only just begun to explore. It would be my greatest wish that we could grow together, each inspiring the other on their journey.'

'In an ideal world perhaps; it may be your path to walk alone.'

Later that afternoon, massive clouds rolled in from the mountains spreading like a Gothic veil over the ocean. A giant cosmic sponge, the clouds soaked up the weight of the water until they hung heavy in the sky, hovering just out of arm's length. Drawing me like a magnet, I walked down to the water's edge, intent on reaching up and touching the roof of heaven.

Colours of sunset spread across the sky in a brilliant rainbow light show. Vivid bands of pink, wild streaks of purple, patches of strawberry, punctuated by the scorching glow of burnt orange. As the sun slipped into another time and place, the sky was flooded with a magnificent indigo. It cast an unearthly glow all around. Every grain of sand pulsated into a single shimmering sea of violet light. Each cell of my body tingled, absorbing the muted pastel shades until my whole being resonated with the vibration.

Intent on capturing the last vestige of light, I sat down on the warm sand to meditate. The beach was deserted except for a scraggy white dog who kept an acceptable distance. Assuming a posture of passive disinterest, he burrowed a hole in the sand and nestled into it.

Surrendering to a gentle meditative state, I transcended the present and lapsed into an altered state of consciousness. Here, in this place of peace, the troubles of ordinary man no longer existed. I was beyond the need to suffer. Those worries that had racked my mind over the past months were reduced to their proper place - acceptance.

My sojourn into the higher realms was abruptly interrupted by a gentle thud in my lap. Disorientated, my eyes flickered open to an unexpected sight. The ragged dog, drawn by the surge of energy, had plonked itself in my lap and curled into a foetal position. With one eye open, it looked at me pleadingly before falling into a deep sleep.

It was a remarkable scene. All the more so because these animals avoided human contact, retaining a wild instinct, fortified by a fear caused by the people's abhorrence of them. Looking down at the inert form, I thought back to Kate's story. My white dog, puny and battle-scarred, may not have been as impressive as her furry bright friend, but he was equally significant. As symbolic as the majestic sunset, he was in his own small way a messenger of light.

'This is the last straw!' If the Almighty made his presence felt through humour, then Joyce was his consummate vessel. I'd been back at Swaying Palms a few days when the whimsical drama began.

The door to my room banged against the wall as Joyce barged through. 'They're all bloody mad around here!' She crashed onto the bed with the full force of a fighter jet. 'I've had enough of this place.'

'Slow down, take a deep breath and tell me what's going on.'

'You know those weird noises I've been hearing lately,' Joyce snorted, 'the squeaking sound. I finally put two and two together.'

'I thought you had rats in the ceiling.'

'Oh, I found *rats* alright but they weren't in my roof! Last night Sly and I were having a bit and I got a tad vocal.' Joyce's cheeks started to flush. 'Anyway, I heard this same bloody noise again and then it clicked! The noise only ever happened during a nookie.'

'Maybe Sly needs oiling.'

'Very funny. I was in such a tizz that I threw him off, grabbed my nightie and flew out the door. I caught them red-handed - those bloody security guards! One was balanced on the chair, perving through my top window while his mate was propping him up. I chased them down the stairs swearing at the top of me lungs. Lucky I didn't catch them or I would have torn their hair from the roots, and I'm not talking scalp here!'

'A true Kodak moment - I wish I'd had my camera.'

'By the way,' Joyce asked, her bloodhound instincts mounting, 'where have you been hiding? I've been trying to track you down.'

'Hanging out at Kate's, living in the lap of luxury.'

'Don't you go getting all hoity-toity on me, you'll end up a snob with all those fancy friends of yours. I envy Kate her house, I've been stuck too long in a hotel room. Now that things are getting serious with Sly, I need my own place.' I wanted to comment, but the bottom line was that he made Joyce happy. It was as simple as that.

'Are you planning to move out, then?'

'Not till after *Nyepi*, there's no way I'm staying cooped up for that. Anyway I want to start the New Year off with a bang. In the meantime, feel like partaking in a friendly game of cards? I'm bored.'

'Only if you promise not to cheat.' As many times as I'd played with Joyce, she had inevitably won. Frustrated, I plotted revenge.

•

'Gin!' Joyce slapped her winning cards onto the table. 'I've earned the title of Rummy queen.' Celebrating her victory, she plunged her fingers into the bowl of chips. 'You lose, so you owe me twenty-five packets of peanuts and the remains of your chocolate bar.'

'I'm good for it,' I replied, nibbling away at her profits.

'Where's lover boy shot off to today?' Joyce asked, dealing out the next round. 'Now, let me guess - a cremation or a tooth-filing?'

'A bit of both. He's guarding a body that went out a little early. The poor soul died before his teeth could be filed so they have to do it before the cremation can proceed. The canines are associated with monsters and the like, so usually they're smoothed down at puberty.'

'I know, to sever any link with evil. Would that it was so easy.' Joyce sorted through her cards. 'Remy's not around much these days.'

'His continual disappearing acts are driving me crazy.' Fiddling with the empty cigarette pack, I reduced it to a crumpled mass. 'I can't seem to shake this dreadful feeling of impending doom. For some reason I feel like my life is about to unravel at any moment.'

'Are you sure you're not being pre-menstrual or something? Us women can be such victims of our hormones. Pull yourself together, otherwise you'll end up causing what you fear the most. As humans we have the uncanny knack of creating our own worst nightmare.'

'Ah ladies, playing a friendly game of cards.' Gusti stalked up the stairs followed by a flock of hotel trainees, all looking eager and brightly scrubbed. 'And which one of you is winning?'

'Me,' Joyce proclaimed, throwing her cards on the table. 'Gin!'

'Here,' Gusti handed us a sheet of paper, 'for your information.'

Nyepi. Day of Silence.

Nyepi is the Balinese New Year in the Solar calendar. This holiday is observed as a day of complete stillness. No fire may be lit, no transport taken, no work done. No-one is to be seen on the road.

One day before Nyepi, the last day of the old year, purification sacrifices and offerings are made all over Bali. In the evening, there is a parade of monsters to chase away all evil spirits from the island.

The next day, Nyepi, all is silent. No activity is done and Bali appears to be deserted. It is hoped that all demons and evil spirits aroused the night before will find Bali barren of life and leave.

'That sounds pretty thrilling,' Joyce said. 'When's this?'

'In five days time,' Gusti replied. 'We will have a skeleton staff working to ensure that basic meals are provided, but bear in mind you will not be allowed to leave the hotel for twenty-four hours.'

Joyce looked deflated. 'I could go mad if I'm not allowed out.'

'Sorry, no exceptions, but please be my guests at the temple ceremony the day before Nyepi. It's really quite spectacular.'

'My, don't we look charming,' Gusti enthused, admiring our temple dress as we paraded down the hotel path. All our efforts had paid off. Joyce and I had spent the last week searching for tailors to whip up two lace blouses that would fit our ample bust-lines. The local cut didn't even come close. 'Might I say you ladies look almost Balinese.'

'Thanks for the compliment,' Joyce smiled, twisting her sarong so she could walk, 'but I haven't seen many plump redheads around these parts. You don't look half bad yourself,' she added, deciding a little flattery wouldn't go astray, 'most regal and distinguished.'

Gusti smiled in appreciation, acting the perfect gentleman as he helped us into the car. Once behind the wheel, his demeanour changed. 'This traffic is a nightmare,' he said, overtaking a galloping horse cart. 'Many people return home to their villages today in time for Nyepi, and many will be going to the temple for the ceremony.'

'Gusti,' Joyce stared out the window intrigued, 'why are those people sitting on the side of the road around that upturned basket? It's an awfully dangerous place to be, right in the middle of the traffic.'

'Alas, one of their family has been injured in an accident and blood has been spilt. It must not be left unprotected in case evil spirits capture the soul of the loved one, so relatives keep a vigil day and night until the danger passes.'

'I heard a story the other day,' I said, taking the opportunity to bring up a few issues. 'A petrol truck skipped the traffic lights on the highway and hit someone on the footpath and he died. An angry mob attacked the driver and his passenger, killing them both on the spot.'

'Ah yes, emotions run high here. After an accident it is often better to flee the scene and go to the police, rather than risk reprisals.'

'And I thought you people were so calm.' It made little sense, in spite of the grisly repercussions everyone still drove like maniacs.

'Our thinking is very different to yours. In our community if there is a robbery, a gong is sounded and all the *banjar*, village members, will run out to try and catch the culprit. It is a group mentality, everyone has an innate obligation to protect and maintain it. In exchange for loyalty is the assurance that one's family will always be supported in times of need.'

'What happens if you catch the thief?'

'If he is caught, he may be beaten to death. Such is the punishment for the crime. Last week a water pump was stolen in my area. Before the police could arrive, the robber was found hanging from a nearby mango tree.' I muffled a gasp. 'We believe if the person is not dealt with, he will go back onto the streets and steal again. A beating will usually suffice but if the thief uses magic it is useless for they feel no pain.'

'Pardon me,' Joyce's ears bristled, 'this I've just gotta hear.'

'You can be cynical but I've seen it with my own eyes. Needles under the skin and magic amulets with secret formulas make the body impervious to pain. Even if beaten severely, they do not react.'

Joyce looked over at me with raised eyebrows but I shrugged it off. Way out of my depth, I dare not refute what was beyond my level of comprehension. Sensing our doubts, Gusti spoke again. 'I myself attacked a man with a knife but he was powered by Lombok magic. It was like stabbing a stone, I couldn't dent his skin.'

'That's remarkable.' All the more so because mild-mannered Gusti could be a potential killer when provoked. Through the window, I looked at the stream of faces. Stonily detached, their eyes betrayed a more elusive persona, one riddled with mysterious undercurrents.

'We're here!' Gusti pulled up outside a modest home in a side street of Denpasar. His wife welcomed us with a pleasant smile, and after offering us a cool drink, bade us follow the rest of the family.

'I can't walk in these sandals.' Joyce hobbled up the road. 'My feet are killing me and my sarong feels like a straight jacket. Why do they wrap yards of this black elastic around your waist?'

'It's supposed to make you look svelte.'

'Now there's a lost cause.' Women, lithe and agile, passed by dressed in exquisite outfits. 'How come they're so elegant?'

'Years of training, and a life devoid of chocolate!'

Taking the sticky remains of a Mars bar out from her sarong, Joyce chucked it in the gutter. 'I'm starting my diet as from now!'

Gusti led us past the stoic statues, adorned with flowers and draped in fine cloth, that guarded the temple gateway. Weaving among the mass of kneeling bodies we searched for a good vantage point.

'See those three altars,' Gusti said, clearing a place for us on the ground. 'One has been erected for our ancestors, one in honour of the sun, and the third for the *kalas*, the evil gods. They must be cast off the island before dawn, before the sun rises on our New Year.'

A line of Brahmanic priests were seated on a bamboo platform behind a huge stack of offerings. Garbed entirely in white, sashed in black and topped with black velvet crowns, they looked inspiring. Embedded in each of their crowns was a stunning single crystal. Reflecting the sun's fire, each stone radiated brilliant rainbow beams that cast celestial lights into the sky.

Humming softly, the priests chanted in unison. The sound intensified, creating a wave of pulsating energy. *'Omm ... omm ... omm ...'* Reverberating through the temple, it bounced off the ancient walls, hushing the crowd into silence. *'Omm ... omm ...'* Building to a spiritual crescendo, it was impossible not to be swept up in the magnificence of the note. *'Omm ... omm ...'*

Caressed by the tinkling of fragile silver bells and the fragrance of burning incense, the priests sent mantras into the heavens. The atmosphere was sacred, imbued with incredible mystical power. A wave of people bowed their heads in prayer, casting flower petals to the wind.

'Over there's the *senggu*, the low-caste priest,' Gusti whispered, pointing to an old man sitting below the others. Ravaged by the passing of time, his face was gaunt and ashen, his beard matted. Uncut hair twisted around his head under a massive turban. 'His job is to lure the demons here so the high priests, the pedandas, can expel them with their combined force. Eight priests are needed for this formidable task, one for each direction.'

'See the pattern on the centre of the ground,' he continued, 'that is the Rose of the Winds, an eight-pointed star. Four animals, each covered by a coloured cloth, have been sacrificed and placed at the cardinal points. In the North a black goat, a white goose for the East, a red dog for the South and a yellow calf for the West. In the centre is a multi-coloured chicken. It is all very symbolic.'

'Everything seems so precise,' I commented.

'Thousands of years of tradition lies before you on the ground. Even the rice has been dyed into eight different colours as is the custom. There are samples of each kind of seed and fruit grown on the island, all the beverages and the dried flesh of every sort of native animal, over eighty different species. We have only until daybreak to rid the island of its evil.'

'Might we have the opportunity to pray,' I asked, wishing to dispel the uneasy feeling troubling me over the past weeks. I felt the need for an exorcism of the soul, all my worries absorbed by way of the massive shift of energy that was about to take place on the island.

'Of course,' Gusti replied. 'Bow your head and follow.'

Closing my eyes, I let myself be swept away, past swirling grey mists to a brilliant white light. A ray of hope in the distance.

We made it back to the hotel before evening despite the skirmish on the roads. The frantic beating of *kulkul* drums heralded the setting sun. The pace became more frantic as the deadline neared.

'I'm too tired to go out,' Joyce pleaded. 'Let me die in peace.'

'There's no way we're missing the parade. Each village has been preparing their *ogoh-ogohs* for ages, all those giant paper-mache monsters! Tonight they come out to do battle. I'm not going out there on my own.' I hoisted Joyce to her feet. 'You have to come.'

'Then let my death be on your conscience.'

An electric bolt of excitement seized the night sky. The procession crept along the darkened street, the muffled sound amplifying with every step. Tense with anticipation, the crowd jerked forward. Suddenly, there was a loud gong and a rush of bodies. Rank with paint and passion, groups of men appeared from the darkness shouldering massive monsters.

A huge gorgon loomed from the shadows. A twisted effigy with matted hair, sharp talons and glassy eyes, it spun out of control into the crowd. Everyone panicked and moved out of the way. 'Over here!' Joyce dragged me into the shelter of a dingy doorway.

Gigantic ogres, one more grotesque than the next, stomped by in a cavalcade of monsters. With flashing teeth, drooping breasts and vicious dispositions, they challenged the evil spirits to emerge from their hiding places. Groups of youths, whipped into a frenzy by the violent mood and too much arak, jostled each other for supremacy.

The banging of metal drums and clanging cymbals escalated to an ear-splitting crescendo. The noise grew impossibly loud in a bid to drive all darkness from the night. Troops of men flailed the air with fiery batons, ensuring no bhuta could escape the deadly trap.

A flash of light and then an intense smouldering heat as a bunch of fire-crackers exploded near my feet. Burning poles sparked the black night with tongues of blue, singeing our eyes with bitter ash, as we broke through the throng. A ferocious demon with gigantic fangs, lurched madly, trampling everyone in its path. Joyce went down in the rush. With one huge yank, I pulled her to safety. 'Whew, that was close,' Joyce moaned, wiping bits of gravel from her shin.

'Don't worry, I wasn't about to let the dark forces run off with you. I don't think they're quite ready for you yet!'

'Now at least I know why tomorrow's the day of stillness.'

'Why?' I asked, following her down a deserted alley.

'Because I'll need at least twenty-four hours to recuperate!'

Nyepi. The day of silence. Not allowed out of the hotel, I lay by the pool, too exhausted to turn the pages of my book while Joyce was passed out next to me, rousing only for the occasional drink. Under a canopy of listless palms the sun too was lethargic, battling to break through the thick layer of cloud that engulfed the sky.

'How come you opted to stay here for Nyepi?' Joyce muttered through her coma. 'I thought you'd relish the idea of being confined with Remy for the whole day, especially when he couldn't run off.'

'He did *sort* of ask me to spend the day at his house but the idea of being stuck with his gracious auntie was too much. I figured it would be more fun here with you, or at a wake for that matter.'

'Wise choice,' Joyce laughed. 'Sly's gone bush to his village. At first I protested but when I found out you're not allowed to have a nookie for twenty-four hours, I gave him his marching orders!'

'Happy New Year,' I said to Gusti as he sheltered under a tree, escaping the intense heat. 'Pity we can't go out and celebrate.'

'Oh no,' he countered, 'no-one is allowed outside. Four things are strictly forbidden today. No lights or fire, this is symbolic so that the fire of lust and desire within us can be extinguished.'

Joyce's eyebrows arched. 'You can count me out then.'

'We are supposed to meditate, fast and purify our souls. No physical or pleasurable activities are allowed and no traffic at all, the evil spirits must believe the island is deserted and go elsewhere.'

'Darwin's just down the road, they could all slip over there.'

'By the way, what year is it?'

'1915,' Gusti replied, 'according to the Balinese calender.'

'I have no comment,' Joyce retorted under her breath.

Throughout the day nothing stirred. The staff lolled about, guests grew restless, all unable to leave the hotel's grounds. The beach was close by but there was an invisible line one was not permitted to cross. Patrols roamed the streets ensuring nobody violated the curfew. The spirits had to believe the island was deserted.

Night passed by slowly with only the comfort of veiled light to read by. Curtains were drawn, lamps dimmed. A mantle of darkness enveloped the entire island. Everyone slipped into fitful sleep, sucked under by the surge of dormant energy being released into the sky.

Nervous and isolated, I became the fabled Sleeping Beauty. Stranded in her castle by a maze of thorns, separated from the one she loved by a suffocating force far beyond her control. Falling into a sleep that lasted an eternity as a year rolled by in the span of a single day.

After an interminable period of darkness, the sun rose again on a new age. Bali was freed of its ancient curse. Mine had just begun.

CHAPTER NINE
A Ghostly Vision

Violent bursts of thunder echoed through the night. I shut the windows tight and bolted the door, barricading us from the sudden deluge. Remy lay sleeping on the bed, ghostly pale. A sharp bolt of lightning slashed through the electrical wires, shrouding the room in total darkness. I lit a candle and sat beside Remy.

In the flickering light, he looked gaunt and weary. Nyepi had affected him badly, enforced contemplation leaving him depleted. He argued that he was just over-tired and would be better after a few day's rest. Remy's woes however, were more deeply ingrained.

Over Nyepi, all demons had been exorcised from the island, in the process a few personal ones had seeped to the surface. I had been aware for some time that something was troubling Remy, the problems were now festering like an open wound about to be exposed. Remy clung on tightly to his devils, pushing them further under where they would cause most harm. By night-time his body was burning with fever.

The following days were a nightmare. Despite constant efforts, the electricity could not be restored, the driving rain hampering all efforts. In the dim candlelight, I watched Remy writhe on the bed, a victim of the fire that consumed his body. Confused, he called out in his sleep, the garbled messages the key to the anguish that racked him, *'Run ... escape ... before the snake destroys us both.'*

Alone in the dark, I begged for the torment to stop. Cradling his head tenderly, I tried to ease his pain and break the horror of his visions. The agony continued until at last my prayers were answered; the thick clouds faded in the morning sky, taking the terror with them. Remy opened his eyes with a vague but perceptible smile. At last he had come back. Back from a brief dark passage of the soul.

The river coursed over polished stones, the thick bamboo screening all light from the secluded glade. A fine cotton sarong was the only thing between us and the spiky blades of grass growing amongst the scattered pebbles lining the riverbank. Remy was propped up on one elbow, contemplating the steady flow of water over the rocks.

'Any room for me inside your head?' I asked, draping my body across his. 'Your thoughts seem so deep, you're lost inside them.'

Remy chewed on a blade of grass. 'Since I've been sick I've had a chance to think things over. Certain issues in my life need to be dealt with, others clarified. I'm going through an emotional catharsis.'

'Change isn't achieved overnight.' Had Remy's issues surfaced because of his illness or had they in fact been the cause of it? Whatever the answer, Remy was altered by the experience.

'I've decided to go away for a few days to meditate, and collect some water from the holy mountain. Before you ask to come along, I want you to know this is something I need to do alone. There's still a lot of sorting out to do and I need distance.'

'That's one thing we already have, how can you want more?'

'I know we're not together as often as you might like, but you have to believe I've never felt so close to a woman before in my life. You reside in a perfect place in my heart, nothing will ever alter that.'

'I feel that less in body than in soul. Tell me, why do you need the holy water, doesn't a healer have the power to heal from within?'

'Yes, but the water is believed to embody the power of a god, and so contains a mysterious force. By virtue of this, it can cleanse all spiritual impurities, ward off evil, or repel any negative attack.'

'Dare I ask which category you fall into?'

Remy thought long and hard. 'When I was ill, I was plagued by dark visions somehow of my own making. These warped images were reflections of my own truth. Holy water is sacred; it strengthens and purifies everything it touches. The more sacred the place from which it comes, the stronger the mantra chanted over it and the more exalted the person making it, the more magical it becomes. I'm in need of the strongest, for the monsters loom heavy in my soul.'

A quiet hush fell over the forest. Not a sound could be heard, not a cricket nor a bird; even the river ceased to flow. I was lodged within a silent void, Remy's voice trailing into the unheard. Unable to hear his words, I no longer needed to grapple with their meaning.

'Please enter my humble home.' While Remy went forth on his mystical quest, I sought the company of friends. Joyce's new house was large and cavernous with only a handful of furniture to break the monotony. A bowl of limp roses graced the sideboard next to a gilt-framed photo of Joyce in gold lamé. There were fewer traces of the discontent that plagued her before - fewer empty bottles. A couple of extra inches around the middle and a rosy glow to the cheeks were sure signs that she was settling in nicely.

'Delicious,' Joyce pulled the roast out of the oven. Wearing a frilly gingham apron, she was the picture of domesticity, except for the rhinestone drop earrings. The kitchen steamed up with the smell of sizzling chook, sending my taste buds into a frenzy.

I offered to help with the carving, but Joyce made it clear the kitchen was her private domain. Sitting down at the heavy wooden table, I flicked through some photos I found wedged in the fruit bowl. Sly's face beamed out from every shot, Joyce standing devoted by his side. Despite the odds, he had taken on a prominent role in her life.

'Those were taken when we went up to Sly's village a while back,' Joyce said, stirring the gravy. 'I quite like it up there in the hills, it's a little primitive but I'm a nature girl at heart.'

'Is that where Sly's gone now, back to the village?'

'Yes,' Joyce plonked down the plates, 'and if you want to know the truth, it's a blessing. The man's smothering me to death, he's suffocating me with affection. One *can* get too much of a good thing.'

'I wouldn't know. Life's no picnic with an aspiring priest.'

'Trust you to pick a holy man,' Joyce chortled, pounding the mashed potatoes. 'Mind you, last time I saw him in action down at the club he didn't seem so holy! Think of it as a challenge. In any case, you're entering your goddess stage like me. I'm Juniper, the goddess of berries! What would we be doing with any *mere* mortal?'

'Then I must be Tenacity, the goddess of spunk. Any lesser being would have given up by now.'

The laughter continued throughout dinner, a glowing reminder of the gift of a woman's friendship. While men may be the bane of our existence or the pinnacle, women invariably provide the safety net. There to catch us when we fall, inspire us with their own broken tales and provide us with the courage to get up and do it all over again.

'Some things in life,' Joyce enthused, fossicking in the fridge, 'are better than men. Feast your eyes on my masterpiece, chocolate mousse à la Joyce. I used to think chocolate was an oral substitute for men but now I know it's the other way round.'

'We definitely have a penchant for the dark variety!'

•

The conversation exhausted and my appetite appeased, I fell onto the bed in the guest room in a bid to sleep. The air was stifling, both windows jammed shut. Joyce crashed out, the sound of her snoring rippling through the walls. Turning off the light, I had almost dozed off when a cool breeze crept by. It gently caressed my face.

My body, alerted by the strange presence jerked upright. Surely I must be dreaming. A shadowy figure was floating at the end of my bed - a poignant woman transparent in light, peering at me through soft, caring eyes. So comforting was her closeness that I felt no fear. Clearly I heard her speak. Not words. Thoughts.

'Your life here is an illusion. Like the puppet play, you see only a shadow of the truth. Look past the shadow and find the truth.'

Smiling, she dissolved into a fine mist. I fumbled for the light switch, knocking over the bedside lamp. It fell onto the floor with an almighty thud. Woken by the commotion, Joyce stumbled in.

'What's wrong?' she asked. 'You look like you've seen a ghost.'

'This house isn't haunted by any chance?'

'As a matter of fact, I do seem to have my own resident spook. Was it a young Balinese woman?' I nodded mutely. 'The first time I saw her she was putting offerings in the temple. She smiled at me serenely, then vanished in a puff of smoke! It frightened the life out of me, but since then I've seen her a couple of times hanging around the temple. My neighbours told me that a young girl used to live here but she died, some sort of tragic accident. They say her spirit is lost and roams through the house. I've come to think of her as my protector, I'm sure she's looking out for me.'

Spurred on by the words of my ghostly visitor, I returned to my hotel room several days later expecting the worst. I wasn't disappointed. Was it a tragic stroke of fate, or simply the right time for the truth to emerge? If I'd stayed away longer, could I have eluded destiny and stayed within the safe cocoon of deceit? Maybe if I had, my life would not have caved in as it did. Could circumstances be manipulated so easily, or was everything that happened inevitable?

'Ben, what a lovely surprise.' I wasn't expecting any visitors, least of all Ben. With his time split between two wives, it was rare to see him.

'I hope you don't mind me coming around unannounced,' he said, hovering at the doorway. 'Is Remy here by any chance?'

'No, but he's due back sometime soon. Would you like to sit down and wait, or can I give him a message?' Ben seemed in a hurry.

'Well actually, I've come to say good-bye. I'm leaving Bali.'

'What! You've never mentioned this before.' Ben had become a good friend and he'd be sorely missed. 'Where are you going?'

'To Java. My wife's got a job promotion close to her family, so she's decided to accept. I've been offered a position in a hotel there.' In Ben's predicament, this was bound to cause complications.

'What about your second wife? I'm sure she'll be very upset.'

'No, I've thought it over carefully. I can't leave her, or my son for that matter, he's only six months old. They'll have to come along.'

'But I thought your first wife didn't know about her?' How Ben had kept up the lie for so long was beyond me.

'She doesn't. There's a small village close to my wife's home where I can set up my second family. It's not too far, I can visit them during my lunchtime. I'm convinced it will all work out in the end.'

'Ben, that's madness! One day it will come out and a lot of people will get hurt. You can't keep this deception going on forever.'

'Yes I can,' he pleaded. 'Remy's gotten away with it for over a year, why can't I?'

Ben's face collapsed as he realised what he had said. At that moment, if he could have reversed time, he would have.

'What?' I asked, staring at him glassily.

'Nothing.' Biting his lip, Ben stepped away, 'Say good-bye to Remy for me.' He backed further down the path. 'I'm so sorry, Lia.'

Steadying myself on a chair, I felt my body go numb. 'No, no,' I repeated over and over, hoping the very word would deny the reality. 'No, you're wrong Ben.' I hammered the words into my brain in a hopeless attempt to alter the truth. My greatest defence was delusion; I still continued to deny that which I had always suspected. Yet, unequivocally, I knew he was right.

Almost as if bidden, Remy walked into the room. One look at me and he knew that the ruse was over. 'Lia,' he said, uncertainly, 'let me explain.' He reached out but I recoiled from the duplicity of his touch. With eyes downcast, he struggled to say what had to be said.

From the look that passed between us, Remy realised there could be no more excuses. His only defence was the truth. With surprising candour, Remy confessed all his sins. The fabric of my life buckled under the strain of each cruel word. Shockingly implausible, the situation was more disastrous than I had imagined.

'It's true, I am married. I have been for over fifteen years. The woman you believed to be my aunt is really my wife ... yes the woman in my house.' My throat began to dry up. 'Kadek is not really my sister, she's my daughter ... I have three daughters and a younger son.' Just when I feared it could get no worse, the onslaught continued, the facts exploding through my psyche. 'The woman who wrecked your room, well she's my second wife. At least she was ... I left her the day I met you. The divorce is final now.'

'You bastard!' I screamed, forcing myself not to lash out. 'How could you lie about your own children, about two wives as though they never existed - what sort of man are you? Get out, out of my sight.'

'Please, give me a chance - I only did it because I love you. Do you have any idea of what I gave up to be with you? The agony of the deception? The toll it took on me was terrible, for I knew the truth.'

My soul wrested inside out, was unable to listen. Repelled by his sight I could no longer see. Torn apart by the extreme agony, I lost the capacity to feel. Realising that he had pulverised our love into a wretched painful pulp, Remy turned to walk away. Not without one last pleading look. It hurt much more than the rest.

I almost succumbed, despairing for a way out, a way to pardon the man I had loved so much only a fractured moment ago. But the annihilation was complete. What Remy had done was unforgivable. He had violated my soul with his lies, all at once I felt dishonoured and defiled. No amount of love could surmount it.

Remy was the perpetrator of the most diabolical of crimes, yet it was I who was to pay the price. Sentencing myself to solitary confinement, I refused to come out of my room. Intent on obliterating Remy from my mind, I systematically destroyed anything that reminded me of him. Any trace of the man I loved, erased in the smouldering flame of charred photos. If only I could burn him out of my brain with the wanton flick of a match, but the bond between us was too intense to incinerate.

Unable to come to terms with the depth of my despair, I made a choice. With every measure of strength I possessed, I packed my bags and walked out the door. Whatever it took to survive, I would do it. Even if it meant leaving forever my precious island paradise, drenched with sweet dreadful memories, and the man I loved.

I headed straight for the bus station. Sitting on my suitcase in the grimy heat among a crowd of faceless strangers, I was stricken. Never before had I felt such despair, nor been so emotionally bereft. In the absolute isolation, I heard the ring of prophetic words. The words of my ghostly custodian, echoing in my head.

'All is an illusion, go beyond the shadows to find the truth.'

The mysterious spectre was right. My life had been one grand illusion. But if it was all an illusion, why did the pain feel so real?

CHAPTER TEN

Mermaid Goddess of Java

The first bus out of Bali was headed across the Bali Strait to Java, destined for the city of Surabaya. I didn't care where it was going; I just had to get away. Zooming down the highway, I willed the bus to go faster, to get far away from the personal disaster that was my life. The greater tragedy was the truth, the bitter realisation that no amount of distance could dissolve the turmoil within - I was taking it with me.

Spurred on by the blare of Kung-Fu videos, the driver wove his way dangerously through the convoy of trucks clogging the busy road to the port town of Gilimanuk. The toxic fumes spewed out by the deadly flotilla of traffic added to the nightmare. Faster still, as scattered villages flashed past. A succession of blurred images, people going about their daily lives with no concern for mine.

My body, relinquishing the strength it had needed to get through the ordeal of the past week, gave up the fight. Sinking into my seat I curled up into a tight cloistered ball, shielding myself from the outside world. Even on the ferry crossing to Java, brutal memories flooded my mind, but I fought them. I had crossed water and left Bali far behind. For a few glorious hours I found release in sleep.

Back on the road, the deathly pace continued as the bus tore down the highway. Time sped by as quickly as the changing scenery. Then came the sharp blast of the horn. The driver jammed on the brakes to avoid ramming the bus in front, hurling me out of the seat and onto the floor. It was the final straw. The driver was a maniac and I had no room left for madmen in my life. Reeling from the onslaught, I snatched my bag and got off at the next town, Probolinggo.

From there, I boarded a mini-bus heading west towards the active volcano, Mount Bromo. Ascending through cool greenness and a forest scented with sweet pine trees, I began to unwind. Nature provided the ultimate relief from the tawdry affairs of man.

*

By the time we reached the small village of Ngadisari it was dark, so I found a small home-stay and settled in. For the price of the room, I was promised a guide to take me to the volcano in time for sunrise. Stress had depleted me more than I'd realised. I fell into bed exhausted, with only a few dry crackers to ward off my hunger.

Only now, in this remote room, lined with facets of another's life, did I fully comprehend the severity of my loss. I longed to return to a place of trust, to be lying in Remy's arms. In spite of everything I still loved him, and I hated myself for it. Turning the anger inwards, it became more destructive. *'Damn you Remy* for doing this to me!'

Alone in the unfamiliar bed, I tussled with the blankets to stave off the chilled night air and quell the tremors inside. Worn out from the battle, I fell into a fitful sleep, until woken by a light knock on the door. I looked at my watch: 3 a.m. Where had the night gone?

Dazed, I climbed out of bed. Standing at the door was a diminutive young man in a woollen poncho. 'I'm Udi, your guide.' Sensing by my look that it would take a miracle to move me, he said, 'The sky is clear tonight, full of stars, so your view of the volcano will be most beautiful.' I was wavering. 'The peak will light up golden red at dawn with the sunrise. I suggest you take a blanket, it's very cold outside.'

It wasn't cold; it was *freezing*. Having survived the three kilometre trek to the caldera in the darkness, I clambered down the steep rim of the outer crater, groping for solid ground. Grabbing hold of a clump of dried leaves, I stumbled onto the lip of the extinct volcano.

Volatile Mount Bromo was spewing red in the distance. To reach it we had to trek across the Sea of Sand, the immutable dormant core of the older volcano. Steeling myself for the journey, I took a deep breath. It hung suspended in the air like a wisp of cloud, before being sucked into the dense mantle of fog. The moon too had vanished, swallowed up in the gloomy haze.

The night was thick with shadows, only the faint beam of Udi's torch eased the darkness. It cast a fragile ray of light on the desolate landscape. Trudging across the vast plateau all senses were dim, only the rough crackle of our footsteps on the hard earth disturbed the bleakness. My legs ached, their taut muscles straining against the rocky surface. I wrapped the blanket around my chest, pulling it tighter to fend off the bitter cold. Chilled dew matted my hair, before streaming icily down my cheeks.

There was a brief flicker of light then the torch faded out, casting us into total blackness. 'Udi, where are you?' I panicked.

'I'm here.' His soft voice offered instant relief. 'Don't worry, I've crossed this way so many times before I could do it blindfolded. There are markers to guide our way - see that white rock over there?' I could barely distinguish the outline. 'Take my hand, I'll lead you.'

Blindly, I traced Udi's footsteps in the sand. Heading further into the void, each movement was laboured, as if we were traversing the dark side of the moon. The acrid smell of sulphur singed my nostrils. My mouth recoiled from the foul taste. My vision, slowly restored, was mesmerised by a vivid crimson glow in the distance.

The volcano loomed straight ahead. Spurred on, I quickened my pace, determined to reach the peak. At the end of the wide plateau the mountain merged into hard rock, a steep band of stairs roughly hewn into its side. The earth trembled below my feet and with a sinister growl the volcano called to me, beckoning me on. Drawn by the mysterious pull of the mountain, I climbed slowly upwards until reaching the top. Elated, I collapsed onto the cold ground.

'We're the first ones here!' Distant lights dissected the plain, the dim lanterns of the horse-riders wending their way closer.

'Of course,' Udi remarked. 'Come, I'll take you to the volcano.'

Staggering across the pitted ground to the crusty lip of the crater, I looked down. Deep into the volcano's glowering belly where the earth had cracked open in savage fury and bled fire into its rich, red veins. A cauldron of hot lava gurgled, spewing up fierce jets of steam, harsh reminders of the volcano's unending turbulence. The putrid stench was testimony to its bitterness.

'Why are you so angry, Mother Earth?'

It roared in response, emitted a low menacing rumble, and then, most ominous of all - silence.

Staring into the fiery cesspool I saw a mirror image of myself. Like me, the passion was intense, the wounds ran deep. One moment dormant, the next a torrent of raging destruction. If I plunged into it, returned the anger to its source, could I put an end to my anguish?

'Last year during the *Kesada* festival, a young man fell to his death. Climbing the edge of the volcano to throw offerings into the crater and so pacify the gods, he slipped - an unfortunate accident.'

'Maybe a sacrifice to the gods.'

Udi, perplexed, tried to fathom my meaning. It was impossible, he was too innocent to understand.

Silhouetted by the soft rays of sunrise, a subtle pink haze, tinged with the palest gold lit up the sky, awakening the night from its sultry dream. It illuminated the whole of the valley. Craggy peaks spliced the vast plateau like a spectacular cosmic moonscape. Bathed in dawn's early light, it looked magnificent and I saw our path clearly for the first time. Why had the dark made it appear so threatening? With light came ultimate vision and life.

At last I could recognise the beauty that had always been there.

I spent the next few days recuperating in the crisp air and quiet solace of the peaceful mountain village. The people, wrapped in striped ponchos, with wizened faces and gentle smiles, reminded me of those of the Andes. Safe in these anonymous hills, where nobody knew me and every passing face was that of a stranger, I shed some of my burden. The clouds were lifting. It was time to loosen my shackles and go out into the world.

With no particular destination in mind, I moved onto the town of Solo, where I met an eccentric English woman named Phoebe. In dire need of some creature comforts, we agreed to share the cost of a hotel room. Phoebe, still living in the days of the Raj, walked around the room stark naked, regaling me with wild tales of her travels.

After several days of sightseeing and Phoebe's rantings, I gave up. While my body dwelled in relative comfort, my sanity was suffering. Realising that my own company was vastly preferable to the stifled comfort of a slightly mad stranger, I ditched Phoebe and headed for the magnificent temple of Borobudur.

Rising up from the plain of Kedu in central Java, this colossal stone pyramid is the largest Buddhist temple in the world. Built around 800 AD by a team of skilled artisans, the massive stupa of Borobudur lay buried for centuries under thick layers of volcanic ash, rediscovered only in 1815.

Conceived as a Buddhist concept of the cosmos, the mighty temple was constructed in the form of a giant three-dimensional tantric mandala. Starting the long circular climb clockwise, I passed a stunning sequence of carvings explicitly cut into the huge gallery walls. Spiralling upwards, scenes of Buddha's life unfolded in graphic sequence - impacting on a world far away from the land of his birth. Exotic figures were hewn into the grey walls: dancing girls, dazzling elephants, endless processions of brave warrior kings - a past era vividly brought to life in the ashen stone.

Leaving behind all traces of human desire, I followed the temporal trail until reaching the peak: Nirvana. The terraced roof was decorated with a profusion of bell-shaped stupas and erudite buddhas in varied postures of serenity. As was the custom, I reached inside one of the latticed stone stupas to touch the buddha's foot to bring me good luck.

Suitably blessed, I sat down to meditate in a secluded spot, drinking in the muted beauty of my surroundings. Shady trees tumbled out over the grassland flush with masses of red blossoms. Prompted by the ethereal vibration moulded by aeons of collective prayer, I was overcome by a real sense of peace; a peace amplified in this helix of sacred timeless energy.

There were those who remained impervious to its pull; enlightenment was the domain of the wise. A tour group converged upon the monument, scaling the fragile walls in wild attempts to take photos. Three boisterous men scrambled on top of an ancient buddha, crushing the sign 'FORBIDDEN TO CLIMB' in their haste to get a shot. The security guard sat in a stupor, having long given up the battle to contain the monstrous hordes.

I gazed out over the valley. How long had passed since the inception of this magnificent monument, how much history recorded in the minutest particle of every stone? One of the holiest places on earth, why wasn't it afforded the reverence it deserved?

Yogyakarta, in honour of its treasured history and regal ties, has long been considered the cultural capital of Java. Lying in the centre of Java's 'Realm of the Dead', it is a city surrounded by ancient ruins. An abundance of art, music, dance and theatre flourish within its enclaves. Its artists are deemed amongst Indonesia's finest.

The thick white walls of the *kraton* palace extend one kilometre square, enclosing a small city of 25,000 people. I entered through an impressive gateway and wandered around the classical buildings of the palace, dating back to 1756 and the Mataram kingdom.

Roaming through the old stone bastions, I was flooded with an acute sense of deja vu. The walls, the buildings, even the shadows they cast were familiar. Only the time frame had altered, everything else remained the same.

Under the vaulted ceiling of the Glass Pavilion came the strongest recognition. The glow of the polished marble floor, the intricate carving of the rich red beams, the heavy smell of the wood, all triggered a profound reaction. Footsteps, coming closer. A ghostly procession of attendants, brilliant in royal blue and batik, floated by in a trail of shadows. I blinked, attempting to dislodge the vision. Instead, the scent of a woman, gold and diaphanous, wafted past, accompanied by the hypnotic wailing of an old man.

My head started to spin. I fled to the garden and found a leafy sanctuary next to a preening peacock. Surely it was just the heat.

'Hello there,' a chirpy voice cried. 'I knew you hadn't seen the last of me!' Oh no, it was Phoebe. Fate was cruel. Wiping some wafer crumbs from her chin, she plonked down beside me. 'I've got a bicycle driver waiting, we can tour around town together. Super!'

I was too tired to protest. The driver pulled down the awning of the carriage to shield us from the hot sun and peddled fast. 'To the Water Castle,' Phoebe shouted, waving her guide book in her hand.

The pool had grown mossy with neglect, a hardy lily floating in the water the only reminder of a romantic past. The studded tiles were faded and chipped but the old palace retained its mystique. Phoebe gestured for me to follow her to the crumbling rooms perched by the edge of the pool.

'Absolutely fascinating,' she said, traipsing up the steps to the attic. 'From this window, the king had a perfect view, he'd watch the ladies swimming below, then make his choice. This was the nuptial bed,' her cheeks flushed, 'where they'd consummate their passion. I'm sure it was draped with sumptuous fabrics and cushions,' she said, lustily reliving the time. 'If only I'd been here then, how romantic!'

'The king had hundreds of women, Phoebe,' I said, arguing on the side of reality. 'Can you imagine the jealousy that went on in the court? With all that competition your chances of having a night alone with him might have been pretty slim.' In any case, I was certain that one burst of Phoebe's prattle would have lasted him a lifetime!

'Don't be so sure, look over here.' At the back of the palace was a private pool for the king and his first wife. 'His queen - perhaps I was she.' Phoebe fanned herself briskly, ready to swoon in rapture.

Looking through the arched windows, it was easy to get swept away in the fantasy. Though the building had fallen into disrepair, its secrets were locked within its walls. The underground passageways resonated with clandestine liaisons. The king had left his mark here; the classic nights of love imbuing their fervid imprint for all eternity.

A glimmer of memory surfaced, casting reflections across the water in a mottled prism of light. My liaison with Remy rippled with intrigue, one woman pitted against the other in a battle of wills. Little had I suspected there were those who hated me from afar, plunging us into a cesspool of pathos created by our love for the same man.

Was it a karmic overflow, the leftovers of a past lifetime? Did I turn and run then too, unable to share a love so precious that I deemed it mine alone? Or did I stay to accept an uneasy compromise, bruising my heart badly in the process? Then, came the cruellest awareness of all: the price of love. How many people had to be hurt, how many lives destroyed - all in the undying name of love?

'Last stop!' Phoebe's galloping tour of the old city was taking its toll. In spite of her English rose complexion and delicate air, she had the stamina of a Rottweiler. I trailed her down a small musty alley, ' ... to a special place, secret really ... where the sultan would come to convene with his spiritual wife.'

We veered off into a private courtyard. 'The marriage chamber,' she whispered, stooping into the small musty cavern. Carved from heavy rock, two beds lay side by side. Freshly placed offerings were scattered on both: soft flower petals, old coins, a smouldering candle. Left by devotees who had come to ask for blessings from the sultan and his mythical consort.

'Oh, what a wondrous story.' Phoebe read from her guidebook adding appropriate embellishments, 'In the sixteenth century, King Senopati went to the ocean to meditate. He had a vision of a beautiful woman rising from the sea. Little did he know that she was in fact the goddess of the South Seas. Soon afterwards they fell in love and were married. How splendid!'

'The sultan married a goddess? What a potent combination.'

'Exactly. She taught him how to gain hidden powers and become a great ruler. He built her these chambers as a place of meditation where they could be alone. What a wonderfully mystical culture to have such tales!'

Sitting on the cold slab that was once the bed of a goddess, I hoped she would not take umbrage at my invasion of her private spot. I envied the king his tryst with a goddess - if I stayed long enough perhaps she would honour me with a visit, and empower me with strength and wisdom. The strength to deal with the trials of my life, and the wisdom to learn.

A week came and went. I found a small guesthouse in pretty gardens on the fringe of the city. Phoebe insisted on moving in too, then tagged along everywhere I went. I was considering a midnight flit, but knew that after my disappearance in Solo, she was onto me. She slept with one eye open.

In a stroke of genius, I enrolled us in a batik class. Phoebe was so engrossed in not dripping hot wax on her masterpiece, a detailed study of a constipated duck, that she left me in relative peace. I teamed up with an interesting lady, Amy, a fashion designer from New York. Marvelling at the way her long, delicate fingers worked the wax, I copied her style. My abstract 'Mountains in the Mist' was no match for her 'Opus in Bird Life,' but at the end of the day I was happy.

Each night, having scrubbed off the last remnants of wax and dye, we three would meet in the back alleys of Yogyakarta, in the artists' quarter. Amy's blond sophistication drew admiring glances from the men in the restaurants. However, Phoebe's loud dissertations were enough to keep them at bay. She did have her purpose after all.

Satiated by the interesting conversation, I would fall into bed content, too tired to let thoughts of Bali filter into my mind. One night as I drew back my sheets, my guidebook fell open on the floor. My eyes fixated on a name. '*Imogiri.* Burial place to the sultans.' I knew I had to go. Intrigued by my sudden interest, the girls insisted on coming along too.

It was Friday, the Muslim day of worship. Imogiri was open for pilgrimage, many of the faithful would visit the tomb of the sultans to pray. The heat was unbearable, the copper sun heavy in the sky.

'Come on, chaps, let's get a move on,' Phoebe coaxed, bounding up the mountain of steps as if running in a decathlon.

Amy gracefully manoeuvred her way up while I lagged behind, stopping often to admire the locals stream past, adorned in their impressive ceremonial dress. Their costume was different to that of Bali, the ochre tones more subdued and mellow. The people, too, appeared more restrained. Everything in Bali was so dramatic, here the atmosphere was infinitely more sedate.

At the top, I found Amy admiring the view. Phoebe had wandered off so we headed for the cemetery grounds. The tombs were clearly sign-posted, those of the Susuhunan kings of Solo to the left, the sultans of Yogya to the right. In the central courtyard lay the burial place of Sultan Agung and his descendants, the Mataram kings.

'Over here!' Phoebe yelled. 'We must change first.' Visitors were required to don a traditional costume of *kain and kebayan* before being allowed to enter the tomb. Whisked behind a partition, I was snatched by an old man who divested me of my garments and wound me into a brown sarong with a bolt of batik fabric around my chest. Arms and shoulders were left bare, as was the custom.

'We look super,' Phoebe gloated, admiring the finished effect in her compact mirror. 'I think I was born into the wrong era.'

Dressed the part, we strolled through the courtyards, absorbing the arcane atmosphere. Again I was struck by an intrinsic sense of connection, feeling more at ease surrounded by these historic grey walls than I did in any modern city or crowded street back home.

Entrance to only one tomb was allowed, the most revered, that of the Grand Sultan. Only one person at a time was permitted inside for prayer. Impossible to restrain, Phoebe fumbled in first. I sat under a tree while Amy went next. I needed time to prepare, to consider the implications of this legendary site. It reminded me of the land of my birth, Greece, full of fabulous myths about supernatural alliances between gods and kings.

Leaving the light of the sun behind, I crawled through the narrow opening that led to the crypt. Bending low, my hands carved a pathway along the smooth stone, my eyes powerless in the darkened alcove. Drawn on by the sweet scent of sandalwood and flickering candlelight, I saw the shadowy form of a priest stooped over the heavy coffin.

He motioned for me to come over and kneel down beside him, then handed me some petals to place upon the grave. I dropped the fragile pink rose petals onto the cold stone. As the old priest began to chant, a blissful state engulfed my being. The vibration within the tomb was overpowering; an emanation so divine that I was flooded with unparalleled ecstasy.

Rich incense wafted around me in thick drifts. With each breath of the fragrant smoke my spirit soared, radiating out in brilliant shafts against the dim walls. I felt all at once invincible, empowered by the Sultan's force. In a sudden flash of light, the energy burst. Fine hazy particles fell upon the soil as I merged into the earth, entering its sacred womb, the place where I was conceived and was one day destined to return.

The steely casket of the Sultan began to vibrate. A golden ray emanated from it, flooding the cave with an incandescent glow. Ashen hands grappled with the stone. A shadowy figure fought to emerge from the coffin. 'Oh, my God.' I stared in disbelief as the ghostly form took shape. The eerie haze pulsated then faded into sheer light. Although I could no longer see it, I knew it was there.

The delicate smell of frangipani flooded the cave. From deep within the rocks, I heard a voice. Soothing and clearly omnipotent. *'Make a wish,'* it commanded. I was overwhelmed. Where did the voice come from? Was the ghost of the Sultan speaking to me?

In spite of the awe, I wasn't afraid. The fear had been drained from my soul by the benevolence of the tone, clearly inspired from another plane. This was an enlightened entity that wished me no harm. It sought to help - to grant me a wish. I hesitated, it was such a difficult choice. What to decide? Happiness, love, tranquillity? Then the answer became clear. *'The pain* ... please, just make it go away.'

I was not sure how long I stayed inside, time had lost all meaning. Emerging into the muffled rays of the afternoon sun, I found a quiet place on the hillside. Vaguely aware of Amy's presence, I stared out to space lost in a state of bliss. A great burden had been lifted. Phoebe was splayed out on the ground, lying rigid, unable to speak. A living testimony to the Sultan's power.

Unwilling to break the euphoric spell cast over me, I focused on a blade of grass as my senses were slowly restored. Groggily I got up and stumbled over to the edge of the hill, to a view that stretched out to the ocean crowned by the faint outline of lofty Mount Merapi.

Even though my back was turned, I became aware of the presence of a man standing close-by. Drawn, I turned to look. Middle aged and distinguished, his hair streaked with strands of silver, the stranger possessed a definite aura that made him stand out. Casting all inhibitions aside I walked over.

'My name's Soedano,' he said, a gentle kindness emanating from his eyes. They were the colour of soft charcoal. 'Let us sit down,' he gestured with the delicacy of an aristocrat. A ruby ring encrusted with diamonds attested to his wealth, his polite speech and manner an indicator of his breeding. He was the epitome of a true gentleman.

'This place is extraordinary,' I said, breaking the silence. I was groping in the dark, trying to understand the reason for my overture.

'The cemetery dates back to 1645. It's the spectre of Sultan Agung you can feel. He was one of this island's greatest kings, a fine warrior and a true mystic. Legend has it that he possessed remarkable paranormal gifts, and was the most extraordinary of men.'

'Inside the cave I had the most amazing experience. Don't think me mad, but I'm positive I saw the Sultan's ghost. His form manifested right in front of me, he even spoke to me.'

Soedano's eyes arched in curiosity. 'What did he say?'

'I heard a voice - a very deep, wonderful voice. It sounded not of this world, almost heavenly. It told me to make a wish.'

'Then I'm certain it was the Sultan. That's why people make the journey here, to ask him to grant a wish. You were unaware of our tradition so he lent you a guiding hand; perhaps you are blessed, or maybe your need is great ... only the Sultan knows and he never reveals his secrets.' Looking at his watch, Soedano got up. 'I'm sorry, I'm late for a meeting, but I would like the chance to speak again.' He handed me his business card, 'I must go to Jakarta, but when I return please be my guest for dinner. I will expect you.'

'I'm so glad you could come,' Soedano welcomed us to his house.

Phoebe was beside herself with gratitude. 'Are you sure you don't mind us tagging along?' she asked, handing her shawl to the maid.

'Not at all.' He gestured for us to follow him into the living room, overflowing with valuable paintings and rare works of art.

Amy sat down on the lounge and crossing her legs demurely, leaned over to admire a porcelain vase. 'Your home is exquisite.'

'Thank you, you are most kind.' Soedano was dressed in a fine sarong, his royal blue shirt spun from the best silk. His hair, perfectly groomed, was topped with a matching turban.

The maid returned bearing a tray of sweetened ginger tea and cakes. Phoebe tucked into them as if she hadn't eaten for a week. 'Delicious,' she mumbled, 'I must admit, sweets are my weakness.'

Soedano smiled, ignoring Phoebe's excess, and outlined the evening's program. 'This is a most fortuitous time for you to come. *Lebaran* is a time of festivity, the end of *Ramadan*, the month of fasting. You will first join me for dinner and then be my guests for the formal ceremony. Excuse me for a moment,' he said, responding to a knock at the door.

Taking off my shoes, I sank into the rich Persian carpet and padded around the room examining the impressive array of artefacts. Taking pride of place was a magnificent kris dagger, framed on the wall. The gold handle was elaborately engraved and studded with precious gems. Its blade, powerful in icy steel, exuded a subtle glow.

'I see you're admiring the family kris,' Soedano said, returning with a young man. 'This is my nephew, Arifin. He is studying law at university. I'm rather busy so I've asked Ari to look after you.'

Handsome and tall, Ari had a noble patrician face with high

cheekbones, aquiline nose and eyes of soft gold. His hands were smooth and refined, betraying a life devoid of physical work.

'This kris,' Ari explained, 'has belonged to our family for centuries. As it was passed down from generation to generation, it collected the power of each ancestor and so became the repository of their combined strength. Thus it is revered and considered a source of great supernatural power.'

'That could explain the glow, it seems to have a life of its own. The carving is so detailed and elaborate.' I strained to make out the finer points. 'Some of the figures look a little evil.'

'They're meant to be. They're *raksasas* - monsters that ward off bad spirits and protect the wearer from black magic. It is believed that the kris will rattle in its sheath as a warning to its master of impending danger.'

'Why is the blade wavy?' Amy got up to take a closer look.

'Carved in this way, it inflicts more damage. One plunge can bypass the bones, leaving a mortal wound that will not heal. The number of curves varies. This one has five, representing the five brothers of the Pandava clan in the legends of the *Mahabharata*. Have you read it?'

'No,' Amy confided, 'just extracts from the *Bhagavad Gita*. I'm afraid I didn't get very far.' Amy's admission absolved me of my own ignorance.

'I don't blame you, it is believed to be the longest poem ever written, over twenty volumes, each one over a thousand pages. Tea?' Ari asked, pouring some from the large silver pot. Sitting down, he sipped delicately from a china cup. Each movement was studied, his manner friendly yet reserved. 'You are very fortunate to be here tonight. This ceremony is of great importance, culminating in our trip later to the ocean at Parangtritis.

'From what I've read,' Phoebe said, 'the beach there is very dangerous, many people have drowned in the strong currents.'

'Ah yes, true,' he replied. 'That is because it is the domain of the goddess Nyai Loro Kidul, and her powers are considered awesome.'

'Ah yes, the marvellous Goddess of the South Seas.'

'Legend tells she was the beautiful daughter of an ancient king. Her ugly stepmother was so jealous, that with the help of an evil wizard, she cursed her with leprosy. Horrified by her deformity, the poor girl threw herself off the cliffs near Parangtritis. She was transformed into a mermaid queen, ruling over a vast underwater kingdom.'

'That's a fascinating story,' Amy said. 'Do you really believe it?'

'Our culture has a tradition rich with myth. Nyai Loro Kidul personifies the spirit of the sea and the land. Ruling over the volcano, Mount Merapi, as well as the ocean, she is both unpredictable and powerful - a potent mix of fire and water. The first half of the month she is seen as a young nymph, the second as an ugly old hag. It is essential to honour both sides of her equally.'

'Is that why we're going to the beach tonight?' I asked.

'Yes, each year on the Sultan's birthday, offerings must be made. The Sultan himself presents a full set of clothing and nail and hair clippings. The Goddess is considered the protector of the Royal House of Mataram.'

'So the belief in their union is still retained until today?'

'Indeed, for if she is slighted she makes her presence felt. In 1966 for example, the current Sultan officiated at the opening of a hotel on the south coast of Java. An old man approached him and told of a dream, a woman in green asking for offerings. The Sultan refused to take heed, not wishing to mix mystical matters with official duties. The sea was calm, but suddenly a huge tidal wave appeared out of nowhere. Trees were knocked down and everyone was drenched. The Sultan conceded, made his offerings to the Goddess and the sea was calm again. The room he used, 319, is kept forever locked and reserved for the exclusive use of the Goddess.'

Our conversation was halted by the arrival of an elderly woman. Ari rushed to help her to a seat. Austere in grey, she was so slight and fragile that she was swallowed up by the deep red lounge.

'This is Ibu Jepara,' Soedano said, showing in more guests. 'A most gifted woman, she will act as our medium tonight. May the spirits give their blessings.' Amy looked at me sceptically, but I knew better. This confirmed my original attraction to Soedano, the psychic tie. No matter what, I was always drawn to spiritually kindred souls.

Dinner was announced. We sat down around an immense mahogany table, spread with a feast of local delicacies. Everyone ate their fill. Phoebe was in her element, hoeing into the goat sate and lamb kebabs with a vengeance. Meanwhile more visitors kept arriving, packing the drawing room at the front of the house. Several buses were parked outside ready for the journey to the ocean which was set to take place after the meditation.

After dessert and coffee, Soedano motioned that the ceremony was about to begin and went off to organise the final details. One of the female guests offered to help us into the appropriate dress. Soedano had thought of everything; three sets of clothing had been left on the bed.

Dressed in our sarongs, with red batik scarves wrapped around our chests, Amy and I sat at the back of the room wishing to remain as inconspicuous as possible. Phoebe was busy parading around the room, convinced she was one of the locals. A few scant looks from some of the devotees and she scooted up the back to the mother flock.

A hush fell over the crowd as Jepara took her place at the front. Seated on the lush red carpet next to Soedano, she closed her eyes and soon slipped into a trance. After a lengthy silence her body started to contort and her speech became distorted, her delicate voice replaced by that of an old man, deep and gritty. It seemed inconceivable that such a frail body could contain such a powerful presence. Soedano leant over to support her, all the while straining to listen to her words. Nodding, he got up slowly.

'What's going on?' Phoebe asked. I was too enthralled to reply.

Walking quietly towards the back of the room he paused, searching through the crowd. All eyes were riveted on him. When he spotted me he stopped, then pushed his way over. My discomfort intensified as he walked closer. I wanted to merge into the wall and become invisible.

'The spirits have spoken,' he said staring straight at me. 'We cannot continue the ceremony unless you lead it.' Phoebe's chin plummeted to the ground. 'Don't be afraid,' he said, responding to the misgiving in my eyes, 'believe in yourself and those who guide you. It's your gift, you must use it.'

A collective buzz spread through the crowd as word spread. Thoughts flooded back. London, the Psychic Society, ten years earlier. 'Every year we select a new young medium, skilled in the ways. You are chosen, it is your turn to stand on the platform.' The same terror I felt then, gripped my stomach now.

Amy squeezed my arm. 'You can do it,' she whispered in encouragement. There was no backing out, I could neither refuse Soedano's request nor that part of myself I had long since denied.

Kneeling on the ground beside Jepara, I prayed for guidance. Even though my eyes were closed, I could see subtle blue rays impregnate the room with fine beams of light. The ghostly ectoplasm spread in silky bands into the crowd, enmeshing everyone within its fibres. Linked in the infinite web, there were no lines of separation.

Suddenly, a blaze of light. Then *he* appeared: Sultan Agung, in all his ghostly glory, his sublime hands bestowing blessings upon his gathered flock. His face, bathed in golden shadows, shimmered with radiance, an angelic glow emanated from his being, swamping the room in rapture. There was no escaping the ecstasy, not a sound could be heard; all were touched by the divine presence.

As the energy intensified, the strength of a thousand lifetimes coursed through my veins, the wisdom of ages flashed before my eyes. Seeing my life clearly through the mind of another, I was flooded with clarity. With insight came forgiveness, then acceptance. My life was vindicated; my weaknesses had been my greatest strengths. I was on the path to salvation.

A higher voice spoke out. I absorbed its counsel to the very core of my being. 'The path you have chosen is demanding. In the awakening of your innocence, you can touch the minds of others. There are many spans of time still to be crossed, the choice of passage is yours. Choose wisely.'

I drifted into a frozen state, gripping tenuously to the vision, far too inspiring to release. Only the crowd's rumbling brought me back to reality. My eyes blinked open unsteadily, I had no idea how much time had passed. People were getting up and trickling through the door to the waiting buses. Ari shuffled across the carpet to me.

'You looked so peaceful, I didn't want to disturb you.'

'I'm still in a daze. I went to an incredible place, somewhere deep within my soul. It was so wonderful that I didn't want to return.'

'I understand, for I went there too. Come,' he said, walking me out to the buses, 'it's time for the second part of your journey.'

The trip to Parangtritis lasted an hour. Featureless images flashed past the window, forming shadows on the glass. I lay back in my seat, elated at what had passed, excited by the prospect of what was yet to come. It was nearly midnight by the time we arrived. Drawn on by the mighty roar of the waves, I walked down towards the beach.

The foam fell like thunder onto the shore, the sound almost deafening. Climbing over the brittle dunes, I was met by an immense wall of ocean. It glowered black velvet, only the white peaks of the waves saved it from total obscurity. Strong winds whipped past, charged with the scent of distant lands. A gust from the east and the ripe lusty smell of Bali swept by, lashing against me. I stood resolute.

Then came a strange voice, howling from the wind. *'Come, come,'* it called, urging me onwards, *'follow me.'* Hypnotised by the flow of the sea, I gazed deeper within until a hazy form took shape. The sketchy outline of a woman flickering through the waves. Beautiful beyond belief, her hair flowed strands of seaweed studded with nacre pearls. *'Follow me,'* she crooned, beckoning with her deep emerald eyes. A crash of waves and she was gone, and in her place was an awful crone, grotesquely wrinkled in the waters of time. *'Follow me,'* she rasped, her cold eyes unflinching.

My body was anchored to the sand, but my mind plummeted downwards. Iridescent fish swam by, further within the ocean's depths. A lone mermaid vanished into a maze of rainbow coral. I caught the strum of gentle harps and the spark of a crystal dolphin as I sank lower. Floating in the seabed, strands of seaweed branched out like deadly tentacles and wrapped around my throat, pinning me to the ocean floor.

Then a voice called out in rescue. 'Come back,' Ari shouted, jolting me back. 'Have you fallen under the Goddess's spell?'

The watery haze began to lift. 'No, no. I'm fine.'

'Don't underestimate her power. Many enter her kingdom but few return, drowning on these very shores. She prefers men as her servants, especially if they wear her favourite colour, green. So strong is her power that mothers lock up their sons when her dance is performed for fear she will take them captive to her ocean realm.'

Across the cold sand, a large group of people had gathered around the old mystic, Jepara. Laid out in front of her was a clutter of mysterious objects. In the middle was a large tray, covered by a white sheet and festooned with flowers. Jepara's gnarled hands ran over the cloth and in one sudden, graphic movement she removed it.

Underneath was the neatly decapitated head of an animal. A buffalo. The moon cast an eerie reflection in its hollow eyes. Blind from the shock, I stumbled to the water's edge. The offerings were dumped into the hostile waves and the people followed.

Cast into the icy depths, the first wave struck with a vengeance, sucking me to the bottom. Someone's hand grabbed mine and plucked me from the ocean floor. A second wave hit with even more ferocity. I struggled to keep my sarong from being swept away, and my dignity along with it. A third wave, and I was plunged into the hostile depths once more. In desperation, I choked to the surface, escaping the terrifying grip.

With every ounce of strength I had, I dragged myself out, collapsing in a sodden mass on the sand. Everywhere men and women were gasping for breath, thankful to be alive. They too had underestimated the might of Loro Kidul. Her power was staggering.

A haunting wail pierced the air. Jepara looked to the heavens as if to receive divine guidance, running her bony fingers through the wet sand, and began to draw mysterious symbols in its grains. Everyone fell silent, waiting for the announcement. Jepara looked up triumphantly. The Goddess, appeased, was in a generous mood. The next year would be a good one. The people had been spared.

CHAPTER ELEVEN
Terror in Sumatra

My first glimpse of Sumatra was through the night sky on the approach to Medan airport. Muted lights twinkled through the thick haze of grey smog covering the ground below. A strange mood permeated the darkness, casting an eerie net over the city.

The flight had been delayed, so it was after midnight when we landed. Wearied by the long trip, all I wanted to do was find a hotel room and drop into bed. The airport terminal was deserted, with only one cab left at the rank and it had just been claimed. I didn't relish waiting for another, feeling threatened by the desolation of the place.

As the taxi pulled out from the kerb, the passenger motioned for the driver to stop and wound down his window. 'I don't think this is the safest place to wait alone,' the handsome stranger cautioned, 'especially not at this time of night. I'm going to town, like a lift?'

'Are you sure you don't mind?' I answered, relieved.

'Not at all,' he smiled, getting out of the car to help with my luggage. 'My name's Matt - Matt Sloane.'

I looked into the brightest blue eyes I'd ever seen. Even in the dark they shimmered like topaz. 'Do I detect an American accent?' I slid into the back seat. 'You're a long way from home.'

'My dad's from the States, but I live in Guam. I work as a pilot in the airforce there.' Matt had the rugged physique of a man honed into shape by the rigours of the armed services; even through his jacket it was obvious. 'I'm here on leave, catching up with a friend.'

As he spoke, I felt a tingle run down my spine - a powerful surge of chemistry. This was the last thing I needed so I forced myself to look away, out into the dark of the city. The streets were empty and despondent, doused in a sombre undertone. The taxi snuck down back lanes past shops and houses that were heavily padlocked, steeled from outside assault.

'This city looks pretty mean.' Matt peered through the window. 'Not the sort of place you'd go for a walk late at night.' There was a vapid scent in the air, a biting edge that was almost tangible.

When we arrived at the hotel, Matt paid the driver and the taxi screeched off. 'He's in one hell of a hurry!' Handing the bags to the porter, we made our way to the reception desk. A bleary eyed clerk, roused from a sound sleep, looked flustered as he rustled through his list. 'Reservation for Sloane - one single, and a room for the lady?'

'I'm sorry sir, but we're completely booked out. There's a conference in town and all the hotels are full. I tried to find a room earlier but none were available. What would Madam like to do?'

'Madam would like to sit down,' I replied, collapsing into the nearest chair. 'I think I'll sleep in the lobby. I'm too tired to move.'

'Nonsense,' Matt protested, 'my room's a twin, you can stay with me. Don't worry, I'm harmless!' My spent body didn't put up a fight. 'It's late and we both could do with some sleep.'

The room was large and spacious, furnished in soft peach. Paintings of exotic wildlife decorated the wall above the plush beds. The room-boy closed the heavy cream curtains and turned down the beds, winking at Matt on his way out. He was rewarded with a tip.

It only added to my discomfort. Here I was in a strange city in a hotel room with a man I didn't know. Oblivious to my unease, Matt retired into the bathroom. 'A quick shower and then sleep, I'm beat!'

'I'll have one in the morning.' I snuggled into bed listening to the sound of running water. When Matt came out, I pretended to be asleep. He was naked except for the scant towel wrapped around his waist. Grabbing his bag of toiletries, he went to the basin to shave. The door was ajar, the light bright enough to give me a good view.

Matt was so gorgeous I had to muffle a groan. His muscles melted into an awesome maze of curves. I yearned to run my hands over every groove, along the smooth flawless skin that glowed in the dark, to feel the perfection of the man that stood before me.

It wasn't fair. No man had the right to be so damned attractive. No woman deserved to be marooned in a room with such a man and not be able to touch. It was torture. Matt slid into bed and turned off the bedside lamp. 'Sweet dreams,' he said, his mellow voice melting through layers of frustration. I scrunched the pillow over my head.

'Goodnight,' I choked, having to forcibly restrain myself from jumping into bed with him. I admonished myself for being depraved and promised the Almighty any sort of penitence to erase these lusty thoughts once and for all from my brain. I knew it was a test.

With the sound of his snoring, I lifted the pillow. In the still of the night I watched in silence; his gentle breath, the rise of his chest, the flutter of his long eyelashes. Immersed in his beauty, I wished the moment would never end. For a brief interlude, Bali was thousands of miles away, no more than a mere ripple in space.

The following morning we ate breakfast together in the hotel dining room. Surrounded by businessmen in crisp shirts engaged in heavy conversation, the room clouded with cigarette smoke and the smell of stale cloves, it was not the ideal setting for goodbyes.

'I'll be heading off soon,' Matt said. 'I've arranged for a car to take me to Dolok where Yudi, my friend lives. What about you?'

'I thought I'd go to Lake Toba. I've heard it's really beautiful.'

'Hey, Dolok is on the way.' Matt pored over his maps and pointed to it. 'Catch a ride with me, at least you'll be halfway there.'

'Coming to my rescue once again. I won't be in the way?'

'Are you kidding?' His eyes twinkled with delight. 'I'm getting used to having you around, might even miss you when you're gone.'

Leaving behind the urban sprawl, we drove along narrow roads lined with small villages and open fields until we pulled into a small dusty town. Matt paid the driver before leading me to a nearby cafe. 'Let's have a farewell drink. Two cokes, real cold.' A scraggly young boy dug deep into the icebox, groping for the bottles. Wiping off the grit, he handed them over. Matt guzzled his down in deep, thirsty gulps.

'I guess the buses run fairly regularly,' Matt said, gathering his things into a neat pile. 'You'd better head off soon if you want to reach the lake before dark. I don't want to have to worry about you.'

I had the strangest compulsion to grab Matt's hand and not let go. Instead, I said good-bye. 'Have a safe trip, and thank you.'

Heaving his bag over his shoulder Matt headed towards the door. 'I hope we meet again one day.' He turned and shot me one last glorious grin before disappearing onto the busy street.

I sat alone at the table feeling dejected. 'This is ridiculous. You've only just met the man.' I stared longingly into my bottle.

'Is Lake Toba really as beautiful as they say?'

I looked up. There was no mistaking that voice. 'What are you doing back here?' I felt butterflies doing swan dives in my stomach.

'I couldn't stand the thought of you having all that fun by yourself. I can ring Yudi and stall. Want a travelling companion?'

'We catch the bus from here,' Matt said, setting the bags down on the roadside. 'It could be a long wait so let's have a rest.'

We sat down on a grassy verge under the shade of a stringy tree. The bark was thick and knurled, its only defence against the cars and trucks that roared past in a continuous convoy. The ground was littered with scattered paper and plastic bottles. 'Nice spot.'

'Relax, it's all a question of state of mind.' Matt started to rub my back. 'Hey, you feel real tense, what's got you so wound up.'

'It's a long story.' My stiff muscles yielded to his touch, his fingers were the feel of cool ivory, broad and solid yet incredibly light. He wore no rings. His hands embodied the spirit of a man unencumbered by life. 'Matt, you enjoy your freedom, don't you?'

'I love flying, the feeling of absolute freedom and space. No boundaries, only those set by my fears. I try to conquer them and go beyond. I've tried jumping out of planes, deep sea diving, martial arts. Aren't you overcome by the urge to discover who you are?'

'Of course, otherwise I'd be home leading an ordinary life.'

'That's the point, you're not ordinary. Nobody is, only you and I have the guts to find out what makes us special and do something about it. There are no guarantees in life, just plenty of opportunities.'

In a crunching rumble of gears the bus arrived. Matt helped me up the creaky steps and along the aisle, through a tangle of people and livestock. We squashed into the back row next to an elderly lady clutching a squawking basket. There was a wild flurry of feathers.

Staring in disbelief at the blueness of Matt's eyes, the old dear reached out to touch his flaxen hair. He winked at her, sending her into a spasm of mirth. She spent the rest of the trip chatting away happily, never once pausing for a breath. It made not the slightest bit of difference to her that we couldn't understand a word of it.

After many futile gestures, she took Matt's hand and placed it on mine. Looking at him expectantly, she waited for a response. 'She thinks we make a good couple,' he said, planting a loud kiss on my cheek for her benefit. She was beside herself with joy. So was I.

'Lake Toba!' a loud voice called from the front.

'This is us,' Matt said, pushing through the throng to get off. 'Bye, darling,' he called, blowing our friend a kiss from the roadside. Her face lit up the sky as the bus sped off into the distance.

We turned to a magnificent sight. Lake Toba spread out in all its glory. The largest lake in South-east Asia, it is a huge volcanic depression filled with water. Inhaling the cool mountain air we gazed over a vista peppered with pine trees, sandy bays and steep ridges.

A small boat carried us across the lake's glassy surface towards Samosir Island. Traditional *Batak* cottages lay sprinkled over the verdant hillsides. Intricately carved in dark wood, patterned in bold red and ochre, they stood out against the leafy trees and blossoms.

'Looks like there's plenty of places to stay,' Matt shouted above the noise of the engine. 'That one look's pretty good.' The hotel jutted out onto a rocky point and the boat driver dropped us off at the jetty.

Nestled into the hillside, our cabin overlooked the lake. Sipping drinks on the terrace we watched the calm waters change colour from soft pink to dusky orange, reflecting the hushed tones of sunset. Flashes of gold mirrored the lake's surface with the last dying embers of light as the sun slid effortlessly off the edge of the earth, vanquished by the darkness of night. The first star appeared in the sky, twinkling silver in a tapestry of blue.

'Make a wish,' Matt said, 'something special.'

'I have,' I replied, 'but it's a secret.' Secret or not, I sensed he knew. He knew exactly what I wanted.

That evening we walked to a small village nearby, enjoying a simple meal accompanied by the gentle strumming of a guitar. The local Batak people, naturally gifted, sang along to the music while Matt joined in happily, making up his own words as he went along.

Matt had no inhibitions, he held nothing back. Life was his for the taking, one big, marvellous challenge. His energy radiated like the full blaze of the sun, attracting anyone within reach. I drew closer.

Satiated with music and hoarse from singing, we strolled down the leafy path under a sky swollen with clusters of stars. Matt gently took my hand. No words were spoken, none were needed.

When we got back to the bungalow, Matt sat outside smoking while I crawled into bed. It had been a long day. As I lay dreaming, I sensed Matt's shadow glide into the room. Then the subtle indentation on the bed as he sat down. Stroking my arm, he leant dangerously close. It was impossible to escape the magnetic lure. Maybe sleeping with Matt could redress the balance, make up for the pain that Remy had caused. I longed to have him, but something inside made me stop.

'Matt,' I said, fraught with mixed emotions, 'I want you so much but

I'm scared it's for the wrong reasons. You deserve better.'

'I couldn't get any better.' He took my hand tenderly and kissed it, 'if you change your mind, you know where to find me.'

The next morning Matt's bed was empty. Serenaded by a small bird hidden in the bushes, I sat on the terrace thinking. Why had Matt appeared now, precisely at the point in my life where I'd made a silent vow never to get involved again? He seemed so sincere and kind, but I knew I could not trust my instincts again.

What of Remy? Had our tie been severed now that I was attracted to another? Was I free, absolved of a connection that caused me untold damage, or was this a feeble attempt to mask my true feelings? Could a love so deep be erased so quickly? I feared not.

'Breakfast, miss,' the room-boy said, placing the tray down onto the table. Trying his utmost to look efficient in his frayed shirt, he started shovelling teaspoons of sugar into the cup. 'Tea or coffee?'

'Did someone mention coffee,' a voice called out from down the path. Matt jogged up towards me, his strong muscles glistening with a potent mixture of morning dew and sweat.

'How come you're so active this early?'

'Got to keep my strength up,' he smirked, 'never know when I might need it!' Having whipped up a fierce appetite, Matt demolished several helpings of toast and eggs, washed down by lots of coffee, then shot off to find a motorbike. There was no holding him back.

'It may be decrepit but it'll do the trick.' The bike was ready to expire from erosion, well past its use-by date. Matt couldn't have cared less. 'Time for some adventure,' he said, ramming his foot down hard on the pedal.

Pottering around the island, we covered a fair bit of ground. Exploring ancient gravesites and *adat* houses lined with buffalo horns, we drifted through aromatic plantations of cinnamon, coffee and cloves. In the end, the old bike, burdened by its load, coughed to a halt and deposited us in a picturesque field sprinkled with flowers.

'Lunch time,' Matt said, spreading out a checked cloth over the thick grass. For him, every disaster was an opportunity. 'I got the hotel to pack us a picnic.' We dined in grand style - grilled chicken in banana leaf, spicy vegetables, boiled rice, followed by freshly cut papaya. All washed down by a thermos of sweetened tea.

'I'm stuffed.' Matt fell backwards onto the grass. I lay down beside him staring at the clouds. 'What can you see up there?'

White drifts swirled past. I tried to fixate on one with meaning. Then I saw it. 'Pegasus - the winged horse,' I replied, pointing to a bright equine shape lined with silver. 'I want to be like it - free to go wherever I want, in any direction the wind blows.'

'That's what it's like to fly. Alone in the endless blue with no beginning, no end. I wish I could take you up there with me, so you could feel what I feel.' Matt gazed into my eyes, then pulled me closer. My spirit soared into the sky; Matt had taken me with him.

It was evening by the time we reeled back to the hotel. I was weary but happier than I'd been for ages. The excitement was contagious. The staff were in the throes of preparing for a celebration. A brewery had booked the restaurant for their annual party and we were invited.

'Feel like having some fun?' Matt said, pouncing on the bed.

'Stop,' I pleaded as he tickled me, 'stop making me laugh.'

'Why, you look beautiful when you're happy.' Quickly dressing, he blew me a kiss as he walked out the door. 'I'll be down at the bar waiting. Don't be too long or I'll send out a search party!'

I sifted through my bag looking for something to wear. I was sick of all my clothes. Like me, they had acquired a jaded feel after weeks of travelling. Depression had engulfed me in a dark cloud, but Matt's energy had lifted me beyond it. He made me feel alive.

Soaking in the bath, I scrubbed away the layer of gloom that had tarnished my body for so long. Choosing a teal blue silk outfit, I slipped on a gold chain then carefully applied my make-up. I stepped back and stared into the mirror; the fire in my eyes had returned.

The restaurant was packed with guests, the buzz of laughter flooding the hall. I brushed through the crowd, searching for Matt. He was standing in the corner in the midst of an animated conversation with some local men. He turned slowly as I approached.

'You look stunning,' he gaped. Aware of the appreciative stares of the other men, he pulled me toward him.

A wave of music flooded the room as the band began to play. The beer taps gushed while waiters rushed around, swaying under the weight of giant food platters. Everyone swooped down on the feast. After eating their fill they started to dance, swept up in the mood.

'Time for some action,' Matt said, whipping me into the crowd. His enthusiasm gained momentum with every song, his energy escalating to a new high. We danced until my head was spinning.

'Can we get some fresh air,' I pleaded.

Swamped in the scent of white lilies, we sat on the pontoon listening to the waves lap against the rocks. The crescent moon shone overhead, lending an intimate glow to the night. Nothing disturbed the stillness, only the lonely chirp of a cricket in the bushes, calling to its mate.

With the gentlest touch, Matt turned me to him and looked into my eyes. Responding to their call he kissed me. Softly at first, then more urgent, spilling over with desire. Realising where we were, he drew back, 'This may not be the best place. Let's go back to the room.'

Flinging aside the sheets, Matt collapsed onto the bed dragging me to him. His touch was electrifying, my body yielded in total surrender. Struggling to keep pace with the urgency of our craving, his lips suffocated mine with passion. I yearned to feel his body inside me, to capture his spirit. There was a deep hunger in my soul.

We were poised on the precipice of union when *it happened,* shocking us to the core of our beings. A presence, diabolically sinister, entered the room, trapping us in its insidious embrace. An eerie wind swirled all around forming a morbid spiral of negativity.

The temperature dropped to a bitter cold. The air became dense and clammy, reeking with the staleness of crushed tobacco. The curtains rustled, the heavy fabric fluttering visibly, yet the windows were shut tight. The ashtray on the bedside table began to shake. Louder still, until the sheets rippled with the deadly touch.

A shiver ran down my spine. Petrified, I lay frozen in fear. Every hair on my head rose in abhorrence of the vile presence. My body was paralysed, crushed by the weight of its force. Creating an icy wedge, it forcibly separated Matt from me. Nothing was visible, yet the pressure was so intense that I was scared it would mangle me.

'What the hell's going on?' Matt demanded, beads of sweat dotting his forehead. He tried to get up but was pinned to the bed, his body unable to obey his mind. Stimulated by the throbbing adrenalin, he jerked free. 'Let's get out of here!' he shouted, grabbing hold of me.

His eyes, glazed with terror, betrayed the depth of his fears. Taking sanctuary in the garden, soothed by the moonlight, we struggled to make sense of it. Defying reason, it was impossible.

'What was that all about?' Matt lit up a cigarette. 'I've never felt anything like it before. It scared the hell out of me.'

'Maybe the hotel has a resident ghost.' The other alternatives were too ghastly to contemplate, the implications terrifying. Surely Remy's power wasn't strong enough to reach me here? Had he cast some sort of fiendish spell to keep me his forever? Worse still, was I carrying the ghost of my memories and had they finally come back to haunt me? I shuddered; this was my worst nightmare.

'I don't get it,' Matt sighed, wrapping the blanket around me. 'If I knew what I was dealing with ... maybe I could fight it, but I haven't got a clue. All I know is that we're not going back in there tonight.'

Propped up in the settee on the verandah, Matt held me close to him as he fell into an uneasy, fitful sleep. I stayed awake, racked by a barrage of questions that tore my mind apart.

At daybreak, the staff began to arrive for work so I hauled Matt back into the room to escape their questioning looks. There was no way that I wanted to be drawn into an explanation of what had happened.

'Matt, please don't argue,' I said, hushing his protests as we lay on the bed. 'I think it's time you went to visit your friend.'

He stayed gallant to the end. 'It's not safe, there's no way I'm leaving you here by yourself. Who knows what's going on.'

'Your staying here will only make things worse. I left behind a lot of unresolved issues in Bali ... I need time to sort them out.'

Despite his protestations, I convinced Matt to leave. After breakfast I walked him to the jetty. He jotted his address down and stuffed it in my palm. 'If you're ever in Guam, look me up.' Trapping me up in a giant hug, he kissed me good-bye then reluctantly boarded the boat.

As it pulled out, he smiled in his own special way and blew me one last kiss. Brushing a tear from my eye, I felt myself weaken.

'Hey, if you start crying,' he yelled, his voice vanishing into the wind, '*I'll* come back to haunt you.' He waved until he faded from sight. I fought back a flood of emotion, wondering what I had done.

When I returned to the room I still sensed a definite presence. Was it the eerie apparition of the night before, or was it Matt? His energy permeated the room, leaving a clear imprint. Whatever the case, I could not stay here alone. Escape was my only option.

Crossing the lake one last time, I looked into the balmy water and saw a reflection of Matt's eyes. Our time together was etched in the waters, our souls captured deep within. Destiny was not ours to share, only a precious sliver of time which I'd treasure always.

The road to Bukittinggi was a nightmare. Wary of the treacherous route, the bus twisted uneasily through a maze of winding paths and hairpin bends. Few of the passengers survived the journey without yielding to a wave of nausea. I escaped unscathed, engrossed in the beauty around me. Rugged gorges, laced with mountain streams, cut into a maze of deep volcanic valleys and rich grassland.

Staring into the craggy canyons, fragmented memories flashed past. Faces, people, places, all competing for my attention. I pushed them aside. Concentrating on the scenery, I forced my mind to stay blank.

The trip was long and gruelling. After twelve hours of constant climbing, we reached Bukittinggi. The town was quaint and cosy; horse carts, festooned with bright red pompoms and jingling bells, trotted through the flower-lined streets, bearing groups of ladies veiled in chiffon. This was the home of the Minangkabau people, a proud, matriarchal society.

I found a pleasant hotel bordered by sharp peaks and sunshine and spent the next few days recuperating from the long trip. When my body had sufficiently recovered, I set off on a walking tour.

Scaling the southern outskirts of the town, I reached a promontory overlooking the deep Sianok Canyon. From my vantage point I had a perfect view of the rocky chasm carved deep within the mountain. I climbed down into a labyrinth of underground caverns. Built by the Japanese, they had served as a wartime prison. Those bleak years had left their morbid stamp on the dungeon walls. Sad voices, racked with melancholy and pain, infiltrated the dank air. Claustrophobic, I had to escape from the stale corridors. Out in the refuge of daylight, shrill cries beckoned me up the hill to the zoo.

Aghast, I wandered through the compound. Animals trapped in small horrific cages shrieked in anguish. Their howls were the same as those I'd heard in the buried prison, their cages replicas of the cells from which I'd just escaped. Most seemed to have lost their will to survive, mere shadows of a species whose spirit was now broken.

A spindly black gibbon was banging his head against the concrete wall of his cage, having abandoned all hope of reason. Another in the next enclosure was reaching out to comfort him through a small crack in the floor, screeching in desperation.

A third, autumn red in colour, was sitting quietly in his cage refusing to take part in his neighbours' hysterics. I walked up to his cage and started talking to him. Intrigued, his bright amber eyes lit up as he loped over. Clinging firmly to the wire mesh he started chatting away happily. Halfway through the conversation he poked his arm out, his tiny palm beckoning to me. Thinking he wanted some food, I gave him some peanuts which he threw onto the ground. 'I know what you want,' his eyes widened as I spoke. 'You're in there all by yourself, give me your hand.'

I took his tiny palm in mine. Surprisingly, he offered no resistance. Very gently I started to massage it, working up his arm to whimpers of approval. Satisfied, he withdrew the arm and offered the other. I rubbed that one too, trying to soothe away his loneliness. Next came the legs, followed by his little rounded stomach which he pressed up against the wire. I tickled what I could, as he giggled happily.

Meanwhile a small crowd had gathered, watching our performance in amazement. Unperturbed, the little gibbon stretched out his arm and curled it delicately around my neck, pulling my head close to his. Unwilling to break the bond, I stood still while the small, captivating creature cuddled me. Content at last, he alternated between talking, crooning and singing to me.

It lasted for hours. I stayed until the zoo was set to close. Sadly, I pulled away to leave. As I did, the monkey jerked away from the bars and hurtled down the cage, screeching loudly. With one arm protruding from the cage, his tapered fingers curled upwards, beckoning me back, the other hand tapping its chest where its heart lay. Its sobs were wretched.

I went back and held it until its cries subsided. 'I'm sorry, I have to go, but I promise we will never be apart. You will always be in my heart.' With that he released his hold and I was able to walk away.

The journey to Padang was uneventful. Scenes of tropical vegetation, ancient longhouses, fascinating people and bizarre bullfights flashed by as the bus descended through the highlands. All deserved more attention than I was capable of giving, my body weary beyond recall.

Late at night, on the last leg of the journey, we pulled into a roadside cafe. In the tradition of the area, a variety of pre-cooked dishes were laid out on the table. Everyone attacked the plate of their choice but I passed up the fried fish heads and a dish that looked like boiled intestines, settling instead on some plain chicken curry and rice.

As we ate, two policemen sauntered in and began to inspect the bus passengers. As I was the only tourist on board, and a woman to boot, they stopped and looked at me. The younger of the two, thin and pasty, eyed me up and down. 'Are you travelling alone?'

'Yes,' I replied, wondering why he cared.

He shrugged his shoulders while the older one finished checking the papers. He turned to face me, 'You're a brave lady, very brave.'

'Thank you,' I smiled as they walked away.

I had no idea what they meant. The people I'd met so far on my trip had been wonderful, the places spectacular. The dread I faced was on a much tougher plane, infinitely more challenging and fraught with risk. If I had the courage to face these tests and go beyond, then I could live a full life. Nothing could stand in my way.

CHAPTER TWELVE
The Jewel of Kalimantan

Borneo is the third largest island in the world. Kalimantan, the Indonesian territory, occupies the south; the tiny, oil-rich kingdom of Brunei and the Malaysian states of Sabah and Sarawak lie to the north.

This exotic island had always conjured up wondrous images in my mind, pictures stored in the imagination of a young schoolgirl as she dreamt of a time and place far away. Impenetrable jungles, fabulous wildlife, hidden rituals - all fascinating and impossibly out of reach. Now, fate had intervened and I was on my way.

The plane began its descent into the coastal city of Balikpapan, over a deep blue harbour dotted with tankers and the flare of distant oil rigs. Like a gruesome slick, the scourge of petroleum dominated the scene, extracting a heavy price from the scarred landscape.

Unlike my fellow passengers, businessmen who'd travelled this route many times before, I had arrived totally unprepared. It was time to devise a strategy, so I turned to the man sitting next to me. Engrossed in business reports, he was writing furiously on a notepad.

'Excuse me, I was wondering if you could recommend a hotel in town. I haven't been in this area before so I feel a bit lost.'

He lay down his glasses on the table. 'Hi, I'm Dan Rivers,' he said, extending his hand. Like him, it was sweaty and effusive. 'I'm from the States but I come out here real often to check on the oil rigs, work for the Star petroleum line. I'd be glad to help you out.'

Starting our descent, the plane dropped in altitude and circled for landing. Banging onto the runway, it swerved to a halt. Dan gathered up some stray papers then snapped his briefcase shut. 'Come with me,' he said, grabbing his things. 'I've got a driver waiting.'

Outside the crowded terminal 'Big Red' was leaning against the wall. A towering Texan, his face was weathered in a tough, pitted sort of way. He slapped Dan on the back before giving me a bone-jerking hug. 'A pleasure, ma'am,' he drawled in a broad southern accent, tipping his hat. 'We don't get many ladies round these parts.'

Throwing the luggage into the rear of his red pick-up, Red opened the door gallantly, brushing aside some crumpled cigarette packs and stray cans, then helped me inside. Dan crushed in beside me. As soon as he'd slammed the door shut, Red shot off like a wild man, his tan polished boot pressed firmly on the pedal. Turning up his tape of Willy Nelson, he tapped the dashboard with his broad, knotted fingers and crooned the tune *'On the Road Again.'*

Whipping up a thirst after the first few bars, Red grabbed a can of beer from under the seat, peeled off the ring with his teeth and brushing aside his long titian beard, sculled it down in one huge gulp. 'Now that surely quenches a man's thirst,' he said, licking off the foam, 'I've had a hankering for that all day. Have one, Dan,' he said handing him a cold can. 'What about you little lady?'

'No thanks.' Red deflected the harsh sunlight with his hat and kept on driving. He was as rough and raw as the place he'd chosen to live. The view outside was dismal, the ravaged, pot-holed streets covered in a fine layer of grit belched out from the nearby oil refinery. The relative luxury of the housing estates for the imported oil workers stood out in stark contrast.

'Hey, it's Friday,' Red yelled. 'The club will be really jumping. Free food tonight, all you can eat. Feel like mixing with the locals?'

'I could sure use some air-conditioning,' Dan said, unbuttoning his shirt collar. 'It must be a hundred in the shade.'

'I'm in no hurry,' I said, happy for the distraction. The last thing I needed was to be alone in a hotel room with only my thoughts for company. My brain was desperate for new fodder and a little light relief. I was fed up with thrashing out the same old scenario over and over in my head.

The club was packed with American expats relaxing after a hard week's work. A jukebox blared out old Elvis hits, competing with peals of raucous laughter and loud conversation. I ate prawns till I was bursting, while Dan entertained me with tales of his travels. Red was engrossed in a friendly game of darts with some friends. Everyone seemed intent on forgetting their worries for a while.

After a few too many drinks, Red challenged me to a couple of rounds of pool. Even with a bent cue, I proved a formidable opponent and beat Red hands down. Dan congratulated me on my success, but Red was more reticent, slinking into a vacant corner. Having never experienced such an ignominious defeat, he was taking it badly.

It was dark by the time we arrived in town, saving the need for any real scrutiny. Unlike Dan I didn't have a company account to rely on, his hotel was well outside my budget. 'No worries, there's a reasonable place just down the block,' Red said, 'I'll drop you there.'

'How about dinner tomorrow night?' Dan asked in a cordial manner. 'I know a great seafood restaurant, please be my guest.'

My room at the Imperial was basic yet comfortable. Settling in quickly, I fell into an exhausted sleep, not waking till the following afternoon. I ventured into town only briefly until the fumes and traffic proved too much, and I returned to the relative quiet of my room to spend the rest of the afternoon relaxing and writing up my diary.

I scarcely knew where to begin. How to capture Matt's spirit on paper? Words could not suffice. Much to my frustration as soon as I'd write the first line, my thoughts dissolved into an emotional blur, the blueness of Matt's eyes replaced by Remy's dark gaze.

No matter how hard I tried to eliminate Remy from my thoughts, he would invariably infiltrate back into my consciousness. Never a day would go by when I didn't think of him. Time was not a great healer. Every moment apart heightened the longing.

Fortunately the phone rang, interrupting my train of thought. 'Hi, lovely lady, it's Red. Are you ready to try the best damn eating place in these parts? I guarantee you the best chilli crab you've ever tasted!' I shut my diary. I could put off remembering for another day.

The restaurant was rowdy, crammed with regulars spurred on by enormous appetites and unlimited bank accounts. Oil was still lucrative business. Dan ordered everything on the menu and soon our table was teetering under the burden of dishes piled upon it. Platters of huge prawns, crayfish and other seafood, all personally selected by Red fresh from the tank. The smell was mouth-watering.

I enjoyed the evening thoroughly, the meal was delicious and the men the best of company. Able to switch off from the residue of their stressful day, they were happy and talkative. 'Shame we have to leave tomorrow to start work on the rigs. I was tempted to invite you along but I thought better of it. Hard to climb aboard if the current's rough, besides the insurance won't cover you in case of an accident.'

'What Dan's really trying to say,' Red added with a glint in his eye, 'is that there'll be a mutiny for sure at the first sight of you.'

'What do you mean?'

'Once them strong winds whip up your skirts,' Red blushed, 'and the guys catch sight of your legs, we'll never be able to control them.' Both men laughed. The joke was on them. I hadn't brought any skirts. Not wanting to spoil their fantasy, I smiled inwardly.

With the spirit of bravado born of one's dreams, I set off the following day to penetrate the source of my longings and explore the real Borneo. The trip north cut through a maze of towering trees anchored by huge tangled roots, sumptuous tropical flowers and wild butterflies. The bus wound along the gravel track, cutting further into the thick vegetation.

Cloying humidity drenched my skin. A warning cry echoed through the trees, a rainbow bird swooping past in flight. Bands of monkeys gathered on the road waiting for some tasty morsel to be flung from the bus. Other animals skulked in the bushes, the air quivering with their breath. Stuck to the vinyl seat, I wilted as the heat became unbearable, the buzz of insects intensely overpowering.

Grinding on for hours through the forest, the trees twined into a dense canopy embracing us in its cool, dank hold. No light could penetrate the threaded leaves, rich clusters of fungi thriving in the darkness ... until a strange light loomed in the distance, bursting through with untold brilliance.

My eyes recoiled from the starkness, startled by the abrupt change. All around, the land lay parched and barren, dying in the relentless heat. Vast tracts of primeval rainforest had been devastated, every tree felled. Huge stumps lay wasted on the ground, sad remnants of once magnificent trees. I could hear their ghosts cry out in pain and I wanted to weep.

If only I could release them from their misery, reverse the destruction, but it was too late. Their mighty energy was lost forever; this brutal bare earth was destined to be the burial place of the tree spirits. The desolation continued for miles and I closed my eyes rather than bear witness to it.

I once heard a story about the ancient Chewong tribe of Malaysia. They believed that the trees of their forest had the extraordinary gift of speech. Their *Ruwai,* or soul, possessed profound feelings. Therefore, it was inconceivable that a tree could ever be chopped down. They understood that a tree had a divine spark, a spiritual essence that allowed them to feel. And so in pain they would cry out, in sorrow mourn, and in gratitude give back their essential energy to the earth and all who walked upon it.

When I dared look out again, I saw the fragile shoots of new growth, and with them a faint hope that one day the mutilation would end and that the land would be restored to its natural bountiful state. *One day.*

The bus ground to a halt in Samarinda, a seedy port town located on the Mahakam river. Overlooking the banks of the river, I stretched my tired, aching limbs. The stench of rotting vegetation and diesel filled the air. Giant logs floated past me, a vivid reminder of the unpleasant scene I had just witnessed.

This was the starting point for trips upriver. An array of rickety vessels, all looking completely unseaworthy, were lined up, waiting to make the difficult voyage. The river was the doorway to the many tribes of the Dayak, the infamous head-hunters of the past. I wanted to sail up the river, through the rich forests lush with mangrove and wild orchids. To see the profusion of wildlife, and experience the abundant sensations and secrets of the rainforest.

Staring at the flimsy boats and the crush of people and produce piling aboard, I had second thoughts. The trip was guaranteed to be long and gruelling. The decks were congested and dirty, the prospects daunting. My guidebook told of 'impenetrable undergrowth, choking humidity and days trapped in steaming jungle by endless rain.'

My love of adventure was being replaced by a strong sense of survival. This was one decision I would have to consider carefully. Protected I may be, foolish I wasn't. As I stared into the muddy waters, thinking out my options, a seedy character in torn jeans and faded jacket sidled up and propositioned me. His breath reeked of stale chilli and foul intentions. I grabbed my things and fled.

On a whim, I flew south to Banjarmasin, a floating city built on marshland, a maze of interconnected canals and waterways. To best explore it I hired a *klotok,* a motorised canoe, and skirted a stack of clustered houses, most perching precariously over the murky water on stilts, others floating on bundles of bound twigs and bobbing up and down with the vibration of every passing launch.

Families squatted on wooden platforms jutting out over the water's edge, engaged in their daily activities while children frolicked in the dirty depths. Totally oblivious to the debris floating around them and captivated by the unusual sight of a pale, lone stranger cruising by, they waved happily as my boat passed.

Large vessels laden with all kind of goods sounded a warning as they sailed past in a series of blunt images. In the afternoon sun, the muted umber tones infused the scene with the colours of antiquity. I felt that I'd stepped into a painting, a modern voyeur in an ancient world.

Later that night I wandered through the markets set in the small back lanes. Aromatic scents of pungent food and spices permeated the dense alleys, pierced by the cries of exotic caged birds and rare splendid animals. The display was fascinating.

Above all, the island's stones held me spellbound. The rich dark earth hid a natural treasure trove, superb gemstones buried deep within the island's forested depths. Mines abounded, loaded with gold, diamonds and other precious gems. Beneath a dusty bench top in a dilapidated store, amid trays laden with stunning specimens, a special stone beckoned. Clear blue, it gleamed with an inner light. The stone had chosen, it was meant to be mine. Without a thought, I bought it.

Returning to my hotel room I flopped onto the bed, exhausted. Tainted by the stale odour of passing strangers, I longed for the familiar, something to identify with. Switching on the radio to drown out my thoughts only made matters worse. Music was brutal. Every word was designed to pierce the heart. Songs of love; unrequited, broken, distant. Missing - what was had, what was lost, what may never be. The heart frozen and lonely, longing for reprieve.

The phone rang. Someone knew me, I wasn't alone. It was a man's voice - the wrong number. His voice sounded like Remy's and it set off a chain reaction. My chest throbbed with a dull ache as my head started to pound. Reality hit - I wanted to be back in Bali.

There in the loud, hollow silence of night I fumbled for the phone, overcome by the sudden fear that Remy had stopped loving me. Slowly I dialled the number. Through the echo on the line and the blaring music of the club, I recognised his voice.

'Lia, is that you?' he asked through the crackling line. My heart choked. 'Where are you? In Kalimantan? What are you doing there?'

'I don't know,' I answered honestly.

'Come back,' he pleaded. 'I miss you so much.' Instant relief, the bond between was us still intact. 'It will all work out, I promise.'

'How can you be so sure? Life isn't that simple.'

'All I know is that I love you. That's all that matters in the end.'

The line went dead. Our connection had been cut. Now what to do? Give in and run to him, or stay strong and alone. To explore this magnificent country with such a weight in my heart was to do it and myself, a cruel injustice. Then I remembered the stone.

Unwrapping the package, I removed the gem and clutched it tightly to my chest. The brilliant glint lodged deep within the stone's heart rekindled the glow in my own. A dazzling spark of light penetrated my soul, flooding it with clarity. It all became crystal clear. I was on an inner journey; I had just momentarily lost my way.

CHAPTER THIRTEEN
Rock Graves of Sulawesi

'Sorry, but the plane to Denpasar is delayed. Engine trouble.'

'When will it leave?' I looked anxiously at the departure board.

'Maybe in one or two hours,' the airline clerk said, checking his computer. 'Do you wish to purchase a ticket?'

I thought back to last night's conversation with Remy. *'Isn't love all that matters in the end?'* I knew that until I was convinced of that fundamental truth, it was pointless returning to Bali.

'Where does your next flight go?'

'Ujung Pandang,' the clerk replied, 'in twenty minutes.'

'Perfect.' It sounded far enough away. 'Where is it?'

'In South Sulawesi.'

'I've never been there before,' I said, allowing myself to be swept up in the hands of fate. 'I'll take a one-way ticket.'

'Tanatoraja, the land of the Toraja people of central Sulawesi. Ancient head-hunters, known for their rare culture and unique burial rites.' The entire flight was spent engrossed in the travel brochures planning out an itinerary. On arrival, I raced up to the transfer desk.

A disgruntled attendant, sweating into his shirt, flipped through the clipboard. 'Sorry, today's flight to Torajaland is full. Try again tomorrow.' Despite my pleas to look harder, he could not be swayed.

I had wandered off to collect my luggage when the attendant ran over to me clutching his walkie-talkie. 'Miss,' he yelled above the crackle. 'I've found you a seat but you have to hurry.'

Lugging my bag, I ran through the crowded terminal and out of the glass doors. The parked bus screeched into action, making it to the plane minutes before take-off. Deftly dodging the rotating propellers, I jumped onboard. The tiny plane lurched to one side with the impact. Everyone turned around to look. I skulked down the aisle and merged into the only vacant seat, quickly fastening the frayed seatbelt.

The engines coughed several times before the plane ploughed down the runway. With one mighty surge we were airborne. Shaking noisily, the plane fought to meld into the air currents. Curtained in white, it flew through a layer of thick cloud into a fine blue sky.

My seat was closest to the wing so I stuffed bits of tissue into my ears to prevent permanent damage. The plastic panelling overhead was rattling and looked in imminent danger of collapsing on top of me. Trying to steady the vibration, I grabbed the seat in front and flipped it backwards, sending a fragile Japanese tourist flying. She apologised to me profusely as she returned to the upright position.

In the fray, I dropped my bag and whilst grovelling under the seat found lunch packed in a cardboard box between some stray shoes. The fried bean curd was an acquired taste so I sipped on the syrupy tangerine juice and admired the view. Through the dappled plastic window emerged the faint outline of distant hills and rich green plains.

The scenery became lusher as we flew further north. Veiled in emerald green, steep cliffs cut sharply into the earth's crust before tumbling into deep, luxuriant valleys. Wisps of milky cloud hung low above the ground, trapped in the branches of the trees. Fused in dense canopies, the forest shielded its ancient secrets.

My reverie was brought to a halt when the plane suddenly dropped altitude. Little Yoki in front began to giggle hysterically, grabbing the armrests until her fingers turned a deathly shade of white. The robust Scot opposite did his best to retain his composure but with the next violent jolt, his veneer cracked and he burst into a string of Gaelic obscenities.

Meanwhile, in the cockpit, the pilots were in the throes of panic. Deciding it was time for action, the co-pilot dropped his newspaper and wrestled with the throttle, nearly prising it from the floor. We came in for an abrupt landing, the plane zigzagging across the runway before grinding to a halt in the middle of a paddock.

The hirsute Swiss lady behind me broke into spontaneous applause. Each passenger mumbled their own personal sign of undying gratitude to the Almighty. A stepladder was thrown onto the ground just in time for the rush to the door. In his haste to depart, Yves, a bearded Frenchman with a multitude of wrapped artefacts hurtled down the aisle, nearly mutilating me with an antique wooden spear. All his efforts were in vain. We all ended up stuck together in the same van for the rocky drive to Rantepao.

Being the last off, I was squeezed in the front between the driver and tour guide, Palo. Despite the discomfort, I marvelled at the beauty of the natural landscape flashing by. Ghostly ravines and haunting jade mountains cut into the sky like jagged glass. By rights, I should have been back in Bali. Instead, I was travelling with a busload of strangers in one of the most remote and dramatically splendid areas of the world.

'You're very lucky to have arrived today,' Palo said. 'A very important ceremony is being held in an outlying village, the funeral of one of the most prominent men in the community. If you would like to attend, just take a small gift as a mark of respect. A carton of cigarettes will be fine.'

'Can you handle a long walk?' Palo asked, as the driver parked the van. I had hired it for a few days of sightseeing, local transport being erratic at best. 'The funeral site's a few kilometres from here,' Palo said, pointing up the hill, 'and the path is fairly rough. Follow me.'

Crossing through sharp undergrowth, we traced a makeshift path round the yellowed rice paddies. It was the dry season; there had been no rain for months. The earth was scorched and brittle, parched by the intense sun. Drifting clouds offered some respite, but the heat became so unbearable that I was forced to stop under the occasional spiky tree to recuperate.

'How much further?' I took a sip from my water bottle.

'Not far now, over the next rise.'

Crossing the ridge, we came to a clearing in the grass. In the centre stood an impressive array of traditional buildings, constructed from bamboo. The sweeping curved roofs were draped with lengths of bright red fabric. Long extended verandahs on rickety stilts were crammed with people attending the ceremony.

'Each building houses family members and their guests,' Palo explained as we walked across the field. 'Hundreds of people will arrive here on foot from outlying areas and will stay until the funeral is over, then everything will be burnt down.'

'That's a lot of wasted effort.' The decorations were elaborate and costly. 'Why are the railings painted with white crosses?'

'The man who died is Catholic. Many people converted earlier this century to Christianity but still retain the animistic roots of the old religion, the *Aluk Todolo*. They honour a combination of both.'

As we talked, a young woman with a rounded face and warm smile beckoned to me from a verandah. She was dressed in soft apricot, a wide collar of multi-coloured glass beads adorning her chest. A matching headband was wound around her dark hair which was swept back in a bun.

'You're being invited to join them. Here, take the cigarettes and offer them to the senior member of the household.'

Removing my shoes, I climbed up the wobbly ladder and crept across the slatted rattan floor. It creaked loudly, threatening to collapse under the combined weight of all the guests. I handed the cigarettes to a wrinkled old man puffing a pipe in the corner.

Palo called me to join him on the floor. The younger women were serving hot tea and sticky rice cakes while their elders, swathed in heavy black turbans, gossiped happily. Their lips were red and swollen from the rich juices of the betel nut they chewed incessantly.

'Betel is the seed of the areca nut, it tastes quite bitter. Here it's mixed with a little lime and wrapped in pepper leaves, then put under the lower lip, usually with a wad of tobacco. It's been part of our culture for years, shared around in social dealings like a peace pipe.'

Distracted by shouting, we went outside to investigate. A procession, led by a wily old man wielding a large baton, approached from the distance. A long line of people, dressed in dark colours of mourning, entered the circle bearing gifts. Obese black pigs, secured to bamboo poles and carried by groups of four men, squealed in protest as they were led to their fate. Docile, pampered buffalos followed placidly behind their masters nibbling on clumps of grass, more accepting of what lay ahead.

'A sacrifice must be made for the journey to the after-life,' Palo said. 'Years ago it was the custom that freshly severed human heads were needed for the funeral, but these days buffalo heads will suffice. The number of animals slaughtered indicates the deceased's status. The family has waited a long time until they had enough money to provide an appropriate send-off for their father. This funeral will cost at least ten million rupiah.'

'That's an enormous amount to spend.'

'You don't understand. Here life is a preparation for death. It is more important to be wealthy in *Puya,* the hereafter, than in the present. That is why the animals are sacrificed. It is believed they will follow their masters into heaven and become part of his Celestial Herd in the afterlife.'

We crossed into the *rante,* the village circle, dodging the endless stream of people and livestock. A richly decorated building had been erected to house the remains of the dead man. A steep bamboo ladder led to the upper floor where the elaborate gold painted coffin lay in state.

'This is the death-house. Want to go up and take a look?'

I declined, not wishing to intrude. Guests, studded with fine beaded decoration, climbed up to pay their final respects. Bearing ornate silver platters, they walked past regally in a display of great pomp. Moving out of their path, I stood beside a large solitary stone placed upright in the ground.

'This stone represents the dead man,' Palo said. 'The size is symbolic of his stature. When the ceremony is over, there will be a procession to the death-cliffs so that the corpse can be carried to its last resting place, a grave high in the rock face.'

The old Tominahs say that our ancestors descended from the stars, the Pleiades, on a crescent moon. In death, they are free to find their way back ... back to their eternal homeland.'

Early the next day, we set off along a curving road, heavy with silken mist. Cool dew fogged the windscreen, obscuring the view. Vague outlines of frosty peaks dissolved into the steel grey sky as the sun struggled to emerge. Eventually it pushed through, coating the valley in golden light.

'Today we will visit a number of interesting places,' Palo said, 'starting with Lemo. It is one of the best preserved grave sites.'

Carved into thick granite streaked with orange and black ochre, the huge cliff face stood starkly dramatic in the bright morning light. A myriad of small wooden doorways, gouged into the massive rock, guarded the ancient burial chambers. Tangled roots of overhanging plants cascaded down the cliff providing a further layer of protection for the decaying bodies.

'How on earth did they carve into solid rock?' I asked, mystified. 'Some of those graves are more than a hundred feet high.'

'With extreme perseverance. Workmen would perch on steep bamboo ladders, or swing from ropes using sharp flint hammers. It took three years to carve one small grave used as a family tomb.'

'Why bury people in rock when the ground is so much easier?'

'The earth is considered the giver of life. It cannot be defiled by planting death below it, because it's ability to nourish would be hampered. Inside the rock, the soul is protected from wild animals and preserved. It's also safe from plunder.'

Forged into the hard cliff face were crumbling old balconies lined with lifeless wooden statues. Clad in musty white, they stood like members of a ghostly regiment, a sinister army of the walking dead. Mute stilted sentinels looked down from their lofty towers, watching over the rich green valley below.

'There is a *tau tau*, or statue, for each of the persons buried within the grave. It is believed that there are many layers to the spirit. One will inhabit the tau tau while the soul makes his journey. The Land of the Souls is very far off and it is a long, dangerous trip. The spirit must be protected.'

I looked up through the twisted roots, past poisonous trees of fragrant trumpet lilies, to the sad remnants of souls sombre with the lingering shadow of forgotten lifetimes. Their wide, vacant eyes stared over the valley, far into the unknown, longing for something they'd left behind. Light rain began to fall. Tears spilled as the skies opened up. *'Follow us,'* they cried, *'we shall show you the way to the stars. On the gentle winds of the breeze we shall carry you up high to the clouds until you reach the gates of heaven.'*

'Now where?' I groped unsteadily in the dark. Clambering through the cave's dim corridors, I edged along the cold, glassy rock further into the ancient opening. Stale from the lack of oxygen, the air was compressed, making it difficult to breathe. The cave was permeated with a hollow emptiness, as if time had stood still a long time ago.

Palo was lost somewhere behind in the dimness of the cave. Stumbling over some scattered rocks, I stopped to get my bearings. Slowly adjusting to the deathly half-light, my eyes focused on a gruesome sight. Two ancient skulls with sunken, ghostly eyes were peering down at me from a deep crevice. I backed away in fright.

'Don't be alarmed,' Palo said, looming up behind me. 'This cave is full of old skulls and bones. It's an ancient burial site.'

Up ahead, the passageway opened into a grotto full of wooden coffins. The lids had been removed and the bones scattered on the ground. Once intricately decorated, the coffins had fallen victim to the ravages of time, the rotted hardwood devoid of its original glow.

'The tombs were looted many years ago. It was customary for the dead to be buried with their most valuable possessions for use in the afterlife. A tempting booty, so old *Bugis* raiding parties would come here from the lowlands and pillage these burial sites.'

I sat on the rocky ledge, surrounded by human remains. The bony skulls had been collected and lined up neatly in the limestone cavities of the cave, the final indignity. Robbed of their individuality they had lost their identity, the sense of who they once were.

'Don't worry,' Palo tuned into my thoughts. 'Their souls have departed this plane of existence, only the earthly vessel remains.'

'This is hallowed ground, we're disturbing their resting place.'

'I'm sure they enjoy the company,' Palo smiled reassuringly, 'and are happy to remember what it felt like to be alive.'

A shaft of light filtered through the dusty haze, illuminating the weathered statues. Standing motionless in the grey alcoves, their arms were outstretched in longing, the coarse wood a grim reminder of a soul once vibrant with the gift of life. Theirs was a temporal loss, their bodies might have faded but at last their spirits were free.

'Kamula is a fine example of a traditional village,' Palo said, as we took shelter from the sun under the overhanging roof of a longhouse. Lined up in a row and raised on stilts, the great sweeping roofs looked like the prows of magnificent old sailing ships. 'The Toraja people believe their ancestors came from the sea. Their boats were wrecked in a storm and using the cover, they took shelter under them. Even today the houses all face to the north, the direction from which they are thought to have come.'

'So their houses are designed as replicas of those old ships?'

'That's one theory. The old Tominahs say it is the crescent moon of our ancestors who descended from the stars in them. 'Look,' Palo said, pointing to the old wooden structure. 'The houses have been built without any nails or pegs. They have been slotted together with great accuracy and painted using four colours only - red, to signify the blood of man; yellow, the earth; then black and white to represent the balance of good and evil.'

'Why all the buffalo horns?' A giant array lined the entrances.

'The buffalo is a powerful animal, its horns symbolise strength and fertility. No evil can pass them and so the house is protected. They are also a status symbol, a sign of wealth. That house over there is the chief's, he has the largest collection, as befits his position.'

There was little activity inside the compound, most people escaping the heat and resting inside. Rice had been laid out to dry on rattan sheets. Several young girls sat on the porch of the granary, waving a long pole to distract the chickens from pecking the harvest. Tired from an over-active day, I too was ready for a siesta, but Palo would have none of it. 'There is a special place I must show you.'

*

The car pulled off the road into a shady spot and the driver sauntered off to get some tea. I followed Palo down some stone steps that led to a sheltered grove. Dark and musty, the forest floor was dappled with faint beams of sunlight and the warm smell of fallen leaves. Thick clumps of bamboo grew all around, obscuring entry into the forest.

Palo led me to a majestic tree proudly rooted to the ground. 'See all the small thatched doors on its trunk?' He ran his hand over the rough bark. 'These cover the graves of the babies. Large holes have been hollowed into the tree to place the baby's body inside.'

'Why isn't the baby put into the rock grave along with the rest of the family?' I whispered, in awe of my hallowed surroundings.

'Because it's believed that until the child turns two it is unable to find its way to heaven alone. So young, it needs help.'

'But why a tree?' I stared reverently at the tree's grandeur.

'The tree's a substitute for the mother, the milk nurtures the baby until it's ready to leave. Only trees with white sap can be used.'

I circled the massive tree, enchanted by the numerous gates carved into it to protect the soul's rite of passage. Strong vines had wrapped around the trunk, ensuring no intruder would dare violate the piety of the site.

'See here,' Palo said, pointing to a small slit in the aged bark. 'This grave is very old. The bark has grown over to disguise the hole.'

In nature's infinite wisdom, the tree enveloped the fragile infant replacing its mother's womb. Tapping into a timeless energy source, it gave life to the little souls entrusted to it, sustaining them on their solitary journey to heaven. It had become the primordial mother.

'Would you like to spend tonight in a traditional Torajan longhouse?' Palo climbed back into the car. 'There's a guesthouse at the top of a mountain a few hours away from here. It's pretty cold up there but the view's spectacular, so it's certainly worth the drive.'

The fresh mountain air would make a welcome break from the pall of death that had surrounded me all day. 'Fine, I'd enjoy the change.'

As we left the town limits behind, the sky grew darker and the road bumpier. A sprinkling of stars provided a smattering of light in the heavens. Immersed in the darkness, I imagined strange shadows rustling in the leaves outside. The car's lights illuminated ghostly footprints on the ground. 'Palo, do you believe in magic?'

'Torajans are well known for their mystical powers. In the past only women and transvestites became witchdoctors. If anyone in the village was suspected of sorcery, they were tried by plunging their hand into hot pitch. If it burnt, they were found guilty and beheaded.'

'Not a pleasant end,' I sighed.

'The people here are very superstitious, many strange things happen round these parts. It is believed that if a Torajan warrior dies outside his own rante, a strong shaman can empower him to return home in his death state. During the war there were quite a few sightings of the walking dead. The Japanese occupiers were so frightened they left the villagers well alone.'

'Now I'll expect to see headless zombies with every passing headlight,' I said, settling into the darkness of the night.

After several long hours travelling the pitted road, we reached the guesthouse. Dense fog hung on the mountainside, making it impossible to see more than a few feet ahead. The night air was cold and damp, the chill penetrating through several layers of clothing.

Retreating to the warmth of the fire in the dining room, I downed a hearty vegetable stew to stave off my hunger pangs. Several other guests were writing letters and quietly reading at the tables. The locals sat huddled around a crackling radio.

After eating my fill, I followed Palo outside to a solitary longhouse balanced on the hillside. Boldly decorated in red and black ethnic designs, it's only access was a steep bamboo ladder. A carved buffalo head guarded the entrance. Ducking low through the solid wooden door, I squeezed inside. The huge room was stuffed full of mattresses. I counted fourteen. Recessed into the side was a panel for belongings and several slats that opened to let in air. A number of folded blankets and sheets were stacked on the floor.

'We could certainly have a lot of fun here,' Palo beamed.

'Forget it! See that bed over there, the one in the furthest corner of the room, that's yours. This one's mine,' I said, draping the sheets over a mattress. 'Is there a pillow in here that doesn't feel like a brick?'

Palo threw one over at me, then fell onto his bed wrapping himself in a tidy cocoon. Within minutes he was asleep. I piled as many blankets as I could on top of me but couldn't get warm. Muttering indignantly, I lay prostrate and frozen, my nose becoming less and less a part of my body. The noxious fumes of the mosquito coil invaded the room, bringing on a violent coughing fit. I fumbled in the dark for the water bottle but it fell out of reach down a deep wooden slat. I was ready to commit mental suicide.

None of this activity had the slightest impact on Palo, who was sound asleep. His snoring only added to my frustration. Lying awake in the dark I plotted my escape. Salvation lay just across the ocean.

*

Mount Agung towered seductively ahead in the clouds. Magnificent in grandeur, it inspired reverence. As dwelling place to the gods, it commanded devotion. Jutting into the heavens as the roof of Bali, it invited total awe. Mysticism of such magnitude was clearly daunting.

I knew I was about to tread on very dangerous ground.

CHAPTER FOURTEEN
Return to Paradise

Giant waves pounded the shore. Bands of crimson smeared the sky as dark violet clouds rolled in from the ocean. The steamy scent of Bali, heavy with repressed passion and promise, caressed the breeze. It undulated through the leaves, casting mystical shadows on the sand; familiar, erotic shadows. *'Welcome back,'* the wind whispered, echoing the sentiment of heaven, *'back to the sacred island.'*

Remy knelt beside me rapt in prayer. His face was tender and soft, his eyes shimmering light. His was an image of beauty I had shut out of my mind, but now my heart opened up. Desperate to forgive him, I searched for a way to forget all that had passed between us. Remy had offered me that way. Begging for another chance, he sought absolution for his sins. A cleansing ceremony to wipe out any trace of his blemished past and offer us a new beginning.

A sinewy priest, wrapped in vestments of white, stood on the rock, the restless ocean thundering behind him. His gaunt silhouette etched subtle patterns onto the faces of those souls who had come seeking help. Strained faces, pleading for deliverance. Sitting motionless on the sand, they held on to the last grain of hope that there could be a cure for whatever ailed them.

The priest took a step forward, clutching his precious gourd of holy water. His wrinkled hands offered the bounty to a young girl, beatific in her purity. Without hesitation, she took a sip then raised her countenance towards heaven, beaming blessedly as she opened herself up to the gods.

'A man in her village fell in love with her,' Remy said, 'but she scorned him. Overcome by passion, he cast a spell over her to capture her love. Her purity repelled the full force of the magic but it lodged in her leg, paralysing it. As a last resort, the priest was called.'

Smudged against the horizon, casting secret mantras into the wind, the old priest emanated an abstruse power. 'To the family's horror,' Remy continued, 'he found a horde of grotesque insects crawling inside the girl's leg. Over the months, he worked to force the scourge out, until she was eventually able to walk again.'

When the priest held out the cup to me I drank willingly, hoping to tap an inner strength that had previously eluded me. I had to enter life with a new level of understanding if I was to succeed.

Taking a woven palm frond, the priest strained the water over my head. It trickled down my back, drenching me in a cold stream. Rising unsteadily, the young girl motioned for me to follow her across the jagged limestone rocks to the water's edge. Without a qualm, she stripped off her outer garments and waded into the ocean.

With purposeful breaths I built up the courage, convinced there could be no turning back if I took this final step. Casting aside all fear, I walked towards the raging ocean. The water crashed onto my body in brutal waves as I went under. Engulfed by the swirling tide, I let the last bitter trace of emotional debris be erased forever.

Surfacing for air, I saw Remy complete his rites of absolution on the beach. When the last prayer was over, he dived into the ocean, daring the currents to absolve him of his sins. Once vindicated, he floated untroubled into the arms of the ocean. Even from afar, I could tune into his thoughts. The connection between us was truly palpable, like a pure uncut diamond. Together, we radiated light.

Obsessed in the watching, I lost track of time. As dark clouds flooded the sky, an uncontrollable icy spasm racked my body. Getting out of the water quickly, I sheltered behind some rocks and changed into dry clothes. The young girl sat on the rattan mat beside me. Intrigued, a thousand unanswered questions filled her eyes.

Remy strode down the beach, beaming with renewed energy. He took a large chunk of chicken from the basket of offerings and handed it to me. 'The ceremony is over, the gods have taken the essence of the food so we are free to eat the rest.'

The young girl nibbled on some rice then rose quietly to her feet and limped down the beach with her family. She was the epitome of childlike innocence, barely sixteen. It was so implausible. At such a fragile age, how could such a horrible fate befall her?

Over the dark ocean, lights of the fishing boats twinkled in the distance. The crescent moon inched its way uneasily over the horizon. A silver haze mirrored its spiritual force. There was so much yet to understand, enigmatic powers beyond my comprehension.

'Remy,' I said, unsure of where this was leading, 'what if you'd used a potion or charm to lure me back, or worse still to make me love you in the first place? I mean, how would I know?'

'You wouldn't,' Remy replied. 'I don't deny my powers but I've never used them to manipulate and control anyone in my life, least of all you. Our love would be meaningless, what would be the point?'

'These powers, you've never really told me about them.'

'A few years ago I was so sick that I was certain I would die. For days I hovered between life and death. The doctors did all they could but my temperature soared - even the balians gave up on me. While I was in a coma, I had visions. An evil god came to do battle with the dark forces that were pledged to destroy me. I made a vow, a promise to that god. If he saved me, I would build a temple in his honour and make offerings to him each day for the rest of my life.'

'But why reach out to an evil god? Surely you would ask for help from a benevolent one - good is supposed to overcome evil.'

'It's the opposite here, one must go to the source - to a god more malevolent than the darkness that has been unleashed - only their power is strong enough to destroy the curse. We all have hidden enemies who invariably target the weaker family members. One day my younger sister was bicycling home when she dropped dead, no physical cause was ever found. I had to be stronger to survive.'

'I had no idea, why didn't you tell me?'

'Because secrecy was my defence. I had made a private pact with a god to ensure my survival and trusted no-one with the truth. In the end I got used to the lies, it became a way of life. Then it turned into a twisted nightmare - lying to you, covering up to my family ...'

For the first time able to put myself in Remy's place, I felt a twinge of pity. It didn't excuse his behaviour nor diminish the pain he'd caused, but it was comforting to know that he'd suffered too.

'Words can never express how sorry I am.' Remy took my hand, 'My lies were unforgivable, but I feared I'd lose you with the truth. I make no excuses, I just ask for another chance.'

'Where does that leave us?' I asked, afraid of the repercussions. 'Do we have any chance of a future together?'

'My second marriage is already dissolved. We had been apart for so long, the ending was only a formality. The first, well it's not so easy. My wife is the mother of my children, it would be a dishonour to send her back to her village. She's older, with nowhere left to go.'

An image of his wife's face flashed before me. The essential beauty of her youth had faded with the vagaries of time. Life had been unkind, had dealt her one too many blows. It was written in every wrinkle, every furrow of her brow. She hadn't smiled in a long time. My heart reached out to her, unwittingly I had added to her misery. Deep down I knew that even if I left, the damage could never be undone.

Remy clasped my hand tighter. 'I'm glad everything's out in the open. Now it's up to you. Are you willing to accept a compromise?'

'What sort of compromise?' I willed myself to be strong. If I had nerves of steel, perhaps I could weather the trials of life. I knew this was going to be one of the hardest. 'What are you proposing?'

'I want to be with you - we can get a house together, a real home. My wife will stay with my family and raise the children. The girls will soon marry, but my son is still young. I will go home every day to see them. There is also the temple, my promise to the god.'

'What will happen if you don't pray?' Remy's face was full of dread. 'You're scared that you will die?' Prayer was fundamental to Remy's survival and the implications were horrifying.

'That's right.' His eyes remained downcast. 'That's what made it so difficult for me to break away. You're from a different culture, an outsider, unable to prepare the temple offerings. One day if I am to become a healer, I will need my wife's help. She is wise in the ways.'

'I can't compete with your other priorities, Remy,' I despaired, 'and I don't want to be responsible for the break-up of your family.'

'My first marriage was arranged, my second an accident. You're the first woman I've chosen for myself. Polygamy is part of our tradition; multiple marriages are accepted as long as the first wife gives her blessing. I've discussed it with her, and she has agreed.'

'You're telling me that your wife doesn't mind if you live with me?' I asked, shaking my head in disbelief. 'You realise I could never agree to share you in a physical sense, I love you too much for that.'

'I'd never ask that of you. When both my wives lived together, there was a lot of jealousy. For a while it was so crammed that we had to share the same bed.' I couldn't even begin to comprehend what he was saying. 'After the constant bickering, my second wife left and I had to divide my time between them. I could never go through that again, besides my feelings for you would not permit it. My family want us to be together, they all like you ... the final decision is yours.'

'This is all so alien to me.' Was my love strong enough to be unconditional and allow Remy to retain that which was already dear to him. Deep down I knew I would respect him less if he cared not for these things. They were his private treasures. 'I need time ...'

The house was small and unassuming, but for me it was home. Set down a shady laneway, it was my own special hideaway. Gone were the dreary months in a hotel room surrounded by endless strangers. I had made a decision. The thought of life without Remy was unbearable. Preferring to share him than lose him altogether, I had agreed to his terms.

Aware that the emotional issues would come later, I busied myself with more basic ones. Things I'd taken for granted for most of my life were to become major hurdles. For water, I'd invest in the bottled variety or boil it. No showers, I'd become accustomed to throwing icy buckets over my head. After all this was the tropics. Squat toilets were an acquired art, better for your system in the long run. Toilet paper was a luxury, this culture was environmentally friendly.

When it came to the well, I drew the line. 'Don't worry,' Remy said, 'there's a pump that takes the water into the house. We're not entirely primitive.' There were compensations for the hardships.

My garden was an enchanted glade. Pushing aside fresh palms that spilled over the path, I was enveloped by a mass of flowering fruit trees and pungent blooms. An occasional butterfly would flutter past or a small bird would serenade me from the bushes. It was a far cry from an urban childhood, and I wallowed in the peacefulness.

'This house is quiet?' I'd asked one last time before signing the year's contract. Peace was essential to me. 'I'm sensitive to noise.'

'Miss, this is the quietest house in Bali,' the owner assured me before grabbing the money and making a beeline for the gate.

From that moment, I could track the passage of time by the variation in noise. Never before had the transitions in my life been plotted according to decibel levels; never before had noise presented itself in such unique packages, each a definitive challenge to my sanity.

The first onslaught was from the neighbours on the right. We shared a common wall, and it was definitely a case of sleeping with the enemy. My nerves were stretched to breaking point as a full scale battle of wills erupted. They refused to back down.

It began at five each morning when the family would rise for the daily wash. Water was drawn from the tub and hurled against the tiles, reverberating through the bathroom like a cement tidal wave. Meanwhile, the maid would be busy in the kitchen pounding away at the garlic with a heavy wooden mallet. Heating up the coconut oil to sizzling point, she would fry up a huge batch of fish, meat and eggs. The heady aroma wafted into our bedroom like Dracula's breath, turning the sweetest dream into one's worst nightmare.

By seven, mum and dad would leave for work and the older children would ride off on their push-bikes for school. This was the signal for the maid to go berserk with the radio. The toddlers would scream, trying to gain her attention above its noise. The bass would boom through the dividing wall until I thought my brains would burst from the sonic impact. No quantity of pillows could cushion the blow.

The aural landslide continued throughout the day, climaxing at night when the entire family competed to be heard above a cacophony of electrical appliances. I took to walking around with bits of cotton wool stuffed in my ears, perpetually chewing on the edge of an aspirin until one day, I realised I had become oblivious to the noise and declared myself clinically brain dead.

Joyce was my one true ally, popping in often for a cup of tea and to lend moral support and the odd set of earplugs. 'You've really done wonders with this place. It looks great.'

'It took a lot of work but it was worth it in the end. Now I've taken to *real* painting.' Months of inactivity had prompted me to dip into my creative talents. I pulled out one of my masterpieces from behind the cupboard hoping for a bit of encouragement.

'You're becoming a regular Leonardo,' Joyce said, trying over-hard to look impressed. She was a true friend. 'How are things working out for you and Remy?' she asked, on a more serious note.

I looked at the photo on the shelf. The spark between us was still there, but beneath the smile was a burden that plagued us both. 'It's hard, the pressure on him to maintain two lives is overwhelming.'

'Well, you're a better woman than I.' Joyce praised me in vain. 'There's no way I could handle the other woman living around the corner. It's hard enough having Sylvia a few thousand miles away.'

'Let's go out in the garden and discuss this in peace.' We found a sunny spot, but as soon as we sat down, the stereo began to blare. Barely able to hear ourselves speak, we dragged the chairs through the grass away from the noise. 'At least there's no neighbours over here,' Joyce proclaimed. Little did we know, the best was yet to come.

*

I was soon to discover that the Balinese are happiest with a hammer in their hand. Regardless of whether there's a nail handy, they love to bang. It may be some evolutionary imprint or a psychic memory of beating the *gamelan* over centuries. Whatever the reason, the outcome is the same. Certain madness.

The vacant plot to the left became a major construction site. Strange men balancing on rickety bamboo planks hung over my garden leering and waving. After months of constant pounding, a huge cement edifice loomed overhead cutting out any vestige of light. No way could the sun compete with this towering monstrosity.

A few days after the hotel's completion, the first tour bus arrived. Javanese students by day, party animals by night. Many a moonlight eve was spent exposed in my nightie, shouting at busloads of pimply adolescents shouldering massive ghetto blasters. '*Diam*! Shut up!' I'd scream as they gawked at the mad Western woman knee high in damp ferns. 'And stop flicking your cigarette butts on my frangipanis.'

'Joyce, I'm due to commit manslaughter any day now,' I sighed, collapsing into her arms. 'Get me out of here before I start self-mutilating. I've begun tuning into the Kung-Fu serials on the telly checking out all the moves. What's worse, I'm even beginning to understand them. Hey, have you noticed there hasn't been a tour bus around here for at least two days. Is that a good omen?'

'No, I think it's a case of the lull before the storm. Take a gander.' We huddled behind the curtains trying hard not to be seen. A large truck had pulled up outside my gate and was unloading a convoy of men in khaki.

'Wrong house,' I yelled at some straggling into my garden. My protests were muffled by Joyce smothering me with the lace curtains.

'Don't be hasty - some of those guys are real cute, especially in those tight singlets. Let them do a few dozen push-ups before you turf them out. I'll go and award points, the highest scorer gets me.'

'Great, now I'm living in the middle of the army barracks!'

'At least you can't complain about being bored, now you've got your own private platoon. Want to swap houses for a while?' Joyce urged, frothing at the mouth, 'All I've got is a resident ghost.'

'I'll let you know.' My eyes scanned the rows of bodies, all those months of rigorous training had certainly paid off. Joyce was right, life would definitely be more interesting from now on.

✻

Endless days were spent glued to my window watching rugged males streak past, clad in little more than my imagination. Noise became infinitely more riveting. Collective heaving, sweating, grunting - the sound of sixty men in close proximity. Now this was *real* noise.

Remy remained oblivious to the onslaught and to my pre-occupation with the troop movements next door. He had an inordinate ability to cut himself off, nothing ever disturbed him. I could not fathom whether he could detach from his senses at will, or really didn't care.

Whatever happened, his routine remained unchanged. Every morning he would go home to pray, do what else needed to be done, then return if there were no other pressing engagements. Usually there were plenty, and he would come back only to collapse into bed for an afternoon siesta. Most of *our* time together was spent with his inert body splayed out on the bed. He needed time out to rest; I needed a meaningful exchange.

Remy tried including me in family affairs, but it was an uncomfortable liaison. His wife accepted me only under duress. She remained the senior wife yet her influence was minimal. Beneath the pretence of niceness was an obvious resentment. My presence in her home worsened her frustration, so with due respect, I kept a distance.

For the sake of his children, I made the effort to pay the occasional visit. Remy's daughters were always friendly, greeting me with welcoming smiles. Eager to practise their English, they were pleasantly sociable, but our cultures separated us. Remy's son was more reticent, preferring to stay by his mother's side.

The antipathy that existed between Remy and his family was difficult to accept. Remy would walk into the house and say little. If hungry, he'd eat. Meals traditionally were not shared occasions, only a means to satisfy one's hunger. After praying he would get up to leave. No goodbyes, no fond farewells, no real intimacy. I wanted to reach out and hug someone, but this was my need not theirs and I felt emotionally starved. It was all so superficial, I needed depth.

Discipline was another touchy area. Remy's son, still young, would go wherever he wanted without a word - just get on his bike and leave, often risking the busy highway. Small screaming children would run amok beneath my feet, blocking any hope of conversation.

'They can do what they want,' Remy said, countering my objections. 'They're young, they should be allowed to enjoy life.'

'Fine, what about the rest of us?' I asked as one bellowed in my ear. 'How do expect them to learn respect for their elders?'

'It comes naturally as they grow.' I begged to differ. So many times I'd been trampled in a bank or shop by people who shoved me out of the way, unaware of the concepts of patience or self-discipline. Driving was pure chaos, crossing the road an exercise in terror.

Who's she?' I asked, hoping to avert a potential argument. A young woman I didn't recognise was preparing food in the kitchen.

'My half sister,' Remy replied matter-of-factly, sipping on his hot cup of coffee, 'the daughter of my father's third wife.'

Here we go again. 'Hold on a minute,' I interrupted, 'last count he only had two, how come he's suddenly inherited another one.'

'Special circumstances, the lover of my father's best friend got pregnant. He was high caste and she a divorced woman of low-caste, so it was difficult for them to marry so he asked my father to marry her instead. He offered to help out - that's why she's my sister.'

No matter how long I stayed, I'd never begin to understand.

Alienation became an increasing problem. Surrounded by indifferent neighbours, having no telephone or transport, I was cut off and alone. Only the camaraderie of my friends provided me with the emotional empathy I needed. New ties were hard to form, most people came and went on holiday leaving no time for meaningful contact.

Most of the expatriates in Bali were on work contracts, mixing within their own stifled circles. The majority were deadly boring, doing their best to forget they were actually in a foreign culture. Those souls who stayed out of choice were usually misfits of their own countries, invariably more eccentric and interesting but also a trifle twisted. Strangeness increased with the territory; the price of living in paradise was high.

My attempts to mix with the locals usually failed. People were too involved in their own lives to bother with an outsider. While language was a stumbling block, it was the huge cultural differences that formed an impenetrable wall. In Bali, emphasis was placed on the past, with no roots to anchor me there we had nothing in common.

While days were easier, spent on the beach with a good book or soaking up the sun, the nights were more prohibitive. An empty house was daunting. With Remy at work, my only respite was the club so I would go there often to escape the isolation.

With any luck, there'd be a familiar face hanging around one of the bars to soften the blow. If not, I would derive comfort from the company of strangers. Pleasant conversation, a common language, shared ideas, temporary enough distractions to provide some small measure of belonging. Other times I wasn't so fortunate. Inside those smoky walls, I was sure I'd stumbled onto an alien civilisation.

Tonight was one of those nights. The oddest assortment of people were thrust together, one specimen more macabre than the next. Attempting to escape the hordes, I bumped straight into a grotesque woman with a giant python wrapped around her neck. As its jaws snapped open, I ducked for cover and clawed my way along to the furthest bar.

Froggy broke into a huge grin when he saw me, directing everyone to move over. Plonking a welcome drink on the bar he scurried off to get a saucer of arak for the snake. I scanned the dance-floor searching for somebody who looked remotely human. No luck. There was a definite feral feel about the place tonight.

Leader of the pack was Sludge, a bikie from Tassie, who'd ripped off his vest to expose a startling display of tattoos, stretching from his nethermost regions to the tip of his bald and shiny scalp. His body looked like the UBD street directory for all roads leading south from Cairns. Along the way he was thoughtful enough to include places of interests and local sites. The dog from Gundagai, the occasional scorpion, snake and tree viper, a few Aboriginal rock carvings plus the names of all the pit-stops along the way - Sheena, Tina, Corrina, Martina - to name a few.

His current flame, Roxanne, looked singularly unimpressed, her jet-black talons twitching in search of an acid texta to permanently delete all her rivals from Sludge's epidermal memory bank. Standing at least one foot higher than her mate, she convulsed over him throughout a particularly stirring heavy metal medley. Her jaguar mini skirt roared into life as Sludge retaliated with a round of solid head banging. During the action, Roxy's navel ring got caught up in Sludge's beard, forcing them to retire in disgrace from the dance-floor in a curious lockjaw position.

Frantic to unfurl Sludge from her abdomen, Roxy assumed a variety of exotic postures. The view was sublime. Each one of Roxy's bodily orifices had been pierced and mutilated with a little decorative wiring. Together they made quite an ornate couple.

Back on the dance-floor, hair was being flung around with unbridled ferocity as the music thundered to a shuddering climax, *'Slash me, rip me, swill me, thrill me, kill me.'* In the midst of the onslaught was Joyce, in extreme danger of being threshed to death. Only her will to unleash her latest bit of gossip gave her the strength to wade through the mayhem.

'You'll never guess!' she exclaimed. 'My ex's turned up, my Bill - out of the blue! Can you believe the gall of that man?'

'What on earth does he want after all this time?'

'To try and salvage the marriage.' Joyce was heaving with delight, all those sleepless nights praying for divine retribution were about to pay off. 'It seems life with Sylvia was no bed of roses!'

'Is it ever? And now he's come running back to you as if nothing ever happened. I hope you gave him his marching orders.'

'Not exactly,' Joyce gloated, ordering drinks all round. 'I've decided to relish the moment, make him sweat for a change.'

'What about Sly, isn't this going to complicate matters?'

'Got to keep them on their toes.' Joyce took a swig of her vodka, then turned serious. 'Look, I do care for Sly in my own way, he's good to me. On the other hand it's hard to bury twenty years of your life as if they never existed. I'm so confused, the last few days have been torture. Bill's sleeping in my room on a trial basis - strictly hands off, so I can sort out my feelings. I've got Sly in the spare room pretending to be the houseboy. They're both prowling around like a pair of mooses with their noses out of joint.'

Convinced it was going to end badly, I stifled a small twinge of satisfaction. Two arrogant men humbled. Hopefully, it would clear the way so Joyce could find one truly worthy of her affection.

'I know you think I'm mad, but it happens to the best of us.' Froggy slapped down another round of drinks on the bar. 'Remember Carol, she came up here with her husband and two kids on holiday. Tom was a real gentleman, quite a looker too if I remember right.'

'And she fell for Froggy! I know he can be hilarious on a good day, but he certainly lacks in the other departments. Carol left her husband, came back here dressed like an eighteen year old and took off on the back of Froggy's motorbike.'

'That's before he got fed up with her and it didn't take too long. I found her one night sobbing on the hotel steps, out of her mind with grief when he dropped her. Carol was a vivacious lady of forty who couldn't come to terms with her age. Maybe she married too young, this was her last grab at youth.'

At the opposite bar two women sat drinking alone. Openly available, they surreptitiously eyed off all the men in the room. They looked alike, except one had been ravaged by time, her meridian of fine time lines camouflaged under a thick coating of make-up.

'Mother and daughter?' I offered.

'The mother's the one trying hard to look the youngest. The way she's poured into that dress! A pity, she's an attractive woman if only she'd act her age instead of competing with her daughter.'

'More likely a fight against time. Ageing is more vivid when it's reflected in your child's eyes. Her maturity should give her the edge with any man worth his salt. The deficit lies in man's inability to measure a woman's value. No wonder we feel so unappreciated.'

'Isn't that why we all end up here? All those bold, wondrous lies: "You're gorgeous, beautiful ... oh so sexy." They roll off the tongue like nectar to the love-starved. We believe what we want to, or need to. JOHN, IS THAT YOU?' Joyce yelled above the crowd.

A bespectacled gent with kind eyes jostled over. Short and portly, he strained to give Joyce a giant bear hug. 'You don't know how glad I am to see you. What would you like to drink? My shout.'

'We're right, thanks. How come you're here by yourself?' Joyce looked concerned. 'Where's Eileen? You two are usually inseparable.'

'We were, until yesterday.' Tears welled up in John's eyes and he flung open the floodgates to his emotions. 'She's left me.'

'But that's impossible, when I saw you last week you were both so happy. Whizzing all over the place, having a ball.'

'We were. Gede drove us around like he always does when we're here. He's become a good friend over the years. This time, he even took us to his village to meet the family. It was all one big lie!'

I moaned. Yet another name to add to the list of casualties.

'Eileen ran off with Gede,' John said, choking with emotion. 'She left a note in the hotel room ... after nine years together. How could she do this to me?' John unleashed the full force of his misery. 'If I ever see that lying bastard again, I'll kill him! I swear I will.'

'I think I'd better get you home,' Joyce said, propping him up. 'We'll buy a couple of bottles of brandy on the way. I'll catch up with you later, Lia, when the storm has passed. When will it ever end!'

It was Sunday, ladies day on the beach. A nice, leisurely massage, a few drinks and a private tryst in a secluded spot. I lay back on the hot sand willing Joyce to arrive. I wanted to catch up on the latest gossip. The sun was sweltering, so I waded into the water, hoping to cool off.

The ocean currents were warm, the atmosphere listless. Floating aimlessly on the waves, I revelled in the clear blue of the sky. Only a few scraggly clouds drifted across the surface, wafting down from the peak of Mount Agung. The holy mountain was chameleon in character. Some days it pulsated pure spiritual energy, others it skulked, barely visible in the fog. Now it looked bleak and sinister, a forewarning of things to come.

Taking shelter behind an abandoned fishing boat, I scanned the horizon. A lone plane carved its way across the sky, but there was still no sign of Joyce. I waded out of the water, shielding my eyes from the sharp glare of the sun. My path was blocked by a gloomy shadow. Squinting, I focused until I could see the vague outline of a man standing in front of me. His presence was threatening, the beach was deserted for miles.

'You here alone?' he snorted. I crossed the sand, unwilling to talk. Sinking into my towel, I was conscious that he was staring at me. From the corner of my eye I saw a tiny speck making its way down the beach. As it got closer, the girth spread and the waddling became more pronounced. Only one person could kick sand with such ferocity. Joyce was on her way.

'At last,' I sighed, as she plopped down beside me. 'Where were you when I needed you? There's a revolting man hanging around here.'

'Don't fret pet, one look at Ramboette Joyce and men run for cover. Now no interruptions, I'm dying to tell you about last night. I left John sleeping off the remains of a bottle of brandy and got home to my own private nightmare. It's my ghost, she's running riot again!'

'Wait till I get comfortable.' I burrowed a groove into the sand.

'Last night Sly was paid an unexpected visit by ghostie dearest. He was sound asleep when she woke him, giving him the fright of his life. He bolted out of his room and ran straight into bed with me.'

'A natural enough reaction, I suppose.'

'It would have been fine if Bill hadn't been in the bed at the time. He woke up, took one look at Sly lying next to me, dragged him out from under the sheets and whacked him square in the jaw.'

'Oh no,' I cracked up, unable to stifle my laughter. 'If I was Sly, I would have preferred to take my chances with the ghost.'

'In the end I had to call the police to break them up, they were ready to kill each other. The cops thought we were all mad or at the very least, slightly kinky. They kept them in the clink overnight but couldn't figure out what to do next, so they gave them back to me this morning. I guess they decided that was punishment enough!'

'Speaking of men, and I do use the term loosely,' I said, peering over my glasses, 'check out the fellas strutting their stuff. Fudge's fairly bursting out of his cossie. What's he stuffed down there, the leftovers of lunch?'

Joyce giggled as she handed me a slice of fresh pineapple. It dribbled down my chin as I crunched into it. 'Sandy's spent the whole morning polishing his muscles. He looks like a freshly hung side of beef. God knows, the meat wins hands down in the intelligence stakes.'

'Oh no, the Aussie Dream bus has arrived.' A bright van pulled up onto the sand. 'All those agile young female bodies vying to be caught by the great Kahuna as their parasail floats down to earth.'

'Look out,' Joyce yelled, diving for cover under a beached canoe. I ducked as a pair of dangling Japanese legs swept past, followed by Fudge who was running behind, frantically trying to catch hold of the spindly line. Young Suki squealed from the clouds as her parachute lurched upwards in the strong wind, dumping her in a clump of palm trees.

A band of Balinese ran down the beach towards her screams while the rest of her tour group ran for their cameras. Clicking away happily, they captured Suki for posterity, hanging from the tree branch. She grinned happily in a variety of embarrassing postures until she was dragged free and limped off down the beach, stopping for another full set of shots with her rescuers. Suki bowed politely before being carried off to the bus.

'Now I've seen everything!' Joyce crawled out from under the canoe, 'that looks like an Aussie remake of Beach Blanket Bingo.'

Several of the Dream teen queens were jumping up and down on the hot sand impatient for their turn to go up. Sandy took more than his fair share of time adjusting the buckles on one particularly voluptuous lass, Karen. As the boat took off he grabbed hold of her straps and they lifted off together into the wide blue yonder. The big boss, Kahuna, screamed abuse at them, but his words were muffled by the wind.

Karen was poised to enter the portals of paradise attached to the rugged Sandy. Unfortunately, the journey was short-lived. Kahuna signalled for the boat to stop and they were both dumped into the shallow waves. The sudden drenching failed to diffuse their ardour.

'By the look in Karen's eyes,' Joyce laughed, 'Sandy's added another conquest to his list. I thought Sunday was the day of rest?'

'I can understand the appeal, some of the guys here are gorgeous - take Kahuna for example.' Standing proudly on the shore, his smooth tanned torso glistening in the sun, he looked like a mix of American Indian and Hawaiian. 'With his long black hair and high cheekbones, you'd swear he was a Cherokee. Wild One on the other hand is a deranged Apache!'

'I'm sure a batch was sent down to the wrong place. They might have the looks but they don't have the integrity to go with it. What I can't figure is how they manage not to overbook the girls?'

'These guys have got it down to a fine art, although sometimes they do screw up. Remember when Kahuna had three here at the same time, there was a riot when they all caught up with each other.'

'But they settled it amicably in the end, Danielle waited patiently until Prunella went back to England but missed out when Fuji upped the stakes. If memory serves me well, she offered him a fully paid trip to Japan and a Suzuki jeep to seal the deal. The yen was the stronger currency after all.'

'No wonder the boys are learning Japanese. It's more lucrative.'

'We're talking big business here,' Joyce huffed, realising the implications of what she said. 'Don't worry, I know Sly's not hanging around for the scenery, maybe that's why I'm holding onto Bill.'

'Oh no, I don't believe it.' I yanked up my swimsuit. 'That guy's been watching us all this time, what a nerve!' Brazenly making his way out of the bushes, he stooped down. 'This is a large beach, please find another spot,' I said irately.

'It's *my* country, I can sit wherever I want,' he snarled as he began to pick at his nails and stare down my front.

'In *our* country,' Joyce bristled, rising to the occasion, 'it's offensive for a strange man to stick his butt in a lady's face.' Joyce began a short tirade informing our unwelcome intruder on pointers of quality control when selecting his next victim. 'Now please be off.'

Glaring at both of us he got up. 'Next time stay in your own country,' he flared, as he stood spread-eagled and defiant against the sun. I felt a tangible ball of hatred hurtle towards us. After one last belligerent look, he marched off down the beach carving a furrow of contempt in the sand.

'I'm tired of all this constant badgering - it's driving me mad!'

'Nothing like trying to have a leisurely day at the beach,' Joyce moaned. 'It's impossible to go anywhere without being hassled.'

'I know, a constant battle from morning to night.' These raw encounters were getting me down. 'Everyone is out to profit from your very existence. On one hand they want what you've got, on the other they resent you for having it. One day this hostility and greed is going to catch up with them. I believe in the cosmic power of karma.'

'Not without taking a lot of victims first. We Westerners are far too trusting, gullible to a fault. Remember that nice couple we met at the cafe the other night, they got sucked in big-time. Appeared level-headed enough but they still ended up losing their life savings.'

'Trust is a forgotten issue,' I said disillusioned.

'They'd known Sari for seven years and treated her like a daughter. After they'd set her up in a silver business, she racked off with all their money. They were shattered. And then they went ahead with that hotel deal. A sound enough investment until the local partner got greedy and had them blacklisted - it's in the courts now, but it'll be years before it's settled.'

'They've lost everything; their home, money, jobs - they're over fifty so it won't be easy starting over again. I reckon Julia, that pretty blond, takes the cake. Put a deposit on a fine piece of land and was all set to build her dream house. Only problem, the land wasn't for sale - the guy took her to a vacant block he said was his. The police didn't get back her money, but she did score a karaoke kit.'

'At least she can sing her way to the poorhouse,' Joyce cackled. 'I don't know how they do it, but they get you every time.'

Little did Joyce realise she was going to find out the hard way.

'Not those bloody roosters again. *5.00 a.m.*! Do those birds have any sense of time?' It was dark outside and Remy was sound asleep. I burrowed my head under a stack of pillows, trying to block out the feathered furore.

'This can't go on,' I yelled over breakfast. 'I counted them - seventeen! Can you imagine the gall of our neighbour keeping so many birds outside our bedroom window? Why doesn't he keep them outside his own, so he can drive himself mad?'

'It's his house, he can do what he wants.' Remy bit into the toast, unsympathetic to my plight. 'Roosters are a status symbol.'

'Can you explain how a chicken is more important than me? By the way, did you have to superglue the rat to the bathroom rock? I got the shock of my life when I went in there to wash.'

'You told me to get rid of it,' he replied, stirring his coffee.

'I didn't think you'd paste it onto the rock like a permanent fixture.' Glue was the preferred method of pest control. 'I can still see its paw prints!'

'It worked didn't it? Don't forget I have to do security patrol tonight.' Once a week, it was Remy's turn to roam the streets with a small group of men, protecting the village. The list of obligations to the banjar was endless and I had no choice but to grit my teeth and bear the absences. It was useless to complain, Remy would risk a hefty fine and threat of future reprisals if he ignored his duties.

As soon as Remy left for temple, I took my book down to a shady spot in the garden beside my mango tree. Opening it, the first words were obliterated by a shrill falsetto shriek coming from junior next door. Even the roosters had the sense to shut up and not try to compete. Lugging my chair down to the corner of the garden, I tried again. The next page was interrupted by a snort. A putrid aroma assailed my nostrils. Tottering on the edge of my chair, I peered over the high wall spiked with broken glass. A bawdy black pig grunted at me as it wallowed in thick mud.

Time for decisive action. This was an opportune moment to pay the neighbours a little visit. I smiled sweetly when they invited me in for a cup of tea. They were sociable enough, charming in a Machiavellian sort of way. 'My husband works late at night and needs his sleep. It's so difficult with all those chickens,' I coughed into my teacup. Remy could sleep through a hen-house massacre, but I thought his point of view might carry more weight on an island dogged by male supremacy.

'Oh, your husband has arrived from Australia?' Mr Tour Guide asked with a supercilious leer on his face. 'By the way, we know Remy's family very well. *All* of them.'

This was going to be an exercise in futility. Quickly gulping down my tea, hoping against hope that it wasn't laced with Baygon, I skulked back into the refuge of my home. There had to be a way out.

That night I plotted and planned, then swung into action. Dragging the stereo speakers through the house with the strength of a woman driven to the edge, I plonked them right under *their* bedroom window and waited till midnight. Tripping over a tangle of wires, I pushed the fateful button.

I had chosen well. At full blast, the plaintive howls of *'Stairway to Heaven'* assaulted the airwaves in one supreme sonic attack. How symbolic, the path to salvation. That's all it took. A year of anguish ended with just one blast of Led Zeppelin.

I remain forever in their debt.

CHAPTER FIFTEEN
Healer of Broken Hearts

'Do you think it's possible to project negative energy?'

'What on earth are you on about?' Joyce munched on her croissant, lashing it with strawberry jam. 'This new cafe's a godsend.'

'Pass me the sugar.' I sweetened my tea with several spoonfuls. Normally I didn't take any, but I had been feeling weak the last few days and needed a boost. 'Do you remember the argument we had with that horrid guy on the beach? I swear I could actually feel the force of his hatred like a heavy ball of hostility heading straight for me. Since then I've felt odd, really drained.'

'You're too sensitive for your own good,' she picked at the crumbs. 'It would take a sledge hammer to make a dent in my hide.'

'Perhaps I am over-reacting, it was probably just too much sun ... or maybe I've picked up a bug.'

'Yeah, a big hairy one with a foul disposition! Speaking of flying missiles, did I tell you about the time I was at a friend's house down the haunted end of Sanur. It was around midnight and I was out in the garden having a fag. I heard this strange rumbling sound, then all of a sudden the dogs started barking like crazy. A dark cloud was massing in the sky, heading straight towards me. I nearly pissed myself I was so scared.'

'How weird,' I crunched into my toast. 'Tell me more.'

'A huge swarm of insects buzzed all around, blocking out the moonlight. Then these massive fireballs came hurtling over my head - green spheres of light coming from one side, red from the other. I was glued to the spot, watching this incredible cosmic battle. I wasn't sure whether it was a war between invisible spirits or a contest between rival *leyak* witches, hurling insults over the backyard fence.'

'Either way, that's pretty spooky - giant balls of energy being hurled through the air! Who knows, maybe we're all capable of doing it without realising. A careless comment, one critical word, a destructive look. All negative thought forms flung around, subtle yet powerful.'

'Tell me about it! My house is like a war zone at the moment. Bill's on the attack, Sly's on the defence and I'm in the middle playing umpire. They're throwing their anger around but believe me, it's not so subtle. It's about to explode big-time, right in my face.'

'I warned you this would happen, you've only got yourself to blame.'

'I know, and quite frankly I'm fed up!' Joyce left a thick lipstick imprint on her napkin. 'I'm going to put an end to it before they wind up killing each other or I end up murdering them both.'

'Good luck. By the way,' I said nonchalantly, 'have you seen Linda lately?' Wild stories had been circulating about her husband Ace's antics, he had been spotted many a night in Kuta with a string of different females. Linda would be devastated if she knew, and Joyce having adopted her as a surrogate daughter, would be crushed by the news. Linda personified young innocence in Joyce's eyes and she would not stand by placidly and watch it be destroyed. 'I thought I might drop round there for a visit.'

'I haven't seen her for ages, I didn't want to intrude on their romantic little love nest. Now, if you'll excuse me I'm going home to clean up my own private nightmare. Send Linda my love.'

'What a great surprise, I wasn't expecting company.' Automatically Linda started tidying up, even though very little was out of place. The house still lacked furniture but it was laced with personal expressions of her taste which made it look homely and sweet.

'Are you alone?' I asked, thankful Ace was nowhere in sight.

'Ace is out trying to find work, he spends every moment of the day and night looking.' I kept quiet, determined not to give away any secrets. 'Keep your fingers crossed, I'm tired of rice and vegies.'

'How are you managing?' Linda was thinner, the bloom had faded from her cheeks as if a layer of youth had been stripped off. She wore a crumpled blue sarong, her flaxen hair piled on her head.

'Fine,' she replied unconvincingly. 'Mind coming down the back while I get a start on these?' She picked up a basket of laundry and walked along the overgrown path. A spindly monkey swooped down from the trees and landed on top of the clothes. 'Coco, get off!'

'A new addition to the family?'

'Ace got it for me, he thinks I won't get quite so lonely if I've got something to play with. Cute, isn't he?'

Coco, distracted by the sound of a bird, scooted back into the bushes. Linda stooped over the well and winched down the bucket, her hands callused and rough. Hoisting the heavy bucket back up, she poured the water into a bowl then began to scrub with a fury.

'Tell me the truth, Linda, do you enjoy living like this?'

She dissolved into a stream of tears, then clearly embarrassed, dug into the basket for a hankie. 'I'm sorry, I'm being silly. It's just that I've been feeling homesick lately. I miss my mum and dad so much, and simple things like going to the mall with my friends, or watching telly with my cat Tabby, or being able to walk in the street without people ogling me or calling out things I don't understand.'

'Isn't there more to it?' I detected a deeper sadness, an innate recognition that something was going on behind her back.

'Ace has been at a loose end lately and has been drinking a fair bit, he goes out late at night and doesn't come back for hours. I sit at home alone waiting, agonising in case I've done something wrong.'

'His frustration is nothing compared to yours,' I argued, upset at the state he'd reduced her to. Love was supposed to be uplifting, not destructive. 'You've thrown away so much of your life for him.'

'But he *has* given me so much in return,' she insisted, 'You don't know him the way I do. When we first met, he was so romantic and sent me the most beautiful letters. Wonderful words written just for me. Sometimes now when we lie in bed, he strums his guitar and sings me love songs. He makes me feel so special.'

'But you already are? Can't you see that?'

'All my life I've been told I'm special because of my looks, but Ace makes me *feel* it. There are times,' she said, suddenly forlorn, 'he makes me feel things I'd rather not. When he's angry it just takes one nasty word, and I crumble inside. He stalks off and I'm left feeling miserable. Then he returns acting like nothing's happened, and I forgive him because I need to. I'm lost without him.'

Linda looked up at me with all the fragility of a deer. Doe-eyed and vulnerable, she lacked the deer's instinct to smell out the predator. The loud screech of tyres and her husband Ace appeared. Jumping off his bike, he strutted up the path haughty in black leather. Astute enough to sense the presence of an outsider, he circled his den like a hungry jackal. His territory had been invaded.

'We're leaving,' he commanded, intent on removing his wife from unwanted company. He stood behind her, his dark shadow dimming her light. Not for a moment did he try to disguise his real self; not a smile nor a polite pretence. Ace possessed an abysmal arrogance that he relished.

The laws of karma were perverse, why else would this dear girl be tied to such a nightmare of a man?

'If I find out that even one tenth of what I've been told is true, then Ace is a dead man!' Joyce huffed, storming down the path. Over the past weeks, news had filtered through of Ace's double dealings. The jungle drums had beaten long and hard, stirring Joyce into a frenzy. 'I promise he'll get his. I've got gangster connections that make the Mafia look like a troop of devout boy scouts!'

'Linda,' she yelled as she stomped through the bushes like a mad cow, her temper out of control, 'where are you?'

Linda emerged from the house, her head hung low. 'Maybe it's better you don't come in, now isn't a good time. Ace is due back.' We refused to budge so reluctantly Linda looked up. Her fine alabaster face was marred by an ugly bruise that spread across her entire cheekbone. 'You can't let him get away with this,' Joyce fumed.

'Ace is the only thing I've got left in the world, I can't leave.'

Her spirit had given up the fight, her inner spark weak and starved. Linda believed herself dependent on Ace's love, what she failed to realise was that it was her own love of self that was lacking. Only a mixture of abject insecurity and self-loathing would allow her to withstand such abuse.

'You've still got your family, and above all yourself.'

Wanton strands of hair smeared her face but she was too distracted to notice, or too tired to care. 'My family's disowned me so this is my home,' she replied dispassionately, 'and as for me, I don't know who I am anymore and I'm not sure that I care.'

'No matter what,' I said, 'he has no right to hurt you. No-one has.' Least of all herself - if only I could make her understand.

'He's my husband. Besides this,' she said running her fingers over the bruise, 'was my own fault. Ace's wanted to have children since we got married and his family are beginning to ask questions. He sees it as a threat to his manhood that I haven't conceived yet.'

'That's hardly your fault,' Joyce snapped. 'He has to be patient.'

'But it is my fault. I overheard some Balinese women talking. They said that if you eat enough pineapples, it stops you falling pregnant. I'm not ready for a family so I've been sucking caseloads of them. I'll never be able to look at another pineapple again in my life! Anyway, Ace found out and he totally freaked out.'

'Wouldn't the truth have been easier?' I could understand why she had misgivings, no child deserved to be spawned into this family.

'I didn't dare,' Linda moaned. 'The ironic part is that I still love him. When he comes home late at night I still make excuses for him. Sometimes I suspect he's with another woman but I push it to the back of my mind because I know I'll go insane if it's true.' There was an awkward silence. Could the truth push her over the edge?

'Things have gotten better financially,' Linda said leading us into the house, 'now that Ace's got a job as a tour guide.' The once bare rooms were draped with fancy curtains and heavy furniture. Carved from mahogany the style was oppressively ornate. Impossibly out of place in this mausoleum, Linda looked like a single white lily lost in a dismal, dark pond. Ace was sucking her under quickly. 'Problem is I hardly ever see him, and I get so lonely.'

Linda cuddled Coco who had jumped onto her lap. The monkey stared up at her through vapid amber eyes, with a look bordering on compassion. Having witnessed the cold hours of Linda's solitude and pain, Coco, in his own isolation, had empathised and they had become each other's closest ally. 'Ace gets heaps of commission so our lifestyle's improved,' Linda said, stroking the monkey's belly, 'but it's those extra benefits I'm worried about. All those single women on holiday, he swears he's faithful but who can be sure?'

It was bound to be only a matter of time.

Ace's transgressions became blatant, as if daring life to defy him. He moved his conquests onto home territory, no longer wary of the consequences. Many a night he would be down at the club, parading another cheap bauble on his arm. Whenever our eyes met, he would gloat openly, daring me to expose his tawdry secret to the world.

Words of warnings had no effect on Linda, nothing anyone could say or do had the slightest impact. She refused to listen. Rather than convincing her to leave, his sordid conduct made her more determined to stay. Plagued by doubt, she took on the role of the shrewd hunter with Ace as her quarry. And so the fiasco began.

Relentless in her quest, Linda would appear each night at the club, determined to catch him. Ace had an inbuilt radar that activated whenever she was near. Thus he avoided discovery, vanishing like the wind seconds before she arrived. And so the drama continued, Linda's life falling around her like an unstable stack of cards.

Fuelled by rumour and fanned by the winds of suspicion, Linda's quest blossomed into a full blown obsession. Reasoning was useless. She was enjoying the chase. There was no room inside her brain for anything else. So consumed was she by Ace that she lost herself along the way. In a slow, insidious process, parts of her personality began to splinter and break off from the central core until she was in danger of losing herself completely.

Powerless to stop the onslaught, we watched helpless as Linda's behaviour became more erratic. She took to hunting Ace with all the wiliness of a hungry fox. Investing in secret bugging devices, she tracked his every movement. A diary was kept and the van's speedometer logged daily to verify her calculations. When mileage exceeded expectations, Linda took to hiding in the back under a blanket to keep a personal check. This backfired when she was nearly arrested by police who found her sneaking out of the van's back window after Ace had inadvertently locked her inside.

She was forced to change tactics, tampering instead with Ace's mail. Getting to it first, she would open it and reply on his behalf. Sometimes as the outraged wife full of fire and brimstone issuing a warning never to come back. More often than not, as Ace himself. Fishing for more information to feed her demented brain, many a night was spent boning up on her Japanese so that the numerous postcards could be deciphered and assessed. A war was looming.

'Look at the bright side,' Joyce said, one day as we were lying on the beach. 'When all this madness is over, Linda can get a good job in a duty-free shop back home. She is cultivating her skills after all.'

'This is no laughing matter,' I chastised. 'It's a tragedy really, so much potential gone to waste. I wish we could do something.'

'You carve your own destiny,' Joyce muttered, exhausted from the effort of trying to rescue someone who refused to be saved. 'At this rate, she can join ASIO. From what I hear she's tracked down a couple of her rivals. First the lovely Nicole. Linda caught up with her near the ice-cream stand and it was on for young and old. Lucky for her the only thing she sustained was a barrage of insults. Not so poor Frida. If it hadn't been for the restaurant staff last night she would have been carted off to hospital with a fractured skull after Linda went for her with a broken beer bottle.'

'This is ridiculous. Something has to be done before it's too late and Linda finds herself behind bars or in a hospital ward. What a tragic waste of a young life. All thrown away for love of a man.'

'She won't be the first. Last week a young Aussie who caught up with her lover's infidelity went on the rampage, tearing his house apart. At the end of the tussle, she wound up in hospital with a broken jaw. And believe me, we're not the only whackos, a Japanese lass on discovering that her island lover was messing around with her best friend torched his place to the ground. So much for the Asian cool.'

'All this in the name of love,' I sighed. 'Betrayal is a bitter pill to swallow but I don't know if revenge is the answer.'

'Don't think I wasn't tempted in my time. I could have easily put a gun to Bill's head, but I only ended up shredding his clothes ... oh, and then there was the business with the car ...'

'And now he's walked straight back into your life.'

'Precisely,' Joyce snorted, 'as if nothing ever happened! What's more he's got the gall to start calling all the shots again. Well I won't have it! I won't be manipulated again, I want *my* divorce and *my* money so I can build a house of my own. Sly's promised to drive me to his village to look at some land.' Convinced she was swapping one disaster for another, I silenced my doubts. Joyce deserved the best life had to offer and I had the distinct feeling Sly wasn't it.

One last attempt. I would try one more time to pull Linda out of the dark hole she'd created. Remy warned me not to interfere, adopting the typical Balinese attitude of non-intervention, but I was having trouble living with my conscience and would not be swayed.

In a conniving stroke of genius, Ace had invested in a dress shop to give Linda a creative outlet for her tension. He had gotten his hands on some money, rumour had it by ripping off one of his girlfriends. He hoped it would be the perfect distraction, that Linda would be kept so busy that she'd forget all about him. Turbulent emotions were not so easily quashed.

I found Linda in the shop, sitting on the floor, sorting through a pile of dresses. Crouching down on a mat, I tried to talk some sense into her, but my words had little impact. She stared blankly at me through sad, lifeless eyes. 'This madness has to stop before you destroy yourself.'

'I *can't* stop,' she moaned. 'The voices inside my head are tormenting me, urging me on. I've got no more strength left to fight.'

'What voices?' No reply. Linda's mind was locked tight. 'Linda, I can't help you if you don't tell me what's going on. Please ...'

'No-one can help,' she repeated over and over. 'It's too late, I'm lost.' Burying her head in her lap, she started to rock back and forth.

'I know someone who can.' It was the meek voice of Ida, the shopgirl. Slim and bird-like, she was no more than twenty-five. 'Once I thought I was going mad and wanted to die. Then I found a special man, a dukun, who restored my sanity and gave me back my life.'

'What?' Linda asked, breaking through her self-imposed exile. 'Why didn't you tell this before? I didn't know you'd been in trouble.'

'It was my own private shame, something I couldn't speak about, but now I can see myself in your eyes and I want to help. It is a terrible place to be, this darkness of the soul. I loved Agus,' her pretty face clouded with sadness, 'but he used my love to torment me.'

'I know what you mean,' Linda said, holding back the tears.

'All those years I spent with Agus were so painful. I adored him but over time he changed, he became terribly cruel. One night when he thought I was asleep, I saw him hacking apart a live chicken and chanting. I was terrified for I knew then he was dabbling in magic. With time he became even more depraved. He took control of my mind, and kept me captive with my love. Losing my will, I knew I had to escape to survive. There could be no other way.'

'My love for Ace,' Linda sobbed, 'has turned to hate and it's tearing me apart. He's taken my heart and twisted it inside out and I want to hurt him just as much as he has me. I can't look in the mirror any more and face what I've become.' She averted her gaze, 'I wish it was all over.'

'It can be,' Ida flicked through the dates on the calendar, 'on exactly the right day. Tomorrow is Kajeng Kliwon, we will go then.'

The pallor of dawn heralded a new day. Ida led us through the back alleys of the village, past the snapping dogs and prying looks, until we came to an iron gate. An old woman motioned for us to enter through the rusty creaking metal. Despite the early hour, many people were scattered around the courtyard waiting their turn to see the dukun.

'They come from all over the island, some have slept here overnight.' Ida ushered us through to some seats on the verandah. 'He is well known for his powers, a great healer. Then there are his other *specialities*. See that woman over there,' she whispered, pointing to a wan, acned face in the corner, 'she's a prostitute. She comes here often to get a tonic to make her irresistible to men. Just in case that's not enough, she slips a little something extra into their drinks.'

Attempting not to stare, I tried to fathom what potion would be powerful enough to restore the spark to the woman's eyes. It had been lost many moons ago when the apathy of life had dulled her senses. My attention was diverted away from her torpid form to the elderly man sitting next to me. Uneasy, he was fidgeting in his chair. His wife, stonily silent, sat rigid by his side. You could have cut the air with a knife.

Ida leant across to talk to them. 'Their daughter is with the dukun now, they fear she has gone mad. The doctors want to have her committed, but she is so young they came here as a last resort.'

'What's wrong with her?' Linda asked, mortified by her own fear of madness. Her eyes glazed over as she listened.

'Recently she married a greedy man,' Ida translated. 'Now he wants her family's property and land. With his parent's help he cast a spell over her that has bewitched her into losing her mind.'

A piercing scream shattered the stillness of the morning. The door flung open and a young woman ran out in a state of complete hysteria. Screaming and running amok, she fought madly to break free while several people battled to control her. The face of the old man next to me crumpled as he recognised the tragedy of his daughter's plight. His grip tightened on his wife's arm, restraining her from running over to help.

Then came a deathly hush. From the room emerged a stately man moving with incredible grace and tranquillity. The strong energy field surrounding him was almost visible. 'That's *him*,' Ida exclaimed. 'I told you he was special.' Walking straight over to the girl, he took hold of her. Relaxing into his grip, her sobs abated and she collapsed into his arms, so healing was his touch.

The dukun began to chant. Softly at first, then louder and more pronounced. The girl's body began to throb, convulsing visibly. Then she began to howl like a frightened wolf - a plaintive, eerie cry. Linda's hand squeezed mine as we both resisted the instinct to run.

The screams reached fever pitch, the girl's spirit fighting for release. The dukun remained unmoved, his face showing no trace of emotion. Splashing holy water over her head, he continued his monotonous chant until the girl was drenched in a volatile sea of water and sweat. She pulled away violently, trying to break free from his grip but his piercing eyes held her captive. There was no escaping the intense magnetism of his hold.

Letting out one final ear-splitting screech, she spewed up a vile green foam before collapsing onto the ground. There she lay in a mangled heap, covered in her own vomit. Her frantic parents unable to contain themselves any longer, ran to her side. Her body, freed from the curse stopped shaking, as her mind returned to its normal dwelling place. It had been on a long distant journey. Her parents clutched her to their breasts, relieved to recover the soul of the child they thought they'd lost.

'It's all over,' the dukun said, his elderly assistant mopping his brow with a white cloth. 'The spell is broken, she will be alright.'

Linda, fearful that the same fate lay in store for her, was on the point of panic. Sensing her trepidation, the dukun gestured to us to follow into his private room. It hung heavy with despair.

'Don't be afraid,' he said, 'your release is close at hand. Many have come before you.' Sifting through a box, he passed us some photos. 'Many spells have been removed, many freed of their curse.'

'What do you mean?' Linda asked, sorting through the pictures.

'Circumstances vary,' he said pointing to two photos stapled together. I looked at the faces - unlined but old beyond their years, the man Balinese, the girl Japanese. Without a hint of a smile, the dour expressions revealed a life robbed of lustre. 'They were very much in love but his wife would not give him up, even though she no longer loved him. She put something in his food to make him her slave forever. In desperation, they came to me for help. After much effort I broke the spell, releasing him from his bondage. Now, I believe they are living together in Tokyo - and very happily indeed.'

'But surely if he really wanted to he could have left his wife.'

'You are too naive. A spell robs you of free will. You become a virtual puppet at the hands of a cruel master, your spirit loses the power to fight. Look, here's a perfect example.' Linda snatched the photo of the young man brimming with life, from his hand.

'Why, that's Chad,' Linda gasped. 'I used to buy fabric from him but I haven't seen him for ages. What happened to him?'

'Unfortunately Chad met with an unhappy fate. He died, a horrible lingering death.'

'I don't believe it,' Linda cried. Devastated, her chest heaved under the emotional pressure. 'It can't be true ... Chad was so happy, always joking around and making me laugh ... it's not possible.'

'Alas, I was too late. Chad was something of a playboy. One night his long-suffering wife had had enough, and accused him of being unfaithful. In anger he hit her and she swore vengeance, vowing to use black magic to make him suffer as she had. Chad laughed in her face, infuriating her more. The next day, she went to a magician who cast a dire spell over him, within days Chad became dreadfully ill.'

'Maybe it was the power of suggestion,' Linda said, shredding her cuticles to bits, 'like pointing the bone or casting the evil eye.'

'No, Chad was a sceptic. Not one to believe in the forces of darkness, he made a tragic error. As his condition worsened, his wife, full of remorse, regretted what she'd done. She took him to doctors in Java and Singapore, spending a fortune but to no avail. The doctors were powerless to identify the problem, let alone cure it.'

'So she brought him back here?'

'It was too late, the magic too far-gone. On the night of the full moon, deranged and believing the spell had lodged in the fish-pond in the garden, the wife attacked it with a pick-axe, reducing it to a pile of rubble. She thought by destroying it she could break the curse.'

'And did she?' My mind was floundering to make sense of it. Had the forces of darkness the power to actually inflict death?

'Once such a powerful force has been unleashed there is no turning back. Chad died soon after. Young and healthy, the autopsy revealed no cause. In the end, Chad believed it true himself. On his deathbed, he asked his family to wait a year before cremating him.'

'Why was that?' Linda asked, her face streaked with the remains of her tears. 'Surely Chad would have wanted his spirit to be free.'

'Yes, but he was hell-bent on revenge. He wanted one year to wreak havoc on those he believed harmed him and asked that six items be buried with him as tools - an axe, knife, sickle, and other weapons of destruction. His fury ran deep.'

'I don't think I'd like to have been his wife,' I shuddered.

'She pleaded with his family to cremate him but they refused to budge, respecting their son's wishes. They relished every moment of her agony because they were convinced she had murdered their son. The wife's misery is complete, a vengeful spirit an impossible adversary.'

'This is all too much for me,' Linda rose unsteadily to her feet.

'Don't be frightened.' The dukun, well aware of her misgivings, took her hand. 'I can help.' His look was reassuring, yet concerned.

Linda tried to answer, but was unable to think clearly. Ida, silent until now, sprang to the rescue. Elaborating with the Balinese flair for drama, she gave a lurid account of Linda's dilemma.

'Your situation is complex,' he said, mulling it over, 'but never doubt for a moment that you are in danger. Real danger.'

'What *sort* of danger?' Linda's face flushed red with fear.

'If you do not control the dragon within,' he cautioned, 'you will unleash a torrent of rage. Only your husband has the power to unlock the dragon. Be warned, you tread on dangerous ground.'

'What must I do?' Linda searched for the source of her fear.

'Be alert and prepare to defend yourself. Your God is different to ours and thus far has protected you from harm. You have been shielded from the full force of your husband's evil but it is time for action, you must break the unholy bond that ties you to this man.'

'Does this mean we won't be together anymore?' Linda asked, shrinking to half her size, 'I love him too much to lose him.'

'Lose him or risk losing yourself! I will mix a potion that you must drink every day to protect you from immediate harm.'

Withdrawing into a dusty corner, the dukun took a cracked earthenware bowl then opened several glass bottles from the shelf, releasing clouds of herbal scents into the air. Measuring each portion with care, he added the yolks of several small duck eggs and blended the mixture into a smooth yellow paste. Pouring it into an empty bottle, he sealed it with a cork and handed it to Linda. 'Drink this three times every day, don't forget. It is vital.'

From the loath expression on her face, I knew it would take an act of God to convince her to go ahead with his plan.

'I will meditate on the way to rid you of this evil. The external demons I'm sure we can defeat, the inner ones ... ah, well that's another story. Return on the day of the full moon for the final battle.'

A circle of pale light ringed the moon with flecks of gold. A hushed silence. Nothing moved, not the fragile rustling of a leaf or the merest wisp of a breeze. The earth was awakening from a deep sleep, its senses barely restored. Slowly came the distant trill of a bird, the scent of dawn, the taste of morning dew. Then the merest hint of colour as the palette of light was awakened.

The day had come at last. The day of Linda's salvation.

For weeks she had laboured over the decision, switching from one stance to another. Tossing all the reasons about like mental flotsam, she was set adrift. Nebulous by nature, she had trouble keeping a grip on reality at the best of times - and this was the worst. Her sensitive Piscean brain, unable to tolerate any more pressure, caved in. Realising that she had no choice but to break her ties with Ace, she agreed to go ahead with the unholy plan.

*

The dukun was waiting. As he greeted us, I noticed for the first time the large silver ring gracing his hand, the dark bloodstone pulsing, heavy with cosmic energy. He caught the look of interest on my face.

'Ah, I see you have powers yet uncovered. You must work hard at them to best harness their potential. Somewhat different to the gifts of your partner. I have been told he has quite a reputation.'

'What sort of reputation?' I asked.

'Quite bewitching,' he smiled, 'hard for a woman to resist. I've heard he possesses great powers like his grandfather. Let's hope that he uses them wisely. If he were to abuse them ... perhaps I'm wrong.'

'I'm sorry, you *are* mistaken,' I replied, springing to Remy's defence. 'He's not like that.' Nonetheless, the seed of doubt had been planted in my mind. What was the innuendo of his words?

Blocking any further conversation on the subject, the dukun diverted his attention to Linda. 'Now, what have you decided?'

'I want to go ahead,' she replied, her heart full of trepidation. 'I want to be able to look in the mirror and see myself again without Ace's shadow hanging over me like a dark cloud. I want to be free.'

'Have you bought everything I asked for.' She nodded as she handed him the neatly folded bag. 'And the photos?'

'Yes, I chose the wedding shots. We were so much in love then. Ironic really, I don't know what real love feels like any more.'

The dukun rifled through the bag and picked a photo. Holding it upright, he cut through the image of Linda and Ace with large scissors, dividing them forever in a final symbolic separation. 'The ties that bind are broken and you are *free!*' Linda choked loudly. Mounting each photo on a copper plate, he struggled to be exact. 'The gems must be embedded in just the right place - the diamond in his third eye, the ruby in yours.'

His fingers fumbled with the pliers as he inset the stones in the photos, all the while muttering mysticisms under his breath. 'These needles are platinum,' he said, spearing the pictures. 'Only their power is strong enough to drive out the darkness from your lives. And so it is done!'

Clutching the fruit of his labour close to his chest, he shut his eyes and increased the intensity of the chant until the entire room was pulsating loudly. Incense was smouldering in the centre of the room, the lingering smell melding with stale body sweat. Linda's fine hair was matted to her forehead, her dress sticking to her body.

'Your torment will soon be over,' the dukun announced loudly. 'Hide these in a special place where he can never find them.' Linda slipped the photos into her bag, frightened that they might burn a hole in her trembling palm. A crackle of heat from the burning candle and the dukun looked up in victory.

'What was once bound for eternity, now forever be torn apart!'

CHAPTER SIXTEEN
The Black Magician

The gold Mercedes glinted gaudily in the morning sun. 'An early wedding present from Cliff,' Kate beamed, 'and it's all mine, down to the last spark on the duco and the customised number plates - *KATE*.'

'Your life borders on the obscene,' I sank into the rich taupe leather seat. 'Don't you have even the merest twinge of conscience?'

'For what? Believing I deserve the best in life, for having a man who adores me? If the rest of you wish to suffer that's your prerogative, I have no intention to.' Kate turned up the dulcet tones of Julio Iglesias on the cassette, drowning out the noise of the highway. Cruising along, we passed a battalion of ravaged bemos and trucks.

'Where are we headed?' I asked, lapping up the comfort.

'Remember Drew, that debased designer friend of mine?'

'How could one forget the infamous night at the Flamingo club when he got up on the table and danced the tango with the waiter, a red plastic rose clenched between his teeth? Left quite an impression.'

'The man's back in town, so I thought we'd drive over for an encore. By the way, how are things going with Remy?'

'Good.' It was an inane response, but I couldn't think of anything better to say. Life was drifting along smoothly; there were no real dramas nor any incredible high points. Materially, I wasn't in Kate's league, but on my list of priorities it barely mattered. I was content to putt along and enjoy the simple pleasures of life, in my heart I was still an incurable romantic.

'Have his famous absences improved with time?'

'Some things my dear, never change. It's probably gotten worse now that he's devoting his life to becoming a priest. Strange people keep coming to our house all hours of the day and night, asking for his help. Remy leaves for a while then returns without a word. I've asked for details about what goes on, but he remains tight-lipped.'

'So it's no bed of roses living with a holy man?'

'His identity crisis is giving me my own. I'm not sure where I fit in the grand scheme of things, if there's a place for me in his world. His needs are so demanding they eclipse mine. I have to work hard to define my own identity, then be strong enough to sustain it.'

'It's such a tenuous thing,' Kate replied. 'Look at Linda, she believed she'd be married for eternity, and look where she's ended up.'

'Back where she started from, in Perth with her family. Hopefully she'll emerge wiser for the experience. Nothing in life is ever wasted - it happens for a purpose, even if we're unaware of it.'

'She's certainly better off without that husband of hers!' Kate expertly negotiated the traffic while reflecting on the vagaries of life. 'Linda will make a go of it, she's a survivor. Where's Joyce at?'

'She's gone bush. The old bird's found a home to roost. She got the courage to go ahead with the divorce and demanded a hefty settlement from Bill, then used it to build a love nest up in Sly's village. Packed up all her things and shipped them up the mountain. I haven't heard from her for ages.'

'Joyce is one tough cookie. She's probably taken over the village by now and set up a women's co-op. Mind you, for one smart lady she was pretty stupid to throw away all her loot on Sly.'

'Such is the folly of us mortals! We all have our peculiar brand of tunnel vision, our personal Achilles heel. It could be that very vulnerability which makes us human ... and keeps us that way.'

'Oh,' Drew screamed, flinging his arms up into the air in a flourish. 'What a marvellous surprise!' Sweeping through the hotel lobby, he whisked us past the kidney-shaped swimming pool replete with gushing fountains and artificial waterfalls, to the beachside cafe.

'You old bitches haven't aged a day,' he commented. 'Still as beauteous as ever. Mind you,' he added, his eagle eyes scanning every detail meticulously, 'do I detect a few more grey hairs?'

Drew was one of those men who judged everyone else by his own impossibly high standards. In flowing white crepe, studded with designer accessories, his style was impressive. His marvellously sculptured hands were garnished with a selection of rings modelled from his own designs. The scarab beetle carved from pearl shell was particularly stunning. With his regal style, he looked like an Egyptian prince from a previous lifetime.

Leading the way into the cafe, he demanded the best table. 'I want to hear all the latest gossip ... word for word. Oh no, everybody duck!' Drew hid behind the menu. 'Here comes the old hag who put a curse on me, according to her I should be dead by now.'

'What are you on about?' Kate whacked him on the knee.

'I was lying on the beach yesterday soaking up the sun when this witch comes up to me opening up her bundle of goodies like a mobile K-Mart. I tried to shoo her away, but she stayed put like a bloody leech. Then she got really agro - threatened to kill me off with a bit of local mumbo jumbo.'

'Speak of the devil, here she comes,' Kate laughed.

'Ooh ooh, Zelda,' Drew called, 'over here.' Recognising the voice she beat a path through the hot sand straight to his side. 'You told me your magic strong - I'm still alive! See, your magic no good.'

'My magic plenty good,' she snapped through a face of granite and a tongue of pure bile. 'Still have lotta time, you dead soon!'

'Go away,' Kate seethed. 'No-one stands a chance fighting this lot, some of them are downright rude and abusive. If they don't watch out they'll destroy the very system they're trying to exploit.'

'Worse still, tourists won't see beyond it to the real Bali. The incredible creativity of spirit that makes this place so unique.'

'Not that there'll be any of it left at this rate,' Kate harped. 'It will disappear along with the last rice field when commercialism coats this island in a ton of cement. It's a global tragedy - the demise of paradise!'

Zelda, unimpressed by the serious tone of the conversation, drifted downwind searching for another hapless victim. Targeting a reclining Italian, she got more than she bargained for when Sergio, spurred on by her insults, jumped up in a frenzy clutching his G-string and chased her down the beach.

'Serves the old biddy right,' Drew fumed. 'Next time she won't be in such a hurry to harass people who come here for a little peace.'

We managed two mouthfuls of conversation before another woman, younger but just as weather-beaten, strolled over to our table as if she owned it. Toothless but determined, she looked us over and then picked out her mark. Staring straight at Drew, she winked, then stroked his arm. The fine hairs on his skin stood up in protest.

'I give you good time tonight, honey. What you like?'

'For goodness sake, love, your wasting your time.' Drew pulled away but she clung like flypaper. 'You're *definitely* not my type.'

Undeterred, she went to second best. 'What about you, lady?' she said, putting her hand on Kate's shoulder. 'You like with me?'

'What?' Kate screeched. 'You must be mad! Go away!'

'Now there's a perfect match if ever I've seen one,' Drew cackled. 'Kate, I think you've found your soul mate at last.'

'Give me a break,' Kate fumed. 'Where does she come off?' Realising that she was way out of her league, the brainless wonder joined a gaggle of massage ladies lying torpid under a coconut tree. Kate's eyes lit up as she remembered a story she just had to share, that '... my house-boy, Lele, told me.'

'Trust you to have a male maid,' Drew drooled.

'Listen, Lele had a friend who came down here regularly for a secret assignation with one of the massage girls. Appears that he went for the *deluxe* massage and pretty soon she got knocked up. Well, as is the custom, the poor lad was forced to marry her.'

'What's new?' Drew interrupted, sucking on a large ice-cube.

'Well this chappie was already married but that didn't stop him from doing the right thing - he went ahead and married her too.'

'They certainly have a penchant here for collecting wives.'

'Variety is the spice of life, take it from one who knows.' Drew's legion of lovers was legendary. I never knew him to leave a venue without at least two on tap. From the growing wrinkles lining his face, it was evident his excesses were catching up with him.

'Let me get on with my story,' Kate said, 'I haven't got to the good bit yet. Birth was imminent so missus was rushed to hospital.'

'I wouldn't go there unless I had a heavy death wish,' Drew cautioned. 'A violent nose bleed was enough to put me off for life.'

'Hubby was waiting expectantly in the corridor when the little one popped out. Even the doctors recoiled; the tot had bright blue eyes and blond hair. Not exactly your local variety!'

'Whoops,' Drew chuckled. Looks like the dear girl was taking private appointments on the side. Massage with the works for some frustrated tourists. What an enterprising lass!'

'Well, hubby divorced her right away but got to keep the baby, he thought it looked pretty. Best of all, you know what he called her?' Kate took a deep breath working up to a climax. 'Ketut Tourist.'

'They're nothing if not discreet. I give up!'

'The land must be here somewhere,' Remy said, veering the motor bike a sharp left. 'These new housing estates aren't exactly well sign-posted.' We cruised down the road past a row of half-built mansions. Cliff had bought land in an expensive area, most of the houses being built were of gigantic proportion. This was the moneyed belt; he would settle for nothing less.

'Look, there's Kate,' I pointed over to a large plot piled sky-high with building materials. She was barely visible behind a stack of bricks. At the sound of the bike, she stalked straight over.

'I'm so glad you're here,' she said, taking us for a guided tour of the land. 'Cliff's busy at the moment. He's discussing the plans with the builders, then the priest's due this afternoon for the ceremony.'

'What ceremony? There's not even a temple yet.'

'The priest must bless the land,' Remy said, 'before the building can begin. The priest must advise according to auspicious days on the calendar as to when various stages can go ahead. One would not dare begin, put the roof on, nor move in on an adverse day.'

'When will I get to live here?' Kate tripped over some tiles.

'When the building is complete,' Remy continued, 'the main ceremony can take place. Knowing Cliff, it's bound to be extravagant. Half the village will be there, a full gamelan orchestra and a mountain of offerings, plus a few chickens and ducks to bury in the ground.'

'No way, I draw the line at some things. This is where we're planning to put the main bedroom,' Kate sketched the plan on the ground. 'I did want to put it over there, with a view over the trees, but Cliff said no. He's vetoed a lot of my ideas, it's a bit frustrating.'

'He has no choice,' Remy explained. 'You see this area is *kaja,* it faces north towards the holy mountain, Agung. *Kangin* is east, where the sun rises. The sun is considered an important manifestation of God, so your bed must be placed so that your head is *kaja-kangin,* in close aspect to God.'

'I'm glad someone's taking the time to explain this to me,' Kate said. 'Cliff never bothers. I thought he just didn't like my designs.'

'He may not understand it himself and so is merely following the advice of the priest. The temple must be located near that wall,' Remy gestured to the same holy direction, 'in the most revered corner of the land.'

'So north and east are considered the most sacred directions?'

'You miss the point. It is all relative. Mount Agung lies in the centre of Bali so to someone living in the north, the holy direction is south towards the mountain. It varies according to location.'

'This is a lot trickier than I thought,' Kate sighed, taking Remy's arm. 'What about over there, where my kitchen will be?'

'Ah yes, to the *kauh-kelod,* the impure directions. That is also where you would put your garbage, and any animal pens.'

'Actually, I'm not intending to keep any pigs, but this is very interesting, tell me more.' Following him around the site, Kate was engrossed as he explained the processes involved in building.

Remy was a fountain of spiritual knowledge. I admired that aspect of him greatly even though I was not often privy to it. Aware this was our common link, I realised it was a force to be reckoned with. If he was indeed to become a priest one day as he so aspired, it would put an immense strain on our relationship. That which had drawn us together could become the wedge to drive us apart. Turning northwards to Mount Agung, I looked up at the mighty peak and prayed.

'How's the building going?' I asked Kate as she marched straight into my house, pacing nervously up and down. Since construction of the house had begun, she'd become a nervous wreck, her own stages of breakdown inversely correlating with the various levels of the house going up. With luck it would be finished soon, before she had the chance either to exterminate the builder or self-destruct.

'Don't ask,' she seethed, 'whatever you do, never decide to build a house, especially here. They're driving me round the bend, what with all the delays. Every other day is a ceremony, then they down tools for a month because it's an inauspicious time to put on roof tiles!' The vein on her temple began to pulse. 'Now they're putting tacky beige in the guest bathroom instead of the pink marble I ordered. Do you think the builder takes delight in torturing me?'

'Sounds like you need a break, how about going for a drive? I think its time we went bush to see how Joyce is faring out there.'

'What a great day for a run in the country,' I said, basking in the sunshine as we rambled along the bumpy road. Kate borrowed Cliff's open jeep for the trip, worried that the Mercedes would look a tad pretentious in the village.

'Let's stop for supplies,' Kate said, pulling into a roadside stall. 'We should get some drinks, there's still a fair way to go.'

'Oh, for goodness sake, get a load of that,' I shrieked with laughter as we carted the bottles back to the car. 'I don't believe it!'

A group of monkeys had hijacked our car. One had ripped the screw-top off the water bottle and was guzzling the contents. Another was wiping the duco clean with a cloth while his friend attacked the glove box. The bravest of them was behind the steering wheel, groping for the ignition.

'You can get rid of them,' Kate said, 'I'm sure you have an affinity with apes - I'm not going near them. When I was in the forest before, one yanked off my Rayban sunglasses and another ripped out the gold stud from Drew's ear and swallowed it! They're vicious.'

'Are you sure they're not part of some organised crime ring - a monkey Mafia? There may be some pretty groovy primates hanging up in them trees, tuned into their Walkmans, taking candid snaps of the tour groups.' While we discussed strategies, a passing shopkeeper strolled past and shooed them away, scattering them in all directions.

'That was easy,' Kate sighed with relief, taking to the wheel.

Winding along a road fringed with palm trees, we checked the signposts and headed due north. Kate slowed down often to negotiate a series of hairpin bends cutting through the mountain. The road narrowed sharply, leading into cool dense forest. Sweeping ferns brushed our elbows as we penetrated further into the undergrowth.

'Joyce has really gone remote,' Kate said, pulling a branch off the windscreen. 'She didn't strike me as the jungle type.'

'Secretly she yearns for adventure. I wouldn't be surprised to see her swing past on a vine. The woman's got style.'

'The natives aren't exactly friendly round these parts. Across that lake is Trunyan, a village propped against the volcanic crater. The people belong to one of the original tribes of Bali and are still quite primitive - they dispose of their dead by leaving their bodies to rot in the forest groves. Amazingly the corpses emit no odour.'

'Strange. When Madge and Len went there for a day trip, they fled in terror when the villagers stoned the jeep and attacked the tour guide because they wouldn't buy anything. The poor dears never recovered from the shock. I don't think they'll be back again.'

'I empathise,' Kate replied. 'I went there once with friends. Our boat was moored in a pocket of dank cold air with really bad energy. All these people came down to stare at us, their eyes strangely empty like zombies. We didn't hang around too long, hightailing it back across the lake in record time. As we rowed, a grey hostile mist swirled above our heads in a threatening cloud. It was terrible.'

Jerking along for several more kilometres, the road dwindled into a rubble track. We didn't say much, hushed by the repressive mood of our surroundings. I turned the map upside down, trying to make sense of it. 'I haven't got a clue, let's go straight ahead.'

The jeep ground its way noisily along the pitted road until we came to a small, isolated village. Several children ran out to greet us. By the curious looks on their faces they didn't get visitors here too often. From the top of a distant verandah, I heard an almighty shriek.

'My prayers have been answered!' Joyce shot down the steps at the speed of sound. Flinging herself into our arms, she squawked a greeting. 'God, it's good to see you both again. I don't believe it!'

'We're glad to see you're still alive on your mystic mountain,' I laughed.

'This is perfect,' Joyce warbled, 'Sly's gone to the village for supplies so I can have you all to myself. Come up to my humble abode,' she dragged us bodily up the hillside. 'We can talk for hours. I'm absolutely starved for company, you're a godsend.'

The small thatched house was perched on the cliff-side. Joyce, the proud hostess, ushered us straight over to the terrace. By the dents in the batik cushions slung around the floor, this was her favourite spot. 'Check out the view. Isn't it great.' There was a sheer drop to the valley; a stream of crystal water poured from a chasm in the rock face, cascading into the river below. It frothed white and sparkling over the polished rocks.

'Sit down.' Joyce hastily dusted down the bamboo chairs. 'You two got here in the nick of time, I was on the verge of committing hari-kari with no-one interesting to talk to. I'm truly desperate.'

'What about Sly?' Thrust into such a remote situation together, their relationship must have developed a new level of intimacy. Or conversely, surrounded by his kin, the bond could be sorely tested.

'Please! His idea of witty repartee is asking me to wash his undies. I put my foot down on that one. I'd have had to carry the water up the hill on my head in a metal pot. Would have wound up with a permanent goitre. I don't spoil my looks for anyone!'

'Joyce, I know it's a nice spot and all,' Kate said, trying to be tactful, 'but how on earth do you stand living out here. It's so isolated. I'm sure I'd go potty - there isn't a beauty salon for miles.'

'Believe me, it takes a helluva lot of getting used to, but you know what - I really love it up here.' An old woman entered the room bearing a tray stacked with hot tea and freshly made sweets. 'Sly's mum likes to look after me,' Joyce said, hoeing into a rice cake. Village life had not diminished her appetite. 'All of Sly's family's are nice,' she added, grappling to keep her sarong from spilling open, 'except for his sister. She's peculiar.'

'In what way?' The group hanging about on the balcony all looked peculiar to me, but I didn't want to say so and insult the family. Joyce seemed to have fitted in nicely.

'She's always following me around, I can't take one step without bumping into her and those kids of hers always run around the house getting underfoot. Then again, we are the only house in the village with a telly.'

As we spoke, two boisterous lads barged into the room and scuttled under our feet. Their mother plonked herself uninvited in the seat opposite. Nursing a young infant groping at her breast, she stared at us with a look of total disdain. 'My sister-in-law, friendly isn't she?'

'We may be out in the wilds, but that baby's wearing enough gold to sink a battle-ship. You can see where all the rice crops go.'

'That amulet around the baby's neck,' Joyce explained, 'houses the umbilical cord. The left side is sealed with an ancient coin, the right supposedly with a chip of tiger's tooth to ward off evil spirits.'

'How come you know all this?'

'I was up here for the baby's birth, as a sort of surrogate mother. The baby's considered pure and can't touch the ground for six months. It must be carried around until its *oton*, its first birthday. See that black rock on the left of her front door - when the baby was born the placenta was washed and wrapped in a white cloth and buried under there in a coconut husk.'

'That's fascinating, is that the custom?'

'Yes, the afterbirth is considered one of the four spirit sisters of the child, along with the blood, the amniotic fluid and the yellow vernix. These spirits stay with the person all through their life and even after their death. They become the soul's special protectors.'

'Almost like her guardian angels?'

'Sort of, they're supposed to bring you happiness and shield you against illness and evil. However there's a twist. If they're not treated with respect, they can turn on you and cause all sorts of dreadful problems. Throughout one's life, one must acknowledge the presence of the four spirits - to talk to them before sleeping, leaving them a little food and drink when you eat, and honouring them at all of the numerous life ceremonies.'

'Joyce, you're becoming a real mine of information.'

'I've got nothing better to do up here than snoop around and read my books. Look,' she said, flipping through a particularly well used volume - *'the kanda empat'* - the four siblings. One lives in the heart as the element of wind, the next in the liver as fire, another in the kidneys as earth and the last as bile in one's breath. The irony is that the spirit's power can be used for one's own purpose, good or evil. For black magic if abused, or for meditation and the attainment of moksha, personal liberation, if realised for the good.'

At this point, Sly's sister who had been sitting motionless, bored by our conversation, slunk out of her chair and squatted on the floor, careful not to let the baby touch the ground. She motioned for us to do the same. A sinewy old man was approaching.

'Quick ladies, positions on the mat,' Joyce said as she peered out the window. 'The priest is about to pay us an unexpected visit.'

'Why are we on the floor?' Kate asked.

'Because no-one else is allowed to be the same level as him.'

The old priest, clad in musty white, regally entered the room. Sitting upright in the nearest chair, he attempted to speak to us in broken English. Sly's mother almost crawled past on all fours to offer him some refreshments. The room filled up with visitors all bowing and stooping to pay their respects. We exchanged a few pleasantries before the priest tired, and after a long, strained silence, he rose to leave. Language, once again, had proved a staunch barrier. Everyone followed him out, leaving us alone to relax our cramped bodies.

'You know,' Kate said, as she propped herself back into the chair, 'Sly's sister is really odd, the way she was staring at us.'

'She's harmless enough. Sly's attached to her and I don't want to upset him by kicking up a fuss. Anyway she comes in handy when we have a fight, she's always on my side! Women have this great instinctive bond. Now let me take you down to the river so you can see why I love it so much here.'

Stiff from inertia, we wandered down to the river's edge and skimmed rocks across the glassy water. 'You see, there are compensations for living away from civilisation,' Joyce laughed, splashing us in an icy spray. The sound of a motorbike rumbling in the distance and her face lit up. 'Sly's back,' she said, running over to greet him. Our presence had become superfluous.

'You ladies come here to check up on my gal?' he said half-jokingly. Smothering her in kisses for the benefit of his guests, he acted the part of the perfect boyfriend, having the whole romance thing down pat. Joyce was elated by this raw display of passion, still infatuated by his thinly disguised charm.

We left them to it and strolled back to the car. Sly's hold over Joyce had grown more intense with time. Slowly he had chipped away layers of her past, until little of it remained. He was now in a position to gain complete control. I hoped Joyce still had the ammunition to fight back when the time came.

'Celebrate ...' The Mercedes swerved into the pink pebbled drive before coming to a discreet halt beside some lavish potted plants.

'Close your eyes and don't peek.' Kate exhaled loudly, barely containing her joy. 'Now open them! Well, what do you think?'

'My God, it's a mansion.' I craned my neck to get a better view of the new house. Painted stark white, it was a stunning blend of Balinese design and Western opulence. Sturdy columns stood guard over the front door, intricately carved in classic rosewood.

'I can't believe it's mine,' Kate said, admiring the new batch of palms lining the path. Those months of anguish were worth it in the end!' The maid pulled open the solid doors that led to the foyer. Shuffling barefoot across the cold marble floor, I gaped at the massive sparkling chandelier dangling above.

'It arrived from Jakarta last week along with two men to assemble it, sort of a package deal. Let me take you on a guided tour.'

I climbed up the massive marble staircase. Flickering shafts of coloured light were reflected from the oval stained-glass windows in the walls. The master bedroom was gigantic, the king-size bed swallowed up by a pile of thick designer rugs and batik cushions. An exquisite hand-painted screen of exotic birds formed a dramatic backdrop to the floral spread.

'This is quite something!' I enthused, burying myself in the rich turquoise lounge. 'My whole house could fit into your bedroom.'

'It's like a dream come true,' Kate said, toppling onto the bed clutching a chilled bottle of champagne. Popping open the cork she filled the two glasses to overflowing. 'Everything's happened so fast in the past few weeks - the house, the ceremony and finally, the wedding plans - at long last!'

'I think that deserves a toast. If anyone could swing it, Kate, it was you.' Taking my glass, I held it high. 'I wish you everlasting joy.'

Kate rolled over onto her belly and picked up the silver-framed photo of Cliff from the bedside table. Taking a sip of her champagne, she was lost in contemplation. 'I do love him so very much.'

'I don't doubt it for a minute.' Despite her euphoria, something was troubling Kate. For someone who had just realised her wildest dreams, she seemed tense - like a frightened bird in a golden cage.

She clung onto Cliff's picture, careful not to damage an image fragile in her mind. 'Cliff's been so distant lately, not himself. I know something's really bothering him, but he won't confide in me.'

'With everything he's had to deal with lately it's not surprising.'

'There's more to it.' Kate sighed heavily. 'I know Cliff well enough to know when something's really getting to him. He's not eating properly, he hardly speaks, and sex ... forget it. He's a proud man who won't open up easily. I thought Remy might talk to him.'

'Unfortunately Remy's involved in a temple ceremony over the next few days. He's been promoted as an emissary for his god so he's busy delivering his messages to the flock.' Remy was becoming more enigmatic by the day, his proclivity to his god making him downright elusive. Kate's eyebrows arched. 'Don't look at me like that. Remy won't tell me any more, until, quote, "I'm ready to understand."'

'And I thought I had problems with Cliff! Lia, it's a long shot but would *you* talk to him?' Kate pleaded. 'It's worth a try, please.'

Cliff was alone in the garden checking out the newly installed pool. Kate handed me a cool juice before slipping discreetly out of sight. I rocked on the fringed swinging chair considering my next move. Cliff was far too insular to approach openly, like most men he would not readily admit he needed help.

Sensing my presence, he looked up, and to my surprise walked over and sat beside me. Absorbed in his thoughts, he started to mutter absently, 'I've gotten everything I wanted in life, and I worked damned hard for it. Why should it be taken away from me now?'

'Cliff, you're not making any sense,' I ventured slowly. 'You've got a string of nightclubs and bars, a wonderful woman, this beautiful house, you're successful. What more could any man want?'

'Sometimes I don't know myself,' he smiled, attacking a shock of silver hair that had fallen out of place. 'I feel driven at times - it's never enough. I get so frustrated and that's when I start drinking,' he added, staring blankly into his glass. 'The pressure mounts ...'

Deep lines furrowed his brow. 'I've told no-one this, but I have to let it out before it destroys me. Lia, I trust you ... but you must promise me not a word to Kate, she's had enough to contend with lately.' Taking a large swig of bourbon, he found the courage to speak. 'It all started when I got involved in a business deal with someone I thought I could trust. We invested a lot of money together to build a hotel - that was a big mistake.'

'Wasn't he honest?' Could all this stress be over a crooked partner?

'Worse than that, he was evil. At first I suspected him of fiddling the books but when I confronted him, he denied it of course. That's when weird *things* started to happen. Botched appointments, missing papers, keys gone. Small things at first, but then it began to affect *me* personally. I couldn't concentrate - my mind became confused and disorientated. In the end all I could hear was *his* voice over and over in my head. I tried to block it out but couldn't. He was driving me mad and very nearly succeeded.'

'Cliff, you're much too strong for that. You're upset, over-tired and worried over this whole thing. He's playing on your weakness.'

'No, it's not so simple. It's gotten to the point that I can't sleep anymore. Night after night I'm tormented by terrible dreams and wake up feeling a wreck. Now I'm so frightened, I stay awake most nights. Kate knows there's a problem but I told her I was having nightmares. I went to great lengths to spare her, even about the bird.'

'What bird?' Cliff was building up to something and I had the sneaking suspicion that something was very unpleasant.

'It was my favourite, it sang to me every morning. I kept it on the balcony outside our bedroom. One night, I tossed and turned convinced that monsters were wrestling with my soul. I felt them pressing on my chest, sucking the life force from my body, I couldn't breathe or move ... it was horrifying. Finally I broke free and escaped outside for some fresh air. That's when I found the bird dead in the bottom of the cage. Dried out like a shrivelled leaf, black and hollow, the soul drained from its tiny body.'

'That's awful,' I said, shivering. 'What on earth caused it?'

'Magic!' The hairs on my neck bristled at the sound of the word. 'My partner's put a spell on me and I'm terrified for my life.'

'Cliff, surely you can't really believe that magic has the power to destroy you?' Despite my doubts, I knew he thought otherwise.

'I don't believe it, I *know* it. Last week I attended the funeral of an old friend. His parents were convinced their son died from magic. He had won a court battle over land; his cousin swore he'd get even. Two days later he was dead. Forty and in the peak of health.'

'Perhaps it was the stress of the case, high blood pressure,' I faltered, searching for excuses. 'He could have had a heart attack.'

'His family ordered an autopsy, but found nothing. It hardly mattered, everyone knew what he died from. When I threatened legal action against my partner, he said he would go to any lengths to stop me. Then I found an effigy of me in the drawer, he'd gotten hold of some of my hair. I destroyed it, but it's too late - the spell is cast.'

'What did you find out?' Kate asked breathlessly. 'I've got to know.'

'Cliff's wound up with heavy business stuff, his partner's giving him a rough time, but he told me that he doesn't want you to worry. He's exhausted, he needs a rest.' I wanted to share the truth with Kate, but in reality I wasn't sure whether she could handle it.

'I wonder if there isn't more to this than Cliff will admit. Lele, my houseboy, has been telling me all these incredible stories. When he was young he watched a ceremony in his village where a dead body was carried from the graveyard and brought back to life.' Aware of my scepticism, Kate was even more emphatic. 'He saw it with his own eyes. On the way home in the dark of night Lele's mother was terrified, sure they were being stalked by a leyak. Freaking out, she quickly peed then smeared urine on herself and her child. Urine makes you invisible to leyaks, they don't like the smell.'

'Can't say I blame them! Aren't leyaks people who can supposedly transform themselves into monkeys, headless bodies or bizarre lights, then come out at midnight to cause all sorts of havoc?'

'Yes, but it's their spirit that changes. The physical body stays behind in bed, lying unprotected. Therefore it is an extremely dangerous practice, one that is not undertaken lightly. These people study the *lontars*, the secret books, for years to master black magic for their own purposes, and then leave a mighty trail of destruction.'

'No wonder it feels so scary round here late at night!'

'Not only can they frighten you to death but they can introduce foreign objects into your body, poison your food and cause many types of illness. Amulets, rings and mantras are used for protection, but it is hard to kill a leyak. Knives are useless, but there *are* ways - if one can cause the spirit to die, the human body follows automatically. That's why people who die in bed late at night of unknown causes may be suspected of being a leyak.'

'How come you've suddenly developed an interest, you usually avoid these subjects like the plague.' More instinctive than she realised, Kate's subconscious was tapping into the arcane reasons behind Cliff's crisis.

'It's an endless source of fascination, especially to see how seriously it's taken. Just last week a massive ceremony was held right in the middle of Denpasar to exorcise all the evil spirits in the area. The police blocked off the road and all leyaks were invited in for a challenge of power. When night came, lights were forbidden, and the women paraded together in a circle of protection. Then there was a shadow puppet show and the puppet master named all the women suspected of being leyaks. One old hag horrified Lele so much that he ran off. Her spectre chased him so Lele whipped off all his clothes, because if you're naked, you're invisible to leyaks.'

'Ah, now I understand the interest! Incidentally, remember that dried-up prostitute I told you about, the one who was at the dukun's getting a beauty potion? Well, she was at the club the other night looking rather attractive - there might be something in all this.'

'Are you sure she didn't spend a week's intensive at the Pond's beauty institute,' Kate laughed. 'They could have been testing a new wonder cream for the mildly decrepit.'

'More likely she's been drinking the local herbal mix to restore the goddess energy. Do you know you can get a tonic to tighten the vaginal muscles and raise lust in the old pecker? Joyce told me about it. She was often known to go down to the corner trolley and indulge in a few sachets.'

'Did it work?' Kate asked impatiently. 'If so I'll go out and buy a few truckloads. Mind you I think it would take more than a tonic ...'

'Joyce never got to test it,' I chuckled. 'As soon as Sly found out, he headed for the hills. No doubt the reason that Joyce is up there right now. He doesn't stand a chance!'

CHAPTER SEVENTEEN
The Getting of Wisdom

'Joyce, what are you doing standing out there in the rain?' Huddled in my doorway, Joyce looked like a gaunt shadow of her former self. Sensing the urgency, I pulled her inside the house and found a towel. 'Don't move, I'm going to make you a hot cup of tea.'

Keeping a watchful eye from the kitchen, I waited impatiently for the kettle to boil while ladling her cup with spoonfuls of sugar. Knowing that sweets perked her up, I rifled through the cupboard and found a stale packet of chocolate biscuits. Arranging them daintily around the saucer, I took them out to her doing my best to look calm.

'Don't worry, I'm not about to cark it on you.' Her hands trembled as she fumbled with the tea. 'Do you mind if I stay here with you for a while? I couldn't think of anywhere else to go.'

'I wouldn't think of letting you step foot out of the house in this condition.' A stray tear slipped out from the corner of her eye, but she dabbed it away with her sleeve. 'Joyce, whatever's going on?'

'Sly's gone and done a Remy on me.' Unable to fathom her meaning, I stared at her blankly. 'Remember the sister you warned me about, the warped one with the mean stare. Well, the longer I stayed up in the village, the weirder she became until her behaviour became downright bizarre. It all culminated last night with the full moon. She went crazy! I found her outside my bedroom window bent down on all fours baying at the moon. Sly went out and slapped her, trying to get her to calm down but she kept on. I still get goose bumps thinking about it,' Joyce said rubbing her arm.

'Had she genuinely gone mad or what?'

'I should have recognised all the warning signs, but what they say is true ... love is blind. Why do you think she was following me around, keeping tabs on me to make sure I didn't get too close.'

'Oh my God!' The pieces fell into place. 'Sly's not her ...'

'Husband, right first guess. Let's say the lady was less a sister than a *wife*.' I felt Joyce's pain as sharply as if a knife had been plunged into my own breast. 'Seems like Sly convinced her to accept our cosy arrangement on the basis of a little financial gain, a house in the village, some security for the kids ... problem was she couldn't hack it. Night after night for over a year, watching her husband sleep with another woman proved too much - she cracked under the strain and decided the money wasn't worth it. She wanted her husband back, now I dare say she's got him plus a few accessories to boot.'

Joyce looked crestfallen so I refrained from commenting. Fresh wounds cut deep and took time to heal, so I settled Joyce into the spare room and tucked her into bed. Within moments she had fallen into a heavy sleep, far from her troubled mind.

Distressed, I waited for Remy to come home. Joyce's pain had stirred up my own. Why did the men here have this alarming propensity to lie so easily, about matters so serious. To fabricate a life to suit their own selfish needs? Were women just pawns to be manipulated at will? I couldn't even begin to conceive of the scale of emotional devastation or the karmic cost.

I positioned myself on the front verandah so Remy would be in the direct line of fire. It was nearly sunset; whatever his other duties he would always come home at this time to change for work.

Distracted, I watched a giant sinewy spider dangle from its web above the window. It waited patiently, in silent expectation of its prey. I could do the same. A sudden rattling of the gate and I looked out from the shadows. It was not who I expected.

Remy's wife darted inside the garden. Perplexed by her sudden appearance, I nodded a greeting. Until now she had avoided contact, keeping her distance; this was the first time she'd trespassed on my territory. Passing me by, she walked over to the temple, placed her offerings on the altar and prayed. With a token look, she left without a word. I was mystified. We had a silent pact to respect each other's boundaries, why had she crossed the line now?

'Your wife was here earlier.' Remy's eyebrows arched in interest, but he was not giving away any secrets. 'She came to pray in *my* temple.'

'The owner of this land is family, he could have asked her to come. Someone has to make the offerings daily.'

'Why would she volunteer for the job now, after all this time?' Mildly peeved, I resented her intrusion into my home. Apart from her obvious disdain, I feared she might have a grander scheme in mind.

There was more to this than even Remy was prepared to admit. I had the sneaking suspicion that he was spending less time visiting his home. I too was feeling the pinch as his religious calling impinged on our time together. Was this a last ditch attempt by his wife to lure him back, or a discreet attempt to check on his whereabouts?

'This is an uneasy situation at the best of times - your wife turning up on the doorstep only serves to remind me. By the way, Joyce is staying here for a while, she's having personal problems.'

'Sly?' Remy asked, retiring to the bedroom. I tried to get a bite out of him, but he had already lost interest in the subject.

'How did you guess?' I said, following him. 'He turned out to be as devious as I'd suspected.' No response, his apathy was infuriating. My mind ticked over - maybe he had known about Sly from the beginning and was respecting the male code of silence. 'I spoke to Cliff the other day. He believes someone's put a spell on him and is genuinely afraid. I want to help him but I'm not sure how.'

Remy spun round to face me. 'Lia, I want you to promise me you won't get involved. Never get mixed up in magic - promise me.'

'Yes,' I pledged, taken aback by the urgency of his tone. 'Why?'

'Because you'll get in way over your head. These are matters not to be taken lightly, or to be experimented with by the uninitiated. I have spent my life learning to fight the dark forces, going into caves to do battle with evil in order to release those vulnerable souls who have become possessed. The magic forces on this island are dangerous, too volatile for you to begin to comprehend ... let alone fight.' Squeezing my arms he drew me closer, 'I don't want you to bring up the subject again, or ever forget your promise.'

It was an uneasy pact. With prohibition came increased curiosity. If Remy was capable of holding off the forces of darkness, why did he believe me any less so? Remy was unaware of one major factor, one I was purposely loathe to tell him. In the past I had experienced these forces, unwillingly been tested by them. It was one of the most stormy, difficult periods of my life. Having achieved an uneasy victory, I was plagued by one nagging doubt. The battle was won, but the war was not yet over. I needed to gather as much ammunition as I could if I was to gain ultimate mastery.

To defend myself against the dark side, I needed a full grasp of its methods. This was the reasoning of the Balinese priests. In order to become a white magician, they first had to master the power of the dark.

If not, they could never understand that which they presumed to conquer, and would thus be vanquished in their quest for supremacy.

'You have to help me.' Kate was flooded with despair. 'It's Cliff, I'm really desperate.' My couch was becoming a full-time confessional.

Joyce plodded through the door. Even sedated with half a bottle of Valium and a few shots of gin, her ears were razor sharp. She was not about to be left out from the action. 'What's going on?'

'What are you doing here?' Kate asked, temporarily distracted.

'Suffice to say that by this time Sly's missus has moved into my house along with that brood of hers, and has reduced it to a pile of rubble. As for Sly, he's no doubt already picking out his next victim. The bastard took me to the cleaners - lock, stock and barrel!' Joyce coughed, pouring another gin. 'They say there's no fool like an old fool. What's Cliff's problem?' she asked anxious for the diversion.

'I know it sounds crazy,' she cried, 'but my worst fears have been realised - Cliff has been hexed!' Joyce looked aghast. She'd expect it from me, but from super-rational Kate? 'He's a wreck, he hardly gets out of bed - it's like part of him is missing. I've had a dozen doctors call round but none have offered any help. Now I've heard about this healer, a powerful dukun from Sumatra. He's supposed to be the best. You'll think me mad but I've already sent for him. I can't stand by helplessly,' she protested, 'watching the man I love being destroyed by forces I can't even begin to fathom.'

'Kate,' I said emphatically, 'do what you must.'

'All I want is a bit of moral support. Jai arrives on Monday. I need someone with me that I can trust.' Joyce looked dubious, in her drained condition it was too dangerous to consider. Kate stared at me imploringly. I wavered, remembering my pledge to Remy.

The atmosphere surrounding Kate's house was tense and hostile. It was shrouded in an eerie silence. I trod carefully over the gravel path, not wishing to announce my arrival. A dangling vine wove through my hair, stopping me dead in my tracks. I should have heeded the warning.

The door to the house was slightly ajar, the lights dimmed. Full of misgivings, I paused before entering, then skulked across the cold polished floor towards the sound of muffled speech. It was coming from the lounge room. A group of people were sprawled on the Persian rug in a circle, fixated on the man in the centre. Kate was far too engrossed to notice my entrance so I sat down unobtrusively amongst some strangers.

I focused my attention to the man in the centre: Jai, the black magician. Wiry and sharp, his jaundiced features were singularly unpleasant. Even his aura was polluted, it emanated a toxic, murky green ooze. From the sinister glint in his eyes, I had no doubt that Jai had been mixing in the forces of darkness; a palpable field of negative energy surrounded him in a dark spiral. Jai was profoundly evil. Automatically, I activated an outer psychic shield of protection.

Although the others had barely noticed my arrival, Jai had shifted around cagily. Watching me from the corner of his eye, he locked his arms in front of him, his fists clenched so tightly that the ashen blue veins bulged. Slowly he began to rock his body. 'I am ready for the journey, my spirit tiger waits by my side,' he spat the words into the air. 'Who will be first?'

'I will,' Kate replied breaking the silence. Her voice had lost its strength, her soul parched of fire. It was clear that Cliff was not the only one in danger. I prayed Kate had not invited further catastrophe into her life by bringing this man into her house. 'My boyfriend is losing his spirit.'

'It has been stolen from him,' Jai snapped, 'by one who envies his success and seeks to rob him of it, then claim it as his own.'

With fumbling bony fingers, Jai took a large sheet of blank paper and wrote down Cliff's name. Kate's eyes widened with each bold stroke of the pen. Folding the paper exactly, Jai took the edge and held it close to the candle. The flame sparked, shooting out bright flashes of blue as the paper ignited into a fiery ball. Jai threw the remains into a small brass bowl. Waiting for the embers to die, he dabbed his fingers into the smouldering grey ash then smeared them across the inside of his arm.

Large welts began to form, bold strokes written across his grisly flesh, ghostly letters etched by an invisible hand. Fragments of a word emerged, scrawled in dull grey ash. Faint ... indecipherable ... then growing more and more intense. Clearly visible until there was no doubt. 'W-I-R-A-N-A.'

'Wirana!' Jai shouted out victoriously. 'He is your secret foe.'

'That's the name of Cliff's business partner,' Kate tugged at her sleeve anxiously. Her face, drained of colour, looked pale and gaunt in the candlelight. She stared in disbelief at the letters indelibly printed on Jai's arm. Branded in flesh - irrefutable, fathomless proof.

'Beware,' Jai warned, 'this man seeks total control. He has planted something in the grounds of your house to rob Cliff of his wealth. It is a slow, lingering spell that will ultimately destroy him. When he has lost the will to fight, Wirana will step in and take over.'

'What should I do?' Kate begged. 'I must stop him.'

'I will travel with my spirit tiger into the dark astral regions and we will tunnel through to the source of the magic. It is a long and dangerous journey and I must stop and feed my tiger many times along the way.'

Kate handed Jai a large wad of money. Clenching it in his fist, Jai lay back on the rug with his arms folded in front of him. Closing his eyes, he murmured a string of incantations. His body trembled and jerked as he went into a trance. Too tense to move, we sat, incredulous, as his dream state stretched into an agonising infinity.

After the longest silence, Jai roused unsteadily. When he opened his hands, everyone gasped. The money had gone and in its place was a small, muddy package. It emanated a life of its own, shiny and strangely diabolic. Unwrapping the mouldy cloth, Jai brushed away layers of caked mud. A minute piece of bone, some seeds, a tuft of fur and a pile of nail cuttings, all repugnantly tangled, were inside. Then the final indignity - a matted strand of hair. 'This is yours,' he said, handing Kate the long blond hair.

'That's disgusting,' she gasped, dropping it to the floor.

'Don't worry, he can no longer harm you. I have broken the spell. Your friend is free!' Eyes darted about nervously, each person looking to the other for some sort of explanation. Even the strongest sceptic was astounded, having witnessed something that defied logic. *The items manifesting out of thin air, the letters on his arm ...*

Jai looked at me, a taunting stare. Repelled by the cesspools of darkness within his eyes, I averted my gaze. My feet felt like dead weights below me. As hard as I tried they would not budge and I was powerless to move. A clash of psychic wills was taking place.

'I need help,' a strained voice cried. A middle-aged woman, wrinkled beyond her years, spoke out. 'I have an antique shop; before it was thriving but now I am going bankrupt. Whenever anyone comes into the shop, they turn around and leave. Even the staff are feeling uneasy and quitting. The stress is starting to show.'

Jai smiled wryly before accepting the mandatory payment. Reclining back onto the floor, his body convulsed into a heaving mass. Engaged in a bizarre conversation with invisible enemies, he writhed wildly before snapping back to life. Handing the woman a small gritty parcel, he sneered. 'A cheap trick. I journeyed to your shop and my tiger sniffed around under the earth to find this buried in a very deep hole, the work of an amateur!'

Unwrapping the mouldy package, the woman's fingers shook as she removed the musty layers. Inside was written a name on a tattered piece of cloth. She read it aloud, stumbling over the letters 'S ... ANTI. She's one of my shopgirls,' she said stunned. 'I can't believe it.'

'This girl Santi wants to take over your business, to drive you out. Beware,' Jai branded her with his eyes, 'or she will succeed.'

My head throbbed as I fought to make sense of this nightmare. This had to be a trick, a colossal subterfuge to relieve people of their money, or else this man possessed fiendish psychic powers he was exploiting for a profit. Either option was horrendous.

Others didn't share my doubts. Spurred by what they had seen, many offered Jai money to uncover secret schemes. The scene continued throughout the night as plots were exposed - tawdry webs of hate, revenge and jealousy. It was the worst kind of psychic manipulation.

There was one final wrench to the soul. 'My mother's so ill in Holland,' a frail girl said, her words sticking in her throat like clumps of dead wood. 'I'm sure she's dying. Please do something.'

'I will try,' Jai answered greedily, 'but Holland is far away. It is a long and arduous trip, my tiger will get very hungry along the way.'

'Money is not a problem.' The girl's eyes, ringed with the dark circles of grief, pleaded with him. 'Just help her.' She gave him an envelope bulging with bills. In a graphic display he twirled his hands in the air, and the wad vanished without a trace. Everyone gasped.

Jai was the ultimate illusionist, with a total lack of conscience. Many ancient cultures acknowledged the presence of a spirit animal to aid the shaman on his quest to other realms. Its powers would protect and guide him as he ventured through potentially dangerous territory. Jai claimed to possess the eye of the tiger, its strength and courage enabling him to penetrate hidden mysteries. However, the tiger's spirit was fuelled by the wind and waters of the earth. In this case it was the master who needed the physical comforts along the way.

Bristling with rage, I decided to expose the man as a fraud before his greed could cause further damage. What disturbed me was that nobody else was aware of the deception, all victims of an apparent mass hypnotic spell. Jai was a seasoned black magician whose powers I alone had escaped. How could I defy him openly without unleashing the full force of his evil?

'I am tired now,' Jai said, satisfied with the night's takings. 'We will journey tomorrow.' There were muffled cries of disappointment from those who missed out. *'Tomorrow,'* he promised as the crowd parted to let him through. Jai glared at me as he brushed past, my skin prickled in abhorrence of his touch. He knew the ruse was over.

As soon as the room cleared, Kate rushed to my side. Before she had the chance to extol Jai's virtues, I stopped her. 'Listen, Kate, the man's a fraud. He's stealing money right from under your nose.'

'You're wrong,' she protested, 'he's helping. How else could he know the names? It all makes sense now. Can't you see he's got power?'

'He's got power alright, but he's abusing it. You've got to stop him before he hurts more people. The man's dangerous, you have to get rid of him. Now!'

Suddenly there was a flash of recognition. 'I'll ask him to leave,' she nodded blindly as the fog began to lift. 'In the morning, when I've got more strength.'

There was no need. Jai, astute enough to know he'd been found out, packed his bag in the middle of the night, took the money and fled into the darkness. Gone but not forgotten, he plotted revenge.

'Are you sure you're alright?' Remy asked, for the tenth time. 'You've been acting strange since you woke up.' Remy got on his motorbike, then looked straight at me, piercing through the deception. 'What did you get up to at Kate's house last night?'

'Nothing,' I replied, brushing off his suspicions. 'Don't worry, Joyce is here if I need anything.' I didn't add that she was beyond help herself, spending most of her time passed out on the bed.

Remy left for temple, the germ of doubt firmly evident in his eye. Throwing a cushion onto the sunniest spot on the verandah, I flopped down among a pile of well-chosen books. There had to be some words of wisdom, a fleeting reference that could explain what I'd witnessed the night before. I knew Remy could shed light on it, but I didn't dare broach the subject with him and risk the repercussions.

I had barely turned the first page of my book when I heard a low rumbling sound. A long protracted growl, slowly escalating. Imperceptible waves of energy vibrated around me yet nothing moved. I braced myself for the shock, expecting the aftermath of an earthquake. There was a sharp rap followed by silence. Fine cracks appeared in the thick garden wall. One by one, the large stone blocks shuddered, tumbling lifeless to the ground as if shaken by an unseen hand. As the last stone fell, a flimsy cloud of dust settled over the scene coating it in a deathly shroud.

'What's going on?' Joyce stumbled through the door and stared incredulously at the crumbled wall. 'Was there an earthquake?'

'I don't know, the wall disintegrated right before my eyes.' A lone butterfly strangely transfixed to a large palm leaf was the only sign of life in the garden; nothing else had been disturbed.

'Maybe they used crummy cement,' Joyce shuffled towards the kitchen to fix herself some coffee. I decided to shrug it off, there was no use in over-reacting. Weird things happened all the time, usually with some perfectly logical explanation. There was no connection whatsoever with the events of the previous night. Or was there?

Later that day, I was showering in the open bathroom. Sunlight filtered through the lush ferns as a small lizard scuttled across the rocks. All of a sudden, I smelt something burning. A fine grey haze filled the air. Flecks of ash dropped from the sky, smudging my skin with black soot. Wrapping a towel around me, I drew back the curtains and peered outside. To my horror, the thatched roof of the garden shed was smouldering dangerously.

I tied on a sarong and ran outside. Joyce was already there, screeching in horror. The neighbours, alerted by her screams, scaled the wall and dumped bucket loads of water from the well onto the smoking building. Spurred on less by the need to save me than by their compulsion to stop the fire from spreading, they put it out in record time. I thanked them profusely as they stumbled over the pile of rubble that was once my wall.

'This place looks like a disaster area.' I surveyed the damage. 'Joyce, you didn't sneak into the back shed for a quick fag did you?'

'Scout's honour, I didn't go near the place. I was on the loo when I smelt the burning, and let me tell you I was out of there like a shot. I wasn't about to meet my maker with my knickers down!'

'This whole thing's getting weirder by the minute.' Damage to the building was minimal, thanks to the timely intervention of the neighbours, but I was left with a most uneasy feeling. 'I wish Remy was here, I need him to clear up this mess.' In more ways than one.

'Great, the one time I have an emergency,' I said, reading the note, 'and Remy's going straight from the temple ceremony to work.'

'Is he indeed? Then I guess we'll just have to turn up at the club and surprise him,' Joyce snarled. 'Men, bloody useless! You're surrounded by a pile of rubble and a burnt out-house, and he's off somewhere praying for salvation. Figures! Time for a little direct action, I'm tired of moping around. Put on your best gear, we're partying!'

As I applied my make-up, I was struck by a macabre sensation. I was sure someone was standing behind me. A warped figure staring back at me from the mirror. Even though the features were blurred, I recognised the hatred in the eyes. It was Jai. Petrified, I jerked away and ran for the front door. From out of nowhere, I felt a hand grab my shoulders and push me. A hard, deliberate shove.

Losing balance, I fell forwards down the stairs. Luckily Joyce was waiting at the bottom of the steps and cushioned the blow, stopping me from falling flat on my face. 'Hey, take it easy,' she joked, 'I know you want to see Remy, but calm down before you end up killing yourself.' I smiled, but deep down I was panicking. I hadn't slipped, I was deliberately pushed from behind. My brain went into shock. Did Jai have the power to inflict harm from such a distance? If so, what scourge of destruction had he unleashed?

'You'll never believe it,' Kate said, beside herself with glee. 'Check out the far bar.' I caught sight of Cliff's head before it was obscured by a squadron of American sailors let loose on shore leave. The local 'butterfly' girls were whipped into a frenzy, vying for the spoils before the men had a chance to return to the boats. 'Cliff's up and at it again, this is the first time he's come out since this whole dreadful business began. Look, he's actually smiling. I told you Jai could help.'

'Oh, he certainly has,' I said, rubbing my bruised shin. Kate, a good customer, had gotten what she'd wanted. Cliff was better. At least someone would emerge from this debacle strengthened.

'I'm ecstatic,' she said, wandering off through the crowd to rescue her loved one from the horde of plastic beauties.

'Things are definitely starting to look up,' Joyce said, nudging closer to a particularly muscular specimen of maritime delight.

'Oh dear one, what a pleasant surprise!' a voice cried out. Joyce winced as she recognised the off-beat face, then feigned deafness to the roar of an Aretha Franklin track. 'This meeting must have been ordained,' the woman persisted. In flowing purple robes, a bold silver star glistening around her neck, she was impossible to ignore.

'This is Andromeda,' Joyce said, spreading her girth across the seat to block her. 'We met down at the beach yesterday.'

'Yes, I was in the middle of my water ritual, paying homage to the great Poseidon when I swam right into Joyce. I think we are kindred souls ... and so it is ordained.'

'Indeed.' Joyce had the amazing propensity to attract weirdos, collecting oddballs the way other people saved stamps. Like a reject from a 1960s peace rally, Andromeda's cheeks were splashed with glitter, her mind similarly bedazzled.

'Isn't Bali just the most cosmic place in the world,' she sighed. 'The vibration here is truly amazing. I came back because of past life karma. You see in my incarnation in Atlantis I caused an energy shift in the earth's surface and I'm here to undo the damage.'

'*That* truly is amazing. May I ask how you intend to do that?'

'Of course,' she beamed. 'When my birth star moves in exact alignment with the moon, I shall evoke the powers of the heavens.'

'That's a pretty daunting task,' Joyce chuckled.

'Indeed, but I have the support of my power allies. The spirit of the goanna moves with me. Not to mention my soul mate, Rex. Alas, he is on a higher mission, exploring crop circles in Cumbria. He speaks to me now. 'Oh, Rex, of course I'll dance for you.'

Andromeda sped off onto the dance-floor, twirling around in a frenzy. Her lilac robes ballooned dangerously, wiping out anyone in close range. Even the navy took cover. Those left standing, soon ran off as she began her loud communiqué with her beloved. 'Oh my darling, Rex, we will soon be reunited. My arms are open to you, my body is fertile, come - take me.'

'Joyce, you do have some rather unusual friends.'

'She dropped out of the stars and to the stars she will one day return. Oh my God,' Joyce seethed, her blood pressure soaring, 'I don't believe it, how dare he turn up here.' Sly, pushing aside anyone who stood in his way, marched straight over to us.

'Beat it buddy,' Joyce huffed, her fists clenching for attack. 'Get out of my face before I grind you into the ground. Some nerve!'

'Calm down honey,' he murmured, attempting to stroke her arm. She flicked him off like an unwanted bug. 'We really do need to clear up a few things. How about we go somewhere quiet to talk it over.'

'The only quiet place I intend to see you in, Sly, is a morgue. You're wasting your time, I never want to speak to you again.'

'I know I've done you wrong,' he warbled, 'but I know we can work things out. If only you realised how much I've missed you.'

'Missed my bank balance, more likely. What? Do you need to make another payment on the car or is the family strapped for a little spare cash? Now that I think about it,' Joyce said, almost dislocating his arm from its socket, 'we do have a few matters to discuss. Damned if I'm going to let you get away with it - I want my money back!'

Left to my own devices, I gazed into my glass, contemplating the meaning of life, hoping the bubbles of my mineral water would provide me with a vital clue. Effervescent one minute, then vanishing without a trace. Just like all of Joyce's dreams.

Staring further into the glass, a vague outline took form, etched in soft fluid lines. Mesmerised by the glassy silhouette, I could not avert my gaze. Then I recognised the face - Jai. Driven by the pounding music, I stood up. Remy smiled as he saw me approach.

What happened next was blurred. A steely voice was driving me on. I vaguely recall the stunned look on Remy's face, the icy feel of the glass in my hand as I threw it, the bitter words that escaped from my mouth, harsh words that were not mine. I found myself slipping from reality. Losing my footing, I tumbled backwards.

Plunging down a swirling tunnel, I cried out. Warped images flashed before me, bright whirling forms and colour. Voices screamed out to me from all sides. I grabbed a plant to break my fall, but instead heaved it rudely from its pot. The earth scattered in all directions, spraying the air in a fine mist. A dark snake hissed a warning '*Get out quickly ... before it's too late.*' But I couldn't, I was falling too fast. Coming to my rescue, the snake coiled its body around me, breaking my fall. Dangling on the edge of madness I was detached from my senses and felt no pain.

Time had expanded, my perception unwinding in slow motion. What had taken a few seconds in reality seemed like an eternity. Hands reached out to help me, a familiar voice called out my name to comfort me. Remy's eyes were flushed with concern. Dazed, I got up, disorientated but unhurt. Steadying myself against the bar, I surveyed the damage. The pot plant had borne the brunt of it, lying in a shattered heap on the floor.

'Remy ... I want to go home,' I stuttered, acutely embarrassed.

Wrapping me in his arms, he led me out. I wanted to speak but was unable to. Remy knew something was terribly wrong but was astute enough to know this was not the right time to demand answers. He lay protectively by my side all night, but was his defence too late?

*

I awoke the following day bruised and shaken. My head throbbed as if possessed by a thousand demons. If I could have buried myself in a pit of remorse, I would have. How to excuse what I couldn't explain?

'You look awful,' Remy said, his voice betraying the level of his concern. 'You've got a temperature, I knew there had to be some reason for the way you've been acting. I'm calling a doctor.'

As expected, it was an exercise in futility. Apart from a fever, the doctor could find no problem. I knew there was something more sinister at play, but was unwilling to confide in Remy. I was suffering enough without inviting his contempt at my stupidity.

'You know what I reckon,' Joyce said, sitting on the end of the bed. Checking to see if Remy was out of earshot she leaned closer, 'We've gotta find someone who can fix you up and real quick. Bugger the doctors, you need a real professional. I'm taking you to Kenzo.'

'So you do believe my story about Jai.' Joyce was the only one I trusted with the truth. 'You do believe he's put a curse on me.'

'Listen love, the way things have been happening to you lately, I reckon they're all lining up to have a go at you. Jai's top of the list.'

'Who exactly do you mean by *they*?'

'Well for starters, what about Remy's missus? She's been hanging around your garden a bit too often lately for my liking. Maybe burying a little special something to make sure you keep your claws off Remy. And what about wife number two? Maybe all those lonely years spent mourning her loss are catching up with her.'

'That's absurd, how can you believe them capable of that?'

'Listen, after I saw Sly's wife in action, I wouldn't put anything past them. People may be all sweetness and light to your face, but you haven't got a clue what's going on behind your back. They probably curse the day Remy met you.' My head began to pound. 'If it was me, I'd be covering all my bases. You know how accurate Kenzo was before, what have you got to lose by seeing him again?'

I thought about the last thing the old man had said to me. 'One day, you will need to see me again. When the time comes, I will be here waiting for you.' I *would* go and see Kenzo again.

The room was gloomier than I recalled, a thick layer of melancholy clung to the walls. The accumulated auric debris of many lost souls. I fidgeted tensely waiting for Kenzo to appear. A sudden rustle of fabric, and the old man emerged from behind the dark curtain.

'You carry a great weight with you today.' He shuffled closer. Robed in burgundy, his gaunt face was lined with pathos. 'You are sorely tested. You have many hidden enemies that lie in wait like serpents, poised to strike! Beware!' Kenzo's eyes lit up, 'Those you believed you could trust are in fact mighty adversaries. Listen my child,' he said, responding to my entreaties to reveal names, 'we cannot bring them out in the open and risk exposing their bane to the world. Let it remain hidden where it belongs, in its own pit of iniquity. We must concentrate instead on finding a way to protect you.' Kenzo wrote down a long list. 'Take this, and when you have these things, come back on the day of the black moon. Then we will rid you of this insidious curse.'

Barely daybreak, the market was bristling with movement. Large piles of fresh fruit and vegetables were spread across the footpaths, many people bunched around them, haggling over prices. 'It's five in the morning,' I said, stepping over a pile of rotting garbage, 'and we're scrounging around the markets of Denpasar with a shopping list I can't even read, it's madness!'

'Look on it as an adventure,' Joyce said, placatingly. 'Let's face it, you don't really have any other choice. You're getting crabbier by the day, you snap my head off at the slightest provocation.'

'I do not!' I barked, like a rabid bulldog. As much as I hated to admit it, my personality had altered. Feeling depleted, my tolerance was wearing thin, those around me bearing the brunt of my vexation. Yet it was the inner assault that was the real source of worry.

'We should be able to get everything in there,' Joyce said, dodging several baskets of leathery eels, 'except for the two goose eggs, they're a bit hard to come by. I've had to offer a reward to the ice-seller to find them on his rounds in the village.'

'It sounds to me like the proverbial wild goose chase!' The rank odour of freshly hacked meat assailed my nostrils as we entered the main pavilion. 'One day we'll look back at this and laugh - at least I hope so for all our sakes. How Remy hasn't cottoned onto this drama yet is a mystery, I hate keeping it a secret from him.'

'Tell him and risk being hung up on that.' Joyce pointed to a sharp, bloody hook that was holding onto the remains of a large shank of pork. 'Remy doesn't seem to be in a very forgiving mood lately.'

'That's because he's so suspicious ... I want to get this whole thing over and done with before it has the chance to ruin my life. Ah, that's better!'

We'd stumbled into the floral hall, overflowing with baskets of marigolds, white lilies and soft lilac hydrangea blossoms. 'Perhaps I could buy a couple of bunches of daisies while I'm here.'

'Focus on our mission,' Joyce said, hauling me up the stairs. 'Let's try up here, I haven't got a clue where to find any of these things,' she said, struggling to make sense of Kenzo's scrawl.

'Let's ask her.' An old woman stood behind a stack of archaic earthenware pots. 'She looks like she'd be au fait with an exorcism list,' Joyce said, handing her the crumpled paper. With slow intent she scanned it, her clouded pupils questioning our motives yet well aware of our purpose.

Her scrawny fingers dipped into a cracked clay pot. Clouds of pungent saffron powder filled the air as she scooped deep down. From a rusty tin, came a lump of brittle grey rock which she ground into powder with a heavy wooden mallet. Using an antiquated brass scale, she weighed each ingredient before wrapping them into small tidy parcels. One by one she laboured, until the list was complete.

'That should just about do it.' Clutching my prized booty close to my chest I made a run for it. Joyce was one step behind.

I awoke on the fateful day in the worst possible way. Troubled by a lucid nightmare, Remy struck out in his sleep at invisible demons, whacking me hard in the back. In agonising pain, I cried out.

'What is it?' Remy was beside himself when he'd realised what he'd done. 'Sorry, I was having a bad dream. I was running towards a steep cliff, chased by a band of monsters and I lashed out.'

A faint voice issued a warning in my ear. It was the day of the dark moon, the forces of evil were seizing control.

'Has Remy left?' Sure that the coast was clear, Joyce darted into the room like a frightened rabbit. 'Have you got everything?'

Groping around on the top shelf of my wardrobe, I searched for the parcel. I had it stashed away under some clothes. The source of my salvation, I guarded its contents with unbridled tenacity.

'I have a real bad feeling about today.' Joyce puffed furiously on her cigarette. 'We've still got a few hours to kill, let's go down to the beach and do some heavy breathing. We can cut through here.'

Dark Sands Hotel, not the wisest choice. We scurried through the gardens, anxious not to get caught up in the negative pull. A group of people had gathered around one of the bungalows. Curiosity got the better of us. 'What's going on?' Joyce asked, straining to see. 'Oh, no,' she groaned, 'I don't believe it, it's Andromeda.'

It was hard not to recognise the recumbent figure in flowing robes. 'What do you reckon are the odds of bumping into her?'

'Friends, come,' she yelled, gesturing for us to join the rest.

'This I've just got to see.' Joyce flopped onto the lawn. 'I'm in the mood for a little light entertainment. What's the woman up to?'

Resplendent in magenta, Andromeda sat centre stage on the grass. Beaming like an omnipotent guru bestowing blessings upon her flock, she dangled a crystal pendulum from her hands.

'Who else has a question?' she beckoned.

'Will I be married soon?' a young girl asked hopefully.

Andromeda threw strange mantras to the wind. The pendulum began to swing back and forth wildly. 'Ah, your young man is not your soul mate. *He* waits for you on a fishing boat in the Atlantic.'

'Oh brother!' Joyce whispered. 'What a load of crap.'

Everyone sat riveted, including some staff who had stopped work. Each movement of the pendulum had them enthralled. It never ceased to amaze me how starved people were of spiritual guidance. So needy that they looked in all the wrong places. Andromeda did not disappoint, raving on passionately to all who would listen.

'Now, that's what I call a dangerous woman.' Psychic powers were a gift not to be abused. I was soon to discover just how accurate my words were. Throughout her metaphysical tirade, Andromeda kept staring at me from the corner of her eye. As she became more and more agitated, the pendulum started to oscillate wildly, mirroring her own condition.

Abruptly, as if led by some devilish hand, she jumped up and bolted through the crowd. Waving her crystal madly she ran for me then without warning, attacked. With clenched fists she bore into my chest, driving in with all her might. I struggled to push her away.

'Get off, you stupid bitch,' Joyce screamed, bashing her with her straw bag. People rushed to my aid, including the gardener, brandishing his rake. Eventually they succeeded in breaking her hold. A wave of protest swept through the crowd as they realised the extent of her madness.

Andromeda collapsed on the ground in a sobbing mass. Hanging her head in shame, she screamed garbled messages to the damp earth, scooping up handfuls in her trembling fingers. The crystal's cord twisted tightly around her arm in a tangled knot, the stone glowering in anger at its mistress's lunacy.

'I'm getting you out of here *now,*' Joyce yanked me upright. 'We're going straight to Kenzo's before anything else can happen.'

Waiting in the small dark entrance, I was overwhelmed. The attacks were becoming too blatant, their manifestation sinister. My chest felt as though a silver arrow had been shot into it, its bruised centre radiating sparks. Kenzo emerged from his shadowy den. Aware of my plight, he hurried me to a dim room at the back of the house, a room sealed from all external light. A few rickety chairs were strewn across the floor, a small wooden table lay dreadfully bare in the centre.

'You have come just in time.' A feeling of panic pervaded my being. 'Don't be frightened, for you are number 888 on my list. A most auspicious number.' How could there be so many damaged souls out there in the world? 'Have you brought what I asked?'

'Yes,' I said, handing him the mangled bag. I prayed I hadn't shattered the goose eggs in the melee with Andromeda.

'Good, the sooner we relieve you of this spell, the better. Now, go into the bathroom and wash yourself clean, then wrap this white cloth around your body.' Scrubbing hard, I re-entered the room bound in the stiff cloth. I felt like a helpless moth trapped in its own cocoon.

Kenzo was too engrossed to notice, his energy absorbed in blending the herbs. Under the crude lighting he placed them into a small china bowl, adding water and handfuls of rocky granules. He stirred the mix into a rough powder and scooped his fingers into it, smearing a large clump of the rough black paste across my back. Cold and abrasive, he rubbed it all over my exposed body until my skin felt like it was being ripped from the bone.

'I want you to take some deep breaths,' Kenzo urged, as he lit a solitary white candle. Turning off the lamp, he picked up the two goose eggs which had been lying inert on the table. Glistening in the candle light, smooth and unblemished, they looked strangely enticing. A subtle incandescent glow emanated from their centres.

'We must capture the dark forces and trap them within the eggs. It will not be easy, the evil will struggle for supremacy. Are you ready?'

'Ready,' I choked as a shiver ran down my spine.

Kenzo advanced towards me, the precious eggs clasped in his hands. Muttering a string of invocations, he placed them on my closed eyelids.

The smooth coolness was soothing until the eggs started to pulsate. My body throbbed, swirling patterns bursting into my mind's eye. A cosmic blast and a wild profusion of images exploded in my head, a blaze of unrivalled colour.

At first it was fascinating, luring me deeper into psychedelic realms. As the chanting accelerated, so did the intensity of the visions. Fragments of thoughts spilled over in my mind, faces searching for space. Blurred, they merged into one distorted picture, my brain reeling from the attack. I panicked, fearing I would lose touch with my personal version of reality.

Then, Kenzo moved the eggs to my throat. A giant tremor rocked my body, the eggs started to vibrate madly. Pressed hard against my skin, they sucked at the malevolent energy that had taken over my body. I experienced the terrifying sensation that my life force was being pulled out right along with it. My face contorted in pain, the agony excruciating.

'Take them off!' I clawed desperately at Kenzo's wrists.

Unable to respond, he was lost deep within his trance state. The pain intensified to an unbearable extreme from which I could not transcend. Passing through a tunnel, my senses no longer existed. My spirit, dispossessed, looked down dispassionately upon my poor racked body, gladly liberated from the source of torment.

'Come back,' a voice commanded. *'Now!'* My eyes snapped open and I looked at Kenzo with a vague flicker of recognition.

Slowly, normal sensations returned as I slumped into the chair. Joyce fanned me with her hat, powerless to do more. Kenzo, sweating profusely from the strain, was too exhausted to move.

'They fought with incredible force. I hope we have succeeded in trapping the evil within the shells. After you leave here, you must go to the bridge and throw the eggs into the river. Only in the muddy waters will their negative power be forever contained.'

'I hope nobody's out there bathing,' Joyce said seriously. 'I wouldn't want to unleash these powers on any other poor soul.'

'Rest now,' Kenzo said, seating himself uncertainly at the table and writing something down. 'Do not open this,' he warned, handing me a folded sheet of paper. 'Place it under your pillow to protect you while you sleep. This one, you must memorise, then destroy. It contains a secret mantra that you alone must know. Whenever you feel the presence of evil, recite it. Never forget to do it,' he hissed, his dark eyes flashing. 'Never!'

'Never,' I pledged, subsiding into the aftershock of my ordeal.

CHAPTER EIGHTEEN
Uneasy Compromise

'Everything that goes on around here is a game,' Joyce declared. 'That's why I've come up with this,' she motioned with a flourish, pushing aside the mess on the table to reveal her new project. 'A new board game! I'm all set to make my fortune so I can run off to Monte Carlo and find myself a baron. I think I deserve a title after all I've been through. Do you like it?'

'Most innovative,' I replied trying to make sense of the chart.

'It's a variation of Snakes and Ladders, Balinese style. I call it Sneaky Snakes and Party Penjors. I could think of lots of ways to slide down on this island, it's the ups I'm having trouble with.'

'This is pretty creative,' I said, as she coloured in some more squares. 'Now let me see. *Snakes.* Drop five if you lent him one million rupiah and expect to get it back, or down ten if he's just cashed in that airline ticket you sent him. Lose seven, if you've got a severe case of Bali belly, head lice, cane bugs or fungal spots. How many points if you score the lot?'

'Zillions! It ranges from small-time, say if a gecko shits in your beer from the ceiling, to mega-points if you find out his mother, aunt, or other close family member is really his wife. Then again you go to the bottom of the board if he shows you a photo of a ravishing blond he's cradling and you believe she truly is his penpal from Dubbo.'

'Coming up with the pluses must have been hard.'

'Yeah, it sure was,' she replied, scribbling with a fury. 'I settled on these. Up three if you're out in the sticks and you're forced to pee, wash naked etc, and the whole village comes out to watch. Ten if you went for a ride in a yellow taxi and ended up paying the right fare without shedding blood. Another twenty if you underwent a recent exorcism ceremony and lived to tell the tale. You get top points right away. And whammy - jackpot! Immigration has just given you a free extension on your visa.'

'Let's keep it within the bounds of reality! You're becoming very resourceful, you might just become a millionaire yet. Come to think of it, I could add a few Snakes of my own.'

'Find your own game.' Joyce zealously guarded the board.

'Actually I was thinking more of an environmental version. Like drop one million points for desecration of the island. Minus one thousand to the morons who built a bungy jump on a natural waterfall and dammed up the stream so that all the dingbats could land there without scrambling what was left of their brains. Or to the huge conglomerates carving up the island for the spoils, and the hotel chains that drain the water table dry for their luxury golf courses, leaving whole villages without supply, or despite all opposition, insist on building near sacred sites, causing vast spiritual carnage.'

'Any more?' Joyce asked, focused on a higher mission.

'Tons? What about 'Skirmish in Paradise'? Have you ever heard of anything more obscene than turning one of the world's most beautiful places into a battle zone. Or crunching along the beach past dead fish, plastic, oil slicks, or through the broken coral on some outlying island, destroyed by fishermen blasting up the reefs. Something has to be done to reverse this damage before it is too late.' I knew I was speaking of impossibilities. Green belts could never be recaptured, corruption erased, or trust restored.

'I despair for this place,' Joyce said, suddenly quiet.

'I know, I cling onto the memory of what used to be and mourn for what has yet to come. I don't think I can stay around any longer and watch the devastation of a place that I adore. It's far too painful.'

'So are you prepared to leave, once and for all?'

'Not yet - I can't cut the umbilical cord that binds me here. The bond's absolute. Remy's a big part of it, but even as he drifts further into his spiritual calling, it causes little dent in the connection.'

'Tell me about it.' Joyce had been tight-lipped since her talk with Sly, but it weighed heavily on her mind. 'We're getting back together,' she shrugged, resigned to my reaction. 'Sly's going to live down here with me five days a week. The other two he goes back home to the village to be with his wife. It's a bad compromise.'

'Joyce, you can't be serious? You'll turn out like Sue! She comes back after five years of marriage in Australia, to find a wife and kids he'd 'forgotten' to tell her about. Now there's all these people wandering around her house she doesn't even recognise and she's ended up supporting the lot. She's lost her spirit in the process.'

'Oh heaven forbid! People make their own compromises, however eccentric. Some women know about the wife, and go ahead and get married anyway. They're happy to be part of an extended family. In any case, who are we to judge otherwise?'

'That's fine if *you* get to make the choice. What about those poor women who find out the hard way - like us? We're resilient enough to survive the betrayal, but others aren't. Look at that poor Japanese girl who's so sick with stress she lies dying alone, staunchly refusing to leave the house she's built, worried her husband will move in with either the wife he'd failed to mention or his new Javanese girlfriend. She'll stay put till her last dying breath!'

'Granted it's shocking, but many mixed partnerships do work out, especially if the girl succeeds in dragging the man off the island where the cultural influence is less overpowering.'

'Remy would never leave Bali, his whole being is enmeshed here. I made the decision to stay with him - I don't know if it was the *best* choice but it was *my* choice, so I must accept the consequences.'

'Just think of how much you would have missed out on if you'd left,' Joyce argued. 'The bottom line is, what the hell have I got left? I'm getting on in years and I don't want to end up a crotchety old lady living alone in some flat with only an emaciated budgie for company. It could work out to be the perfect solution - a man to keep the love juices flowing and precious time to myself. In any case, many women back home accept second best as mistress to some measly man, at least here I'm the majority shareholder!'

'Well, that's one way of looking at it, but ...'

'These past weeks,' she interrupted, 'I've had time to reflect on my life. I thought I was happy over the years, business was booming and the money kept rolling in. It made me a free woman. I could have anything I wanted except the one thing that mattered most. *Love.* Bill cared in his own way, but I was more like one of his mates at the pub who never scored an invite. He didn't see the woman in me, so I never recognised it in myself. Sly may be the biggest con-artist of the century, but he treats me like a pearl.'

It suddenly became clear to me why women got sucked in so badly. Many men were content to gain entry to your body, here they wanted access to your soul. Sly had played Joyce well, astute enough to know what was missing deep inside her and fill the gap. Now, she was unwilling to discard the one thing that made her happy.

'I feel like a rosebud that's just bloomed after years stuck in a desert. So I might have to pay to get watered, but then again roses don't come cheap! I know if I stay here I'm bound to get pricked by a few thorns but if I go back home, I'll sure as hell wither up and die.'

There was no way I could object. Throughout my life I had opened myself up to many experiences and no matter the cost, I had learnt much along the way. Of *one* thing I was certain: at the end of the road there would be room for only one regret - for those things never tried. Failure or success were nowhere near as daunting.

All of a sudden the door slammed open and Remy loomed against it. One of my blunders was about to catch up with me. 'What have you two ladies been getting up to?' We looked at him blankly. 'How long did you intend to keep your little forays a secret? A friend saw you coming out of Kenzo's house last week. What's going on?'

'Oh, I just remembered a cake I have to bake,' Joyce said, backing out of the room and leaving us to it.

'OK, I admit it,' I said, cornered. 'I ignored your advice and got caught up in stuff I wish I hadn't. Curiosity got the better of me.' Still no dent in his armour. 'I'm sorry, but actually everything's been much better since I saw Kenzo, my life has returned to normal.'

'Lia,' Remy softened, 'I'm being over-protective because I don't want anything to happen to you. I've warned you that these forces you are mixing with ... well, they can be lethal in the wrong hands.'

'I've learnt my lesson the hard way.' This was the opportunity I'd waited for. 'One thing still really bothers me though,' I started tentatively. 'Why was it that in my hour of need I was forced to turn to a stranger and not to you? It hurt me so much that you weren't there for me.'

'What do you mean?' Remy looked wounded.

'I know you've got the power to help me when I get tangled up in my proverbial messes. You've helped countless other people who have turned up on our doorstep, strangers who asked for help. But when I needed you, you weren't there for me, or at the very least I was scared to approach you. Shouldn't you be more concerned with the welfare of the woman you love rather than that of a stranger?'

'You're right,' Remy said, after a moment's reflection. 'I have become obsessed in my calling, neglecting you in the process. Let's go somewhere we can be alone and talk things through.'

The rock face plunged chalky white into the deep blue ocean. The waves flung hard against the cliff, then dissolved into a thick wash of foam. I peered over the stone wall, enthralled by the magnificent cobalt wall of water spread out below me. There was a sheer vertical drop to the sea.

'Uluwatu,' Remy explained, 'is a narrow isthmus of limestone that was once thought to be the mythical ship of Dewi Danau, the goddess of water. See the turtles over there?' he pointed to several dark shapes breaking through the waves. 'They're coming up for air. A magical place, isn't it?'

The energy was intense, positive and strong. 'Uluwatu is one of the most important temples in Bali,' he pointed to the thatched roof of the white coral temple, perched on the rim of the peninsula. 'It is considered one of the six holy temples of our world. The sage Wawu Rauh who came from Java, achieved moksha, enlightenment, here in the sixteenth century. It was he who helped incorporate the principles of Buddhism into Balinese Hinduism.'

'Remy, do you know how connected I feel to you right now?'

'That bond becomes my ultimate downfall. You asked me why I didn't reach out to help you before, why I was so detached? It's because I fear any personal involvement would cloud my judgement and jeopardise my power. My love for you makes me vulnerable.'

'You're wrong - love is your greatest strength, you just don't see it. Let me tell you something I've never confided before. If we were brave enough to expose our trials and tribulations more often, we could share our anguish with many other wounded souls walking the same path.'

'Lia, I don't understand what you're getting at.'

'Before I came to Bali, I went through one of the most horrendous periods of my life. The more difficult things became, the less capable I was of handling them. It's an insidious process, this negative assault on the soul.'

'What are you trying to tell me?'

'At the time I had become very ill. I woke up in hospital after surgery feeling like a thousand demons were attacking my soul. I dismissed it as the after-effect of the anaesthetic not realising then how diminished the auric field was and how weak I'd become. When I returned home, the onslaught continued. I was terrified.'

'What exactly happened?' Remy's eyes narrowed as he looked past the words, to the rationale of why I had never told him something so crucial before. Simple. It was a savage wound that I'd sublimated even from myself.

'Every night I would be woken by spirits, lost and out of control. I felt they wanted to destroy me ... by attacking me, not so much my physical but my ethereal body. By weakening my auric protection, they undermined my health which was already seriously compromised.'

'That's how they could affect you in the first place - but why would they want to?' While Remy could accept the presence of dark forces on his own territory, he had trouble with the notion that they were prevalent elsewhere. I too had dismissed these nightly visitations as bad dreams until they became so vivid that to ignore them any longer would be dangerous.

'I have no idea. In the end, I embarked on a quest to save myself. It was a difficult task, my world gave little credibility to such forces. The church, despite acknowledging the powers of darkness, shirked away from them, exorcism was a black art confined to the middle ages. The Spiritualist church was more forthcoming, giving me exercises of spiritual self-protection.'

'How could they explain what was happening to you?'

'They said that I had a great task to complete for the powers of Light, and for that reason the forces of darkness would try to stop me. Whatever the cause, I found through my spiritual sojourn that there were a lot of frightened souls out there. People under psychic attack, too scared to admit it; vulnerable through the draining effects of alcohol, drugs, illness or stress. Some, who heard 'voices', probably of dispossessed spirits, were often labelled schizophrenic or mentally deranged, because our society can't deal with it. There's a lot of psychic interference out there in the world, without any proper acknowledgment and no adequate means of handling it.'

'Then you came here, discovering it was a normal part of life.'

'I was led to you for a specific reason. Spiritually charged, you are one of the few people who have learnt how to protect themselves from these forces, so your love became my psychic defence. Your aura was strong enough for two, impervious to outside attack.'

'You believe you were bought here for your own protection?'

'Yes, and because I have so much left to learn. Spiritual knowledge is a major quest of mine in this lifetime. You can teach me so many things, but you guard your knowledge well, almost like you're jealous of my interest in it. This barrier between us is infuriating.'

'I'm just gaining a foothold on my power, having people come to me for help is new and privileged. Maybe you're right,' he added, resigned to his spiritual greed. 'I do want to keep it all to myself. Besides, I rationalise it by saying as an outsider, you have no right of access to Balinese lore.'

A silver-edged cloud inched overhead, filtering light grey until the sky was shrouded in an ashen mist. Dark clouds gathered; a storm was brewing, the sky hung heavy like molten lead.

'The temple here is dedicated to the god, Rudra, the dissolver of life,' Remy said, his words mirroring the spreading bleakness. 'He is the bringer of storms - he shoots poisonous arrows into the sky to rip the heavens apart.' A streak of lightning shattered the air, amplified by the menacing roar of thunder. Rudra had shot his arrow high, piercing the veil that guarded Remy's heart. No words were necessary, Remy finally understood.

'I don't know how the others will accept you,' he said, leading the way along the abandoned path. 'I told them you would be coming.'

In his search for enlightenment, Remy had formed an alliance with a band of like-minded men. This closed circle of aspirants forged an esoteric secret society, made up for the most part by descendants of a long line of royalty. Remy's family had a tie with theirs that dated back many centuries.

Entering the ranks of the chosen, together they would head off on covert mystical crusades. Odysseys to the highest mountains to gather holy water for their sacred rituals; to haunted islands, to sleep on the cold ground and do battle with resident demons; or to remote cliff side caves, lost deep in contemplation. Therein they would experience wondrous visions.

Now I had been granted temporary right of admission. The path led to a building entangled in a bed of ferns. A group of men were gathered on the floor, drinking strong coffee and discussing strategies. They looked up as we approached, their interest piqued.

Reticently, I walked close behind Remy. This was his private domain, I was clearly an intruder in their midst. There was a forbidden energy here, radiating from the beings of these men. I had trespassed on hallowed ground. A woman, and a Western one at that, had entered their secret place.

The men scanned my face for signs of weakness as I sat down in the sacred circle. There was a loud silence until one man took the initiative and spoke up, 'I see you wear a special stone.' I fingered the crystal around my neck, searching for the right words to open a door into their world.

'I wear it for protection,' I said, aware of its inner light, 'and like many of your holy men, to enhance my communion with the universe.'

'Indeed,' his knobbly fingers pointed to the stone, 'crystals are rare and highly prized here, they are usually only found embedded in the crowns of high priests.' Throughout time, the power of crystals had been recognised by the enlightened. Potent transmitters, they were not found in abundance on these islands. Heavy involvement in black magic could make amplification of such energy dangerous.

'What more do you know of the stones' power?' an elder asked, his eyes deeply hooded. I sensed this was a test of sorts.

'Over the years I have built up a collection of stones gathered from some of the world's most potent energy points. I believe that each one of these stones possesses the cosmic emanation of its source.'

The old man stared at me, intrigued. 'I have a stone that was given to me, a special stone. What can you tell me about it?'

He handed me a wrapped parcel, inside was a clear citrine gemstone. Metallic streaks ran across its glassy surface. Placing it in my palm, I willed the stone to reveal its purpose.

'This is a healing stone, the person who owns it has a problem with their blood - their circulation is impaired. It should be kept close to the heart to pump out the poison and aid in their recovery.'

The man muttered something to the others. Several men took off their rings and handed them to me. Aware that many Balinese wore heavy rings studded with gems which were talismans passed down through their families, I hesitated. Thought to possess great powers, these stones were almost mythical in content.

Despite my misgivings, I proceeded. All seemed satisfied with their interpretation, psychic lore transcending cultural boundaries. One man in the centre had remained quiet. From his noble stature, and the reverence with which he was treated, it was evident that he was the most influential person present. The descendant of a king of the local regency, he came from a long line of royalty. He had a cool arrogance about him, an air of superiority that was unnerving.

With steely purpose, he took off his heavy onyx ring and handed it to me. The metal burnt a hole in my flesh. The stone's structure was intense, compressed energy pouring out of each molecule, a dense ebony blackness forged over ages by the volatile forces of nature. 'This piece originates from deep within the earth's crust and exudes power,' I explained. 'Thus spawned in the dark it possesses the psychic magnitude to cut through evil, and so counteract the forces of magic. It is a potent deflector of darkness.'

'Yes, you are right,' he responded guardedly. 'Just yesterday I was called to a stranger's house. He was very ill, on his death bed. As soon as I entered the room my ring began to pulsate strongly, warning of impending danger. The man was the victim of a deadly curse. I immediately commanded the fiendish spirits to depart the place and leave his soul in peace.'

Purposefully, the man turned to Remy. 'Why did you not tell us that your friend possessed such gifts? She could have come before and given us insight into the wisdom of the West.' Caught out, Remy looked to the ground - so *he* had been the block to my progress.

'I wish to learn so much. I have always felt an affinity with the spiritual practices of the East. One of my greatest revelations took place on the slopes of the Himalayas of Nepal. It touched me deeply.'

Even back then on that mystical mountaintop, in the sheer light of a brilliant full moon, I sensed an intrinsic connection between the two places. Not only in an ancient belief that Bali originated from the lofty mountains of Nepal, the last remaining Hindu kingdom in the world; nor just in the sanctity of holy water collected from the mother river, the Indian Ganges; or the sharing of a common religion; not even in the placid faces of the people. More so, the connection came from my heart and I felt indelibly joined with both places without any real grasp of why. Time would prove my greatest teacher.

'Ah, this is the life,' Kate gloated, luxuriating in the warm bubbles. Sheltered by lush palm trees, the turquoise spa was idyllic. 'The wedding's planned for April, it's going to be so romantic ... and lavish.' Kate poured another martini. 'You will be here, won't you?'

'Of course,' I replied, drawing my head back through the water. Kate looked at me quizzically, sensing a hidden worry. 'The prospect of life with a priest is daunting. Remy's become so entrenched in his spirituality, I fear that one day he'll aspire to be more god than man.'

'Don't be so pessimistic. Cliff's always considered himself a bit god-like, a cut above the rest. It's that belief that got him where he is today - it took him from a childhood of scrounging on the streets to a modern-day financial tycoon. Now he's so intent on building an empire for our heirs that I hardly ever see him, but it doesn't phase me. I know I'm an integral part of his life. How he hopes to produce any progeny is beyond me, but I'm patient. I'll compensate by building my own empire one day.'

'You've known from the start what you wanted and went out and got it, all the while expecting nothing but the best.'

'I can't understand why some women settle for less and end up with the crumbs. When I think of the abuse Linda had to endure, the shit Joyce went through or the compromise you've had to accept.'

'Kate, you've been fortunate enough to be buffeted from most of life's hard knocks. You're the sort of person that infuriates the rest of us - great body, health, life and foreseeable future. You only serve to remind us of what we're missing. If a person has been through hell, they become accustomed to it. It's hard for them to realise there's a heaven out there waiting for them, and even harder still to believe they deserve a slice of it.'

'I admit being born into wealth made it easier, but I'm of the firm opinion that you get out of life what you put into it. All I can see is a lot of potential gone to waste. You're an extraordinary woman; are you going to spend your life obsessing about Remy, and neglecting yourself?'

'Of course not,' I protested. 'These experiences I've had over the past few years have to account for something.'

'It's called the getting of wisdom. Why don't you do us all a favour and write them down. Share something of yourself with the world. Heaven knows people need to be warned of the traps which lurk out there, that way all you've gone through will have meaning.'

'A hen's night!' Kate exclaimed. 'I don't care if it *is* three months before the wedding, I want to get into the party mood.' She stepped back to admire herself in the mirror. 'Which one of these goes best,' she asked, fiddling in her jewel box, 'the pearls or the diamonds?'

'Wear them both and save yourself the angst,' I said, draping the rest of the jewellery around me for maximum effect.

'Did someone mention *angst,* my favourite condition!' Drew sashayed into the bedroom, drenched in the scent of unbridled passion. 'This house is like the ruddy set from Gone with the Wind!' Pouring himself a glass of red wine from the crystal decanter, Drew reclined on the chaise lounge and basked in the decadence. 'Here's to a fabulous evening,' he said, toasting us in grand style. 'Unforgettable!'

The doorman nodded as we neared, heaving open the solid wooden doors to allow us entry. Vamps was a large, glowing cavern, peppered with darkened booths, thick with the smell of raw body odour and forgettable nights. I sank into the blood-red cushions as a limp waiter in a starched bow-tie took our order.

Through the smoky haze, a group of businessmen were seated in the next booth surrounded by a string of half-grown girls in scant dresses. The table was strewn with choked ashtrays and cheap bottles of brandy that lay drained and empty, just like the girls by their sides.

'I know how to liven you up,' Drew said, concerned by the dull mood. 'I've got some great stories to tell you.' Another dose of Drew's infamous tales, fantastic but true. 'This is a classic,' he said, sipping his Campari. 'I've spent the last weeks squiring some film folk out here from Holland making a documentary about magic. So far we've been to Java to find out about *Tuyul* magic, that's a spell to make you rich. The only hitch is you're supposed to sacrifice one of your family members every year for the rest of your life.' Kate glanced over at me and grimaced. 'Then there's *Babi Ngepet*, magic that turns you into a pig so you can rub up against someone's house undetected so their wealth transfers to you. As a precaution, you light a candle and have someone watch it. If it flickers, you're in danger and they must blow it out so the pig can disappear. If the pig's seen, *you* snuff it!'

'I'd like to snuff you,' Kate said, smothering him with a napkin.

'Oh, I forgot the best of the lot,' he laughed, repelling the attack. 'The crew went off into the jungle looking for the magic man who worships the goddess of the leech.' Drew had outdone himself. 'Whatever your problem, the dukun sucks it out like a leech. Can you imagine if you went to him with a little prostate trouble or heaven forbid, piles! Unfortunately, we couldn't find him, the poor man was in hospital with a severe throat infection!'

'Drew, you're impossible!' Spying an old friend, Kate found an excuse to run off. Spurred on by the pickings at the bar, Drew went on a hunting expedition, so I was spared any more stories. Sitting alone, I became distracted by a dark figure on the dance-floor. My eyes trailed his every movement, until I forced myself to turn away.

One's best laid plans are often cast aside by a higher power. There was a light tap on my shoulder; it was him. 'My name's Lawrence Lee,' the mystery man said, sitting down beside me. 'I'm here tonight on some business. Meeting you is an added bonus.'

'I'm sorry, you're wasting your time,' I said, intending to rebuff his advance. An innate force stopped me. This was no mere pick-up line. I was meant to meet this man for reasons far beyond me.

'Don't look so baffled,' Lawrence said. 'Sometimes things in life are unclear until we gain the wisdom to decipher their meaning.'

'I haven't the foggiest idea what you're talking about.'

'Special people recognise each other. In my travels, I have met all manner of remarkable people. Unique souls possessing powers that surpass the imagination.' Stunned, I tried to fathom where this was all leading. 'One man stands out in my mind as truly exceptional, Malik, a psychic bodyguard in Java. He protects some of the most influential people in this country.'

'A psychic bodyguard?'

'Indeed,' he replied cuttingly. 'Persons in high positions - politicians, leaders, businessmen, can be attacked in many ways. The most insidious is through magic. Malik is considered unbeatable in this country in the field of psychic defence. He can repel invasion by any outside alien force and deflect it back to the sender. Perhaps in your position, you need his protection too.'

'Whatever do you mean?' I asked, shaken by his candour.

'You don't think I picked you out at random in this crowd,' he said, never once removing his gaze. 'You already know what I mean.'

My mind flooded with a thousand scenarios, my interest roused. 'Where is this man?' I asked, in spite of myself.

'Several hours drive from Surabaya in a remote village in central Java. You will never find him without my help. When the day comes that you are ready to make the journey,' he said firmly, 'I shall fly you there to meet him.'

'This is crazy. I can't do that, I don't even know you.'

'You know as much as you need to. Here - take my number,' he said, thrusting his card in my hand. 'Call me when you must.'

CHAPTER NINETEEN

Pandora's Box

'I can't hear you,' I yelled above the roar of the traffic. The bike wove uneasily through the heavy traffic blocking the road. Remy was distracted, his mind entrenched elsewhere. Again he spoke. Random phrases cast into the wind, a tirade of words that held no meaning.

Much to my horror, Remy got so caught up in the ghostly dialogue that he lost control of the bike and swerved sharply. I yanked his arm to steady the bike, saving us both from being dumped in a nearby ditch. The shock snapped Remy out of his trance-like state back into reality.

'You could have killed us! Don't you see how dangerous this preoccupation of yours is becoming?' He nodded mutely, aware that he'd conducted another deadly discourse with his invisible phantoms.

Remy's spiritual calling was intensifying daily and he basked in the connection. Over the past months he had been honoured by the aristocratic elite for his perceived prowess as channel to their gods. Through his mouth the gods spoke, relaying messages to his eager kin. Officiating at the temple of their ancestors, he became a crucial religious link between man and god. Ostensibly, he had reached the status of priest, but the demands it placed on him were enormous.

While I was proud of his elevation, I was apprehensive of the consequences. Each time Remy returned home he was tired beyond exhaustion. His body was drained, his mind worn out. Although he rarely confided in me, I suspected he lapsed into trance for these forays. Rather than uplifting his spirit, it was sucking his soul dry.

'This can't go on, it's damaging you too much.' Remy was resolute, no words of caution could detract him from his chosen path. 'Then promise me you'll confine your spiritual parlance to the temple in future, where it can be kept under control and do the least damage.'

Remy refused to comment; he'd already given away more than he'd intended. I was soon to find out that once one entered a pact with the gods, it was they who defined the terms of the agreement. Lesser mortals could do no more than just sit and watch, then be swept along by the backlash. The consequences were far-reaching.

'Follow me,' Remy said, parking the bike in thick grass. In the distance an eerie high-pitched whine rustled through the trees, pulsing louder as we neared the cave. Then the sky fluttered with the wave of a thousand wings. The fluid stream of darkness dipped, landing effortlessly on the cave roof, a strange stillness settling overhead.

'This is the *Goa Lawah*, the Bat Cave,' Remy said, locked into the morbid luminosity of the scene. Countless small creatures hung inverted, limp and shiny, shimmering in unison against the bleak cavities of the rock wall. In stark contrast, an old priest, in pristine white, sat quietly chanting amongst a group of devotees strewing flower petals onto the callused stone.

Hypnotised by the surreal sight, my eyes became distracted by a ribbon of movement. A flicker from a deep shelf in the rock, then a slithering swirl as the huge body of a python dangled piously from above. An unearthly hush was cast - not a flicker of a bat's wing, nor the wisp of the priest's breath, just the soundless void of complete awe.

The thick scales of the snake's belly shimmered in the morning sun, it's head swallowed up in the cavernous hole. I turned away. Long gone were the days when the snake had issued its deadly counsel, now I refused to concede that it would reappear.

Surely the time of warnings had passed.

Opening up to his calling, Remy spent all his time at the temple. He had only one aspiration - to become a fully-fledged priest and he was single-minded in his pursuit. The Balinese believe the body stores a magic energy called *sakti*. Some people have a natural capacity to accumulate it, and thus empowered become holy men and priests.

Remy inherited strong sakti from his grandfather, who chose him as spiritual heir. His sacred healing tools were handed to Remy at the time of his death. Remy refused for a long time to open the box, realising that to do so would mean turning his back on his old way of life. Ultimately he made the sacrifice.

When he at last found the courage to open it, he released a Pandora's box into his world. Contained inside were secret formulas - old *lontars*, palm leaf manuscripts, inscribed with ancient calendars and horoscopes, and faded script brimming with medical and mystical text. In a small silver container were rare stones and Chinese coins which, when placed in water, had the power to invoke magic cures.

Remy had been left an awesome bequest. His grandfather's legacy had given him access to great power. In the hands of the wise, this was a great boon, but exploited by the selfish it could become dangerous. Power is corrupting, especially at the hands of an evil god. Remy had made a private pact to honour the god who saved his life. The price of salvation was high, to enter communion with a dark entity demands a heavy tax on the soul.

Many Hindu gods have the capacity to distort their own powers. Siwa in anger becomes the vengeful Kala, his wife Uma the evil Durga. Once provoked, the god can dip into his wicked shadow self and cause widespread destruction. So in a human being, sakti can be contaminated by evil intent or by indulgence in one's baser instincts. Remy had still to develop the ultimate gift of humility, thus true power was beyond him.

In the past I had become used to Remy's various quirks - the bowl of food he left for his ancestors whenever we ate, his private conversations with distant beings, the dreadful nightmares when he lashed out in his sleep fighting impossible adversaries, but now their hold tightened. His emotions suffered from the strain, and mine were trampled in the process. At first the issues were minor, more a nuisance than any real threat.

'What is *that* doing up there?' Remy stormed into the room.

It was midnight. I was sound asleep and hadn't heard him come in. 'Why have you hung your dress up there?' Full of moral outrage, he ripped the offending garment from the wall. 'You know I find it disgusting.' I should have learnt by now, thinking back to the trauma caused the first time I'd hung the undies up high on the washing line.

Clothing below the waistline, especially women's with the possible taint of menstrual blood, could not be placed higher than the head which was deemed sacred. A woman was considered unclean during her time of the month. She could not go to the temple, prepare food, and usually slept separately from her husband. This practice culminated in the fear of being bewitched, the outcome if a man's head was anointed with this blood.

In keeping with his calling, Remy's demands became more extreme with time. Something amorphous was taking hold of him, and I despaired at my inability to win him back. My own clairvoyant prowess proved ineffectual. Remy was intimidated by it and set up psychic blocks. There was only room in our house for one spiritual bastion, clearly it wasn't me.

As he became more devout, his humanity suffered and I was troubled by one nagging thought. If Remy had evolved spiritually as he claimed, where was the warmth and compassion - the mark of a true master?

I was in dire need of help. One day, while rustling through the cupboards, I found an old calendar. From one of the worn pages shone the beaming countenance of an angel. I framed it lovingly and hung the picture on the wall right over our bed where she could watch over us while we slept.

That night, I was woken by a loud bang. On the ground lay my angel picture, in a pool of shattered glass. I got up to investigate. The nail was still embedded in the wall, the plaster intact.

The next day I put the picture back up, securing it firmly in place. There it hung in all its glory until night fell, then another crash. Regular as clockwork, night after night, the angel would fall fractured onto the floor. Remy denied the implications but I could not. Was there some negative force churning around us, or could it be that my beloved angel was trying to tell me something?

Refusing to let my imagination run riot, I rationalised it away. Until one afternoon, when I was lying alone on the bed reading a book. Just as I was crunching into a juicy apple, I was disturbed by a strange vibration gathering around me. All at once, my angel picture started to wobble then with one massive whack it hurtled *across* the room. Almost as though some invisible hand had struck it hard and the force had flung it sideways.

My attention had been captured, but I remained unruffled. If this was the work of a dark force then it was crucial I not be intimidated, nor show any gesture of weakness. Such graphic displays were crude attempts at psychic bravado. Still, if it was a sign from guardian forces that there was real danger brewing, I had to be alert to search for the hidden meaning.

Tapping into an inner sanctum, I began to write down all that happened. My collection of notes swelled into a diary. Each word written, every page filled, was a magnificent release. Once manifested on paper events, could no longer vex me; revelation freed me from the sacred wound.

As my world opened up, Remy's faded into obsolescence. Thus absorbed, I left him to his calling while writing became *my* grand obsession. The threat that Remy's distancing presented, his allegiance to his gods, became less intrusive as I melded with the page. The process was not only cathartic, but enlightening.

Aspects of self well covered began to unfold, my relationship with both Remy and the island started to gain a new perspective. All went well until the day I trespassed on forbidden territory. I had strayed upon an area fraught with danger. *That day,* the fateful day I wrote of *magic* and my words were silenced.

The powers I was invoking were stronger than I could have ever imagined. Challenged by my tenaciousness, they attacked the core of my work - the supernatural. From the very first line written, the computer scrambled. Mysterious symbols flashed across the screen, taunting me with impossible script. Anxious not to lose valuable input, I inserted the back-up disc and watched amazed as the words disintegrated before my eyes. The rest of the work was left intact, only the mystical was lost into space. The secrets were preserved, returned once more to their dark hiding place.

It was nightfall by the time I got home and there was no sign of life. Remy had already left for work. Strange ... he always made a point of leaving the lights on, but tonight the house was swamped in total darkness. In the spidery shadows, I groped for the outside light-switch but to no avail - the electricity was dead. Fumbling for the key in my purse, I realised I'd been in such a hurry on my way out that I'd left it on the sideboard. No need to panic, we kept a spare one inside the window-ledge for emergencies.

In the vague shadow of moonlight, I pressed open the louvre window. I felt a sudden rush of energy pulsate through the glass. Then came a loud crack as the thick pane exploded. I pulled away sharply, a large slice of glass embedded in my finger. Muffling a cry of pain, I plucked the spiked fragment out of my skin, wrapping a tissue around the wound. Stunned, I wondered why the window had burst, its strong louvre pane shattering at my soft touch. No matter, it was only a small cut - it would heal with time.

After a few days, I noticed a strange lump on my wrist. An internal bruise, surrounded by a blue circle. It soon disappeared, but another came and went, and then another, all mysteriously moving upwards, as if some malign force was clawing its way up my arm. The bumps subsided, but my upper arm began to swell, becoming inflamed. Reaching further still, until my neck throbbed painfully, signalling a deeper problem.

Medical tests revealed no physical cause, yet the pain increased by the day. Writing was out of the question, the use of my right arm severely compromised. A nagging doubt developed into a grave misgiving. Could someone or something out there be trying to prevent me from completing my work? If so, why?

I opened my book of prophecy, to find an answer. A card fell out, landing neatly face-up on my desk. It was the card Lawrence had given to me. On it, was scrawled several words. *Malik - psychic bodyguard.* A vital piece of the puzzle was about to be revealed.

Flying across the vibrant blue Java sea, my emotions were electric. Lawrence sat by my side, content to read his business journal. He had not been surprised when I called, making all the travel arrangements with incredible expediency and detachment. In reality, he had known the extent of my concerns long before I did.

On arrival in Surabaya, a car was waiting. Lawrence took to the wheel and headed straight for Bono, the small town where Malik lived. Speeding along the motorway, we passed through urban sprawl, the choked city evaporating into isolated pockets of green and a smattering of villages.

'I hope I remember the way,' Lawrence said uncertainly. 'It's been a long time since I've been here.' After several hours drive and a few wrong turns, we reached Bono. Once there, instinct prevailed. We cruised through a web of unmarked roads, before coming to a dead end. Opposite was an abandoned field, littered with ancient ruins.

'We can walk to his house from here,' Lawrence said, helping me out of the car. Fascinated, I took time to survey the field strewn with old stones. Carved in grey basalt, a shrine stood intact within the ruins. The ancient doorways were flanked by carved towering warriors, two massive stone bodyguards. I blinked, swearing the craggy faces looked down at me and smiled. With true intent I turned around and walked over to Malik's house.

The front verandah was crowded with people waiting to see the celebrated mystic. Finding the only empty chair, I sat down and leafed through one of the albums strewn on the coffee table. Overflowing with photos of those he had helped, it was a glowing testimonial to his powers.

'People travel from all over the world to see him,' Lawrence said. 'His powers are well known to many.'

'How do they find him tucked away in this remote village?'

'You know there is a higher force that guides us along our path,' he chastised. At that precise moment, the door opened and out walked a man of infinite power and strength. Trailed by a field of glowing energy, his form was encompassed in a blaze of pure white light. I was taken aback less by his presence than by the overwhelming feeling that we'd met before.

Ignoring the others, Malik walked straight over and embraced Lawrence in his strong muscular arms, greeting him warmly. Then his attention turned to me. Our eyes met in an intense mystical reunion. 'You have arrived at last, I have been waiting a long time.'

He led me along the hallway, through a maze of stony arches to a room at the back. In the centre of the floor was a secret trapdoor, hidden by a rich woven carpet. Malik pushed it aside, creaking open a heavy wooden door, then climbed down the old ladder to a chamber.

I paused before following, wondering what manner of lunacy could induce me to follow a strange man into a hole in the ground. I took the first step, overcome by a pressing urgency. Having come all this way, fear could not stop me now. There was no turning back.

The underground chamber was small and airless, it had no light except for a bare bulb attached to a crude wire in the corner. Malik motioned for me to sit on the small prayer mat beside him. With a great deal of trepidation I did so, unwilling to relax my guard.

He turned off the light, plunging us into total darkness. Only Malik's heavy breathing punctuated the gloom. Out of the deathly void, spectres appeared. Piercing through the cover of my eyes, I used my inner sight to tap a more profound sphere of vision.

Protracted tongues of mist seeped through the wall's dull brickwork. All at once, the room was flooded with the glow of radiant spirits. Their presence gave sanctuary to my soul. *'These spirits are here to protect you,'* Malik whispered. *'Never doubt for a moment their commitment to you.'* Struggling to identify the nebulous forms, I concentrated hard. Very slowly, the cloudy images began to take on meaningful shape: my spirit guides.

An imposing Indian chief, as timeless as the skies, enduring lines of wisdom etched across his face, spoke to me through the murmur of the wind. The figure of a young woman, swathed in the purity of flowers and sheer chiffon, hovered close by. At my feet, lay a black jaguar, dark and silent as the whisper of a moonless night. Behind me, in white tunic emblazoned by a red cross, stood a brave knight, his sword planted firmly in the ground.

'We are here to show you the way,' they counselled. *'You must fight to win in your life quest ... find your inner strength to succeed.'*

Intense beams radiated all around, swamping me in a ray of divine love. Throughout my life, in the bleakest of hours, I had never been alone. These wondrous beings had walked forever by my side, supportive and accepting. They had paved my path in gold.

As they dissolved from view, I remained empowered by their force, fully aware of their continued presence. Now they would be needed more than ever. Another being was forming in our midst. Spindly cobwebs of grey threaded the air as it skulked hidden in the shadows. Deception was its greatest cover. 'Show no fear,' Malik warned, 'I shall protect you.' I hardly dared breathe as I was enveloped in a pillar of pure white light that repelled the darkness. 'Realise that despite our presence, you alone have the power to overcome your enemy, no-one else can do it for you.'

'But how can I do that if I don't know who the enemy is?'

'Perhaps it is the shadow of your own dark side, or your partner's ghost, or perhaps an outside force that means to stop you from fulfilling your life purpose.' Malik abruptly turned on the light. Shielding my eyes from the glare, I listened to his words. 'Whatever the case, the darkness must be defeated before you can succeed in your chosen task.'

'I know,' I faltered, wishing it was not true.

'Good, for you have found the source of your own strength. Still,' Malik smiled, 'it never hurts to have a little help from one's friends. Your guides will always shield you, and I have been chosen to protect you on the earthly plane. Your body has been considerably weakened by those who wish you harm. Now, we have important work to do - give me your arm.'

Taking my forearm, Malik ran his fingers gently along the skin until small drops of blood began to ooze out. Horrified, I watched the flow gather force, trickling warmly down my arm. 'Don't be frightened,' he said, taking the other arm. 'I am removing the poison that has infiltrated your system. If it is allowed to remain there, it will destroy you.'

Rising onto his knees, Malik ran his broad fingers along my body. Clammy blood seeped through my dress, dripping all over me. I grew faint as the full force of what was happening filtered through. It defied all rational explanation and I was powerless to resist.

'Enough.' He led me out. The fresh air singed my nostrils as I emerged from the dank tomb. 'My maid will help you wash.'

After cleaning the bloodstains, I emerged from the bathroom still shaky.

Lawrence poured some tea, while Malik was busy elsewhere. He returned to the room clutching something in his hand. 'This is for you,' he handed me a silver ring. A superb piece, it was engraved in an intricate spiral design, coiled into the shape of a serpent. A single green eye glowered at me. Had the snake been my protector from the start?

'Wear it and you will be safe.' I slipped the ring onto my finger, it was a perfect fit. 'The power to win is in your own hands. Use this strength wisely and walk forever in the path of the light.'

What followed next was totally unexpected. 'Many people travel from afar to see me - most to ask for help, others to expose me as a fraud. Then there are those who come on a mission of ego, to learn my gifts and master them for their own selfish purposes. Great power used imprudently can be most destructive.' He paused pointedly, 'You, however, are without motive and possess a pure inner fire. Furthermore, you are guided by a band of wise spirits. For this reason, I have decided to take you as my first pupil.'

'What a great honour,' Lawrence gasped, 'to be given the opportunity to learn the secrets at the hands of the master. You are truly privileged!'

'Thank you,' I responded, cautious of the implications.

'Think about it carefully.' Standing behind me, Malik placed his hands over the crown of my head. 'This will strengthen you.' My body tingled with a potent surge of energy. 'If you stay you will accomplish great feats, learn to transcend the ordinary. Breaking through the bounds of matter, you will one day be capable of walking through walls.'

If Malik's claims were true, what could I hope to achieve? Why spend months of study to walk through a wall, when I could simply open a door. It was a crude analogy but it rang true.

'Malik,' I said determinedly, 'I have no desire to master such things.' He made no comment but he understood. 'What I do ask is that you stay close to me, I have need of your wisdom and courage.'

'You already have more than you will ever know.' Clenching my hands firmly in his strong palms, he made a vow. 'Fear not, for I promise to walk by your side always. When you look up at the sky and see a falling star, then you will know. You will know I am standing right beside you.'

CHAPTER TWENTY
Full Moon Rising

Purnama. The night of the full moon. The shimmering distant orb cast silver moonbeams all over the island. Bali was bathed in a gossamer stream of light. The soft beat of temple drums, coupled with an eerie gentle wailing, creased the air. The erotic scent of smouldering incense stirred the senses, leaving subtle trails of jasmine-rose. The heavy, ripe smell riddled the entire island with intense carnality and dark mystery.

Plucking some flowers from my garden, I sprinkled the petals into a hot bath laced with fragrant oils. Immersing myself in the water, I imbibed the healing power of the water. Thus purified, I dressed in a long white gown and wove fresh blossoms through my hair and stepped out into the moonlight.

On a damp patch of grass, I knelt alone in prayer. My cleansed body radiated pure light, glorified by the rays of heaven. In my lap lay four large crystals. Their purpose, to seal off my home from intrusion. Hostile guests, astral or real, would be barred. I had made a secret vow, nothing would interfere with my well-being again.

I walked around the garden, plotting my moves. The first crystal would be planted in the ground under my favourite tree, the pure gardenia. The heady perfume wafted all around as I smoothed down the last clump of earth. 'I ask the spirit of all flowering trees to safeguard this point to the north. Thank you for your protection.'

Searching for a point directly east, I chose a lemon tree, a fruit bearer, to be the stone's sacred guardian. In the south, I found the perfect spot, under my lilies. Careful not to disturb their rounded roots, I placed the crystal in the earth below them. Then, finally, the west. In the dark edge of my garden, I buried the last of my precious crystals beneath some thick shrubs which would provide it shelter.

It was a simple ritual. The plants that I had nurtured for so long would protect me. The crystals amplified their energy, forming a laser field to repel any energy that did not belong within its defensive shield. As a final precaution, I took a dense black obsidian stone and buried it near my back doorstep. Here the land was kelod, most dangerous. Unholy trespassers could intrude no more.

Within my sacred circle, I envisaged a ring of pure white light surrounding me in a fine mantle of protection. Then I recited the words of an old Indian prayer that always induced an infinite sense of peace. Spun inside these beautiful thoughts, I wove a web of safety.

Repulsed by the positive energy of the force field, negative impulses stayed firmly locked outside where they belonged. What I hadn't realised was that these very same impulses were trapped inside Remy, triggered by over-indulgence in his clandestine world.

I had made a fatal mistake. Spurred on by a misguided ego, Remy opened up to these lower realms. Each time he stepped foot inside the house, within its potent psychic screen, the forces rebelled. Caught in a complex cosmic trap, they struggled for supremacy. In an ironic twist of fate, I actually incited what I had hoped to avoid.

'I don't know who my own father is any more,' Kadek sighed. 'He becomes more of a stranger to me every day.' Her pretty face was deathly white, frustration draining her of all energy. 'I miss him.'

'We all do,' I replied, concerned to see his child so distressed. Kadek had never talked to me about emotional issues before, the Balinese were guarded and rarely spoke of such things. Now in my own home, she opened up for the first time, unable to deny any longer the feelings that plagued her.

'My father has always done exactly what he wanted,' she started, 'and no-one ever questions him, because in Bali a man thinks himself a king. Now that he spends all his time in the temple, I fear that he will class himself a god and be lost to us all.'

'Kadek, do you believe your father to be a spiritual man?'

'If you ask does he talk to the gods then the answer is yes. If you mean is he a good man, then I believe he can be. My father suffers from an inflated ego, he has always been treated as special. Being with you has opened up a whole new dimension in him, he has become more humane. Now something has taken hold of him and he is slipping into his old ways. We are losing him to forces much stronger than either of us.'

Remy *was* becoming more evasive, disappearing for days on end. I shared his daughter's concerns. While I had attributed his absences to increased religious fervour, I was not entirely convinced. There was an invisible block that no amount of effort could remove.

'I'm sure my mother was tempted to return to her village many times, especially in the old days,' Kadek said with unexpected candour. 'My father was a difficult man to live with. When he took a second wife my mother was devastated. He never asked her permission; that is wrong. She lost a part of her spirit then. I don't want that to happen to you.'

'What?' I asked, unsure of her meaning.

'On the surface my father appears to be strong, but deep down he's weak. I fear he is falling into bad habits. He never comes home, and now a friend told me she's seen him many times near her home, in a place,' she hesitated, 'that is a well-known gambling den!'

I was shocked, less by the implications of Kadek's words than by the hypocrisy of her father's actions. Gambling was widespread in Bali, but it was also illegal. I didn't want Remy ending up in jail, but beyond this, I wished he possessed the integrity to be honest.

'You know some bad people hang around those sorts of places,' Kadek said, clearly worried, 'women of ill repute and others. I do not want my father to get caught up in this, it's not good for him. Please help me stop him before more damage can be done.'

'Only your father has the power to do that,' I replied, giving her a reassuring hug, 'but I'll do my best to help.'

That night Remy lay beside me on the bed in a deep sleep. I scanned his face searching for clues. The bond of love between us was intact; he was just as beautiful as I first recalled. A strand of silky hair fell careless across his forehead, I pushed it back then traced an imaginary line across the bone. Serene in sleep, his eyes divulged nothing. Shut tight, their secrets were locked far within.

Once this man had been my prince, my shining knight. Together we had travelled to distant spiritual shores, to forbidden places we would never have found alone, on a mystical journey of the soul. Along the way he had been my saviour and my pariah. Loving him with an intensity that hurt, he had the power to edify my spirit or crucify it. He was my primal partner.

Flecked with velvet beads of sweat, his chest glistened in the flicker of the candle-light. Unable to resist the alchemy between us, I ran my fingers along his body savouring the feelings it stirred within. He still had the power to bring me to life. Gently I leant over and kissed him. He began to emerge from his dream state, his body responding. Then his eyes opened.

'What are you doing?' he protested. 'Can't you see I'm tired?' With obvious intent he turned his back on me. That's when I caught it: *the stale scent of a woman.* The musky aroma of a stranger's body imprinted on his. Waves of dread shuddered through me but I stilled them. It was a mistake. My fears flared temporarily out of control, distorting my senses. It was only warped imagination, Remy loved me far too much to ever do *that.*

With the first rains, a plague of flying ants descended like a dark cloud covering the sky. In a surging wave, they blanketed out all light. Then, as swiftly as they came, they lay dying on the ground. Having lived a brief moment of discovery, they found blessed release in a ritual of mass suicide.

The destructive cycle had begun. My mind clouded with suspicion, was plagued with distrust. Giving in to my doubts, I confronted him.

'Why are you checking up on me?' he barked when challenged with the truth. 'Many people gamble here. You have no right to begrudge me that just because you have no vices. You sit on your throne handing down judgements, what gives you the right?'

'I don't pretend to be a saint, why are you being so defensive?'

'It's hard enough having the gods as taskmasters. When they speak through me it is a great burden. Omnipotence is demanding. Then you start with your 'holier than thou' attitude, and it's too much. I need to remember that I'm human, to have the weaknesses that other people have and indulge in some of the pleasures.'

That was the crux of my concern. I wanted to come right out and ask him if in one fragile moment of time he had succumbed. Fearful of the answer but no longer able to keep it bottled up, I hedged around the question, reluctant to accept its repercussions.

'What ever happened to the notion of trust?' he shouted. 'If that's what you think then it's time I started living up to your expectations.' In a fit of rage he rammed his fist into the wall. I was taken aback, this vehement display of moral indignation smacked of guilt. An innocent man would have no need to act so outraged.

'What's gotten into you, Remy? What happened to the man I fell in love with?' He refused to answer, then stormed off into the bedroom. Desperate for comfort, I needed to know the truth. Little did I know that it would come from the one person I least expected it to.

*

Several days later, I was alone in the house, when there was a knock at the door. It swung open and Remy's wife boldly strutted into the room. Without a word she sat down opposite me, her body rigidly tense and guarded. It was the first time she'd come inside uninvited.

'My husband doesn't come home any more.' We'd never spoken before on a personal level and while language was no longer an obstacle, a strong emotional barrier still existed between us.

'I'm sorry, but he's not here either. He left earlier this morning.'

'I know,' she snapped. 'Now my husband is a big man in the temple he has grown beyond us. He reserves himself for the gods and lesser mortals. Many devious women are attracted to men in power, they think him special.' She smiled a demented, half-mad grin.

I wanted her to stop but from the wild look in her eyes, her mind was waging a private war from which there was no retreat.

'Yesterday I followed him,' she sighed, 'down some winding tracks, straight to *her* house.' A cool breeze rustled the palm tree, chilling me to the bone. 'I found them together on the bed, him and that *whore*. I screamed, "How many lives have to be destroyed before you'll be satisfied? When will it ever be enough?" And now,' she sobbed, 'it is me who has had enough! I must put an end to this.'

'Calm down,' I begged, alarmed by her inner glint of madness. Were these the words of truth, or the deranged ramblings of a crazed woman? Either way, a wave of utter disgust flooded my body.

'With my own hands,' she continued, 'I'll take a dagger and kill the man who has caused me so much pain.' Propelled on by hatred, she let fifteen agonised years spill out in a storm of sorrow. 'He has damaged so many people's lives, he deserves to die.' Her body was shaking uncontrollably, her face red with rage. 'Help me.'

'No,' I stammered, refusing to be drawn into this treacherous alliance. By confiding in me, she had made me an emotional accessory to her morbid plot. In a bizarre twist, where mutual love of a man had never succeeded in uniting us, common hatred stood a chance. 'How much more of yourself are you willing to destroy because of him? Are you ready to risk going to jail? Who would look after your children?'

A strange softness swept over her body and her breath became less urgent. 'You're right, he's ruined enough of my life, I'll not lose any more of it over him.' Rising up unsteadily, she left without a word.

The temple ceremony had begun. It was the *odalan,* a celebration to honour the anniversary of the dedication of the temple. Something impelled me to venture within the holy confines of its walls.

The haunting beat of the gamelan lured me on. Relentless and driving, it invited hypnotic fervour. People surged all around, growing restless for the fight. The music rose to a harrowing crescendo as an unholy hush fell upon the crowd.

Rangda appeared, causing a palpable ripple of fear. Rangda, the horrible monster queen. Rangda, the blood-thirsty, child-eating witch of black magic. There stood the effigy of a monstrous old woman, her white body striped with black, cascading white hair and pendulous breasts. Huge, bulging eyes glared into the crowd, daring anyone to approach, warning them off with snarling fangs and a long, red tongue dangling flames of gold. Flames too, shot from the top of her head, her taloned, gloved hands carrying a white cloth. A deadly weapon, one flick could wreak havoc on her unsuspecting victims.

Suddenly, there was a shattering scream, a blood-curdling gurgle. Words spilled out in the ancient tongue of Kawi. With peculiar whining tones, Rangda grunted loudly, then threw her head back in a threatening volley of laughter, shaking menacingly.

Her opponent entered, the formidable Barong, intent on thwarting her bid for supremacy. Barong, the mythical lion representing the powers of good. Embroiled in an ongoing feud, Barong sided with humanity to thwart Rangda's evil intent. His great frame, carried by two men concealed in his shaggy coat, sparkled with golden scales and mirrored fragments. A number of small bells jingled with every movement. It was the Barong's beard that held his real power, a tuft of human hair entwined with flowers.

The two forces faced each other. Rangda, the female, represented the magic of the left, the black of night, the darkness from which comes danger, illness and death. The Barong, the male, was the magic of the right. His was the light of the sun, the antidote for evil, the defender of humanity.

Poised for battle, the music spiralled into a feverish spin. Many of the men in the crowd were touched by the eerie vibration. Their eyes snapped open, they advanced through the crowd as if summoned by a higher force. Half-naked, their sarongs rolled up to their loins, they stepped into the central courtyard of the temple. These men were to be the assistants of the Barong in the fight against Rangda, the defenders of good against evil.

The priest dipped the Barong's beard into holy water, splashing droplets over their twitching forms. Consecrated by the strength of the Barong, they walked menacingly towards Rangda, their kris daggers drawn, but the spell of the old witch turned the power against them. They fell into a mad collective frenzy. With incredible force, they fought to drive the icy steel of the dagger into their own flesh, the sinews of their arms tensing with untold might as they pushed harder. Still the metal could not penetrate the flesh.

The magic of the Barong rendered them indestructible. Every muscle of their body tensed, the cold, rigid flesh of their stomach rock hard to repel the brunt of the attack. The sharp points of the daggers could not pierce the protective shield of Barong. Dark marks rose on their chests where they bruised the skin, but still they could not penetrate. One part of their psyche strove for destruction, another was steeled to protect them against it.

Only in the state of complete trance were the men safe, when any showed signs of returning to consciousness they were violently disarmed; possessed of supernatural strength, it took several men to hold them down. The priest unfazed, wiped the face of each with the beard of the Barong. The men snapped back unsteadily with little recall of what had happened.

The contest was over. The masks were returned to their ritual holy place for the next round. There could be no outright victory, this was less a battle than a reminder of the ongoing balance between good and evil, an intrinsic notion in Balinese life. The Barong was a tangible, physical form of a magical deity. Rangda was equally powerful, and just as fascinating.

And so darkness mirrored the light. Life was less about conquering the dark than recognising it. In the still of the night and the blackness of our bleakest emotion, we are all confronted with the ultimate test. Soon I would be forced to look deep within myself and acknowledge the darkness inside me.

It would have been easier to walk away. In doing so I could have been spared the pain, but would have emerged none the wiser. Instead I stood firm. My motivation was to thwart Remy, to prevent him from retreating into the arms of a waiting love. Many times he wanted to confess his sins, but I wouldn't grant him that privilege. I let him wallow in them, hoping to make his life as miserable as he'd made mine, regardless of the fact that I was torturing myself cruelly.

Confronted by the twisted monsters of his psyche, Remy turned their full force upon me. Aware he could no longer manipulate me with his lies, he tried to crush all that we had built together, foremost our love. Fits of temper became common as his outer shell began to crack. Doors slammed, wood splintered in rage, objects were hurled across the room, hostile words flung brutally - all lifeless casualties of our unconsummated passion.

When he felt the noose tighten, Remy fled to the stony sanctuary of the temple. It was his ultimate escape. Within its stern grey walls, he could communicate with his gods. In his quest for spiritual supremacy, he had relinquished his soul. Having willingly given away his power, it was now the gods who had assumed control.

Remy was lost. The inner spark in his eyes that once captivated me with its radiance, was gone. In its place lurked an evil dark force. Repelled by the light within me, it turned away. Remy could no longer bear to look at me. He constantly wore dark glasses or averted his gaze. He had trespassed into a spiritual cesspool that had sucked him under; in my folly I was dragged down with him.

The struggle gathered force, each harsh word a sharpened deadly arrow, a step backwards from resolution. I launched a massive counter-attack, embroiling us in a gigantic clash of wills. Whatever damage Remy could inflict, I could wreak more. Whatever dingy cave he crawled into, I grovelled further into its murky recesses. No matter the cost, I was determined to beat him. Until the day I broke: the shocking day I realised I had become a dangerous woman.

I found a photo of her, and my world shattered. I smashed our picture against the wall in a symbolic separation. I could no longer tolerate the cruel ruse, the pretence that love conquered all.

It conquered nothing. Not the pain, the sorrow or abject longing, nor that empty space in the heart where it once resided. It conquered nothing but its own myth. Love was the most cruel of emotions, its destruction propelled one to the greatest acts of hatred and degradation.

'How many women will it take,' I screamed, 'before you are satisfied? I gave you all but it still wasn't enough.' Deep down I knew it never could be. This man had such a massive void in his soul that no other human being could ever begin to fill it. 'One day I hope you realise how precious the love we had was, and the lengths you went to in order to destroy it.'

Remy tried to placate me, stirring me up with declarations of undying love. He advanced closer, wanting to sweep me into his arms. It was the final insult. Outraged, I lunged for a knife in the kitchen drawer. The sharp metal blade flashed bright in the sunlight, mirroring the fury in my eyes. I hesitated, unsure on whom to turn my anger, him or me. Where could it do the most damage? Then came the most horrific realisation. I had become capable of the most heinous of crimes - the destruction of life.

The spiritual savagery had to stop. There and then I ordered Remy to leave. The final ultimatum, followed by a dreadful silence. He lingered in the doorway, reluctant to part. Despite the intense pain, neither of us was willing to let go. Our bond, terribly battered and bruised, still drew tight, sealing us as much in hatred as in love.

That night I stood in the garden, shadowed by the glassy remnant of the moon. Its dull timbre enveloped me in a despondent haze. My body was spent, numb from the onslaught of scarred emotions.

'Show me a way out of this hell,' I called to the heavens.

The sky rumbled, thundering with the footsteps of a gallant warrior. Malik's shape took form high among the clouds, in his hands was a mighty sceptre fashioned from the stars. 'Child,' a kindly voice murmured from the ether, 'look to the light.' The stars twinkled as a subtle sheen emanated from the cosmos. 'You have waged war against the darkness, but in your fury you have joined their ranks. If you challenge them to battle, you will surely lose for their evil is infinite; you are no match for their wickedness.'

'What should I do?' I had seen glimpses of my own dark side and it terrified me. Deeds I thought myself incapable of, surfaced like an awful wound, fed by the pain within my heart.

'Like the island on which you live,' Malik advised, 'the forces must be honoured equally. Restore the balance; for only in the depths of darkness can you define the light. Remember the moon glows brightest in the blackest night sky. Remy has been your moon, your mirror, through his eyes you saw yourself.' I cringed. 'Do not shirk from this side, for it saved you in your darkest hour. Anger became your lance, hatred your shield. Now cast them aside for you need them no more. Go beyond and look to the light.'

With a brilliant flash the warrior's celestial rod twisted into a deadly cobra. Its eyes flared icy green, then its jaws snapped open. *'Can't you see,'* it spat, *'the keys to your salvation are in your own hands, as they have always been. Use them now to find the answer you have so long searched for... and thus see the truth within your own heart.'* With one final hiss, the snake dissolved forever in a pile of stardust at my feet.

'You must come,' Kadek pleaded, 'the circle will not be complete without you.' Self-healing had been a long, arduous process. It had taken every last ounce of courage to cast aside my feelings for Remy. I was not about to jeopardise it now by exposing raw wounds.

'The priest says all those close to my father must be present, it is his only chance to break free of the evil that controls him.' With alienation from all that he valued in life, Remy's personality had disintegrated. His family had turned to a priest in a last attempt to rescue him. Remy's soul was in torment, his health failing as his heart suffered under the strain.

The arrogance shaken from him, Remy had learned the hard way that he was not as invincible as he had thought. His treatment of those close to him had been callous and cruel, in the unbending law of karma, he found himself alone. Those he once cared for had withdrawn their love, but the imprint of love still remained. Now in one final act of grace, they had rallied around him. Did I have it in my heart to do the same? Eventually I succumbed to compassion.

Remy's eyes were downcast when he came to my door. For the first time in our years together, the false bravado cracked and Remy allowed his vulnerability to show. His fingers trembled as he tied the sash around my waist. Here, in exquisite detail, stood the man who had such a profound hold over me. In that brief moment, I realised just how much I loved him and the absolute futility of it all.

At this most crucial moment, Remy had chosen to come for me. Rejecting the dictates of the past, ignoring the incongruous ties of the present, he reached out to a place and time that held most meaning. Our bond, which had become no longer viable, was still intact. Together in this final hour, we walked hand in hand towards an uncertain salvation.

The entire family were gathered in the courtyard of his grandfather's house. Remy's wife watched me like a hawk, her bitterness evident. Here, in front of the collective family, she had been relegated to second place. Even now that the war was over, the feud between us was still not resolved. The priest motioned to Remy. Kadek pulled me down on the mat beside her while his elder daughter sat on my right. Their mother's stare intensified.

Remy took his place next to the priest. A wooden platform, heavy with offerings and burning incense, was laid out in front of them. An eerie silence crept over the courtyard; even the birds stopped their singing, sensing the solemnity of the mood. There, in the deathly hush, the breath of unrestrained fear hovered all around.

The priest stood over Remy while two strong men stayed staunchly by his side. Then the chanting began, lulling Remy into a deep trance as he slumped into the chair. The long, terrible silence was abruptly shattered. Remy's eyes snapped open, a blood curdling gurgle hurtling from his mouth. Stroking an imaginary beard, a tirade of ancient Balinese fell from his lips.

'Grandfather is here!' A surge of excitement swept through the family. 'He speaks through my father,' Kadek cried as her grip tightened. The elderly grandmother, responding to the voice of her late husband, collapsed on the ground, drenched in her own tears. Her frail body crawled across to him. Clasping Remy's hand, she hung on his every word, her eyes glowing with love and recognition.

'Grandmother is happy,' Kadek said, 'for grandfather tells her they will be together. He is waiting for her, she will join him soon.'

One of Remy's aunts, so moved by his presence, ran over and flung herself prostrate at Remy's feet. Wailing hysterically, she became frenzied as she called out her brother's name over and over again. Grabbing Remy's arm, she begged him for help. He started to talk to her in a low gravelly voice, a voice I could not recognise.

'She will be better,' Kadek said, straining to hear, 'the pains that ravage her will cease if she drinks the herbs grandfather prescribes every day. She will honour his advice, for even in death he is acknowledged as a great healer.'

I shuddered as I watched Remy's animated body. His hands jerked in unfamiliar gestures, his voice rasped in a raw pitch. The flame in his eye was acutely alien. It belonged to someone else. Another's body had been transposed onto his. His soul had temporarily vacated its earthly vessel to make room for another, the spirit of his grandfather. Their connection had never been severed; instead they had struck up a secret alliance.

Remy was a trance channel. Did I know in certainty the man who had shared my bed for so many years? When he called out in his sleep, was it him, or was there a stranger lying next to me - taking over Remy's body and invading mine in the process? All at once I felt spiritually violated.

The ghostly voice faded, leaving a dull quiet. Grandfather's spirit, weakened by his earthly contact, had departed. Remy recovered slowly, and propped up by his brothers, staggered towards the priest. He knelt down humbly in front of the old man, his head bent. Humming a dull, deathly monotone, the priest circled him holding a cluster of flowers. He dipped them into his wooden bowl and shook the water over Remy's limp body.

The reaction was immediate. Remy struggled to break free from his brothers' grip; they fought for control, but his strength was superhuman. Several people ran to their aid. His mouth choking with foam, Remy screamed out a string of obscenities as his captors pinned him down against his will. The priest dowsed him with more water in a torrent of cleansing, intensifying his pleas with the gods to release Remy from his demonic prison.

Kadek buried her head in my shoulder, and whilst her sister tried to maintain a calmer facade, I could sense her shaking inside. 'The priest must drive out the spirits that have possessed my father. They are strong but he *must* be stronger ... he *must*,' she cried.

She began to sob loudly as her father challenged his invisible monsters. The rest of the family stared on, speechless, a look of real terror in their eyes. Remy's body convulsed as the priest droned his mantras, totally detached from the evil entities that strove so fiercely to take control of his soul.

Overwhelmed by his agony, I felt a tight band of pain constrict my chest as if my heart was being wrenched from its cavity. The man I loved had been reduced to an embittered shadow. Piercing through the icy wall that enveloped Remy, I caught sight of a faint dying ember. A flicker of the original spark of love was trapped there in those dark hollow chambers.

The fire had to be re-ignited before it could be lost forever. I wanted to help, but I was powerless in the face of such a prodigious foe. Prompted by a higher force, I went beyond. I left the fear and anger behind and prayed. As I did, a brilliant shaft of white light beamed down from above, flooding the courtyard in a heavenly glow. Though no-one else could see it, all were touched by its presence. Their distress diminished, the cries of anguish crumbled under the soothing force of such an exalted power.

Gently embracing the light, I cast it over Remy's trembling body. It streamed over him in a soft, radiant flow, expanding into a magnificent crystal pyramid. Within the prism of light, his spirit was shielded from harm, sealed from the horror. Encompassing the spectrum of colour, the light created rainbow hues filtering into the softest blue, a transcendent sapphire healing blue. Remy's terror abated as he basked in its serenity.

Impossible to remain unmoved by the vision of light, all seeds of hatred were erased within me. Scarred ribbons of memory curled out of sight until only a glorious moment remained. The heady perfume of flowers scattered on our bed. Sweet reminders of all that was good and pure between us, strewn on Remy's pillow, as he lay down after prayer. Signs that within the turmoil there had always been portents of unbridled beauty, indicators of God's presence and the infinite glory of love.

Without hesitation, I opened up to Remy. His frightened eyes turned towards mine. Full of forgiveness, I spoke to him from the bottom of my heart, spontaneous words accessing the essence of my soul. *'I love you,'* I mouthed so he could see.

Immaculate unconditional love.

Remy's being contorted, a thousand spirits scrambling for control. 'A daughter of demons,' they raged, 'she has taken you away from the gods whom you chose to serve. Look away!'

Remy's mind waged a silent war. Now was the moment of choice. To accept that part of himself he had renounced, or walk the path of love. It was a crucial decision, and Remy's alone to make. Then came a flicker of recognition. He looked deep within my eyes and caught a reflection of the love that resided within his own soul.

A look of infinite peace flooded his face. He succumbed willingly, acquiescing to a higher force. In that split second, the darkness surrounding him cracked wide open, dissolving into a beam of sheer white light. An ear-splitting scream echoed through the courtyard and Remy slumped to the ground in a heap. The battle had ended. Vanquished by a supreme power, the enemy retreated into the dark, back to its cloistered hiding place.

Suddenly, I felt lighter, as if a great burden had been lifted. The chains that bound me to Remy had been released, the grit of karmic debris erased by the combined power of *light* and *love*. The snake had been right - the keys had been in my hands from the start. In innocence, I had found the truth and stumbled upon the keys that unlocked the gates of heaven.

In reality, I had been Remy's mirror, his moon, his absolute source of reflection. As he mirrored the darkness, I had shone back the light. We had been each other's shadow, as integral to one another as day and night, and now we had come full circle. The balance had been restored. Having accepted both essential aspects of ourselves, the dark and the light, we were strong enough to stand on our own. Now we each were whole.

The Bali moon rose in pure magnificence, shimmering silver in the sky. Another day was over, another chapter closed. Silently I stood up and slipped out of the courtyard. Bands of light glowed from the heavens, illuminating the way. My path was clear.

I was ready to set out on the next stage of the journey.

EPILOGUE

The peak of Mount Agung towered above, forging majestic patterns in the sky. Perched among the gods, I sat on a craggy ridge smudged with the palest shades of day. Never before had I felt so divine as here in this loft of angels, poised on the brink of heaven.

A lone bird swooped down to show me the way. Landing on a rock, it preened its feathers before turning towards the sun. Inspired by the source it set off in flight, soaring into the vastness of the sky. I rose to follow but a thick drift of cloud blocked my way.

Suddenly, the sky gaped open and a splendid ray of sunlight cut through the sultry glaze. Everything took on a bold new dimension. The contours of the earth, each sinewy fold, brittle rock crevice and crusty fissure, could be seen with startling new vision. What once was obscure, was now in perfect focus.

Besakih, the mother temple, stood proudly aloft on the slope of the mountain. Through its ornate gateways, I caught a glimpse of paradise. Every step led upwards, the stone slabs grooved by the force of a million footsteps. Many souls had come before me on their own rites of passage, each with their own road to travel.

It was a reciprocal odyssey, this journey of the soul. Not only had the island inspired those who trod upon its earth, but their presence impacted on it. All had left an indelible mark, an evolutionary imprint of energy upon the land that touched it to the very core. Bali had lodged deep within the hearts of many; it was etched within my own for all eternity.

It had been the supreme quest. This ethereal island of splendid fascination had lured me to its shores then enticed me to stay. Sorely tested by its gods, I had tapped an inner power and found my source of strength. Experiencing a profound love, both human and divine, I'd touched on a universal truth. Transcending the personal, I had been privy to God's master plan and willingly accepted it. And with that acceptance came a perfect peace. The search was over.

I had found heaven inside myself.